Collins

Big book of Crosswords

Book 2

Published by Collins
An imprint of HarperCollins Publishers
Westerhill Road
Bishopbriggs
Glasgow G64 2QT
www.harpercollins.co.uk

10 9 8 7 6 5 4 3 2 1

All puzzles supplied by Clarity Media

ISBN 978-0-00-827966-0, 978-0-00-796950-0

Printed and bound by CPI Group (UK) Ltd, Croydon CR0 4YY

A catalogue record for this book is available from the British Library.

If you would like to comment on any aspect of this book, please contact us at the above address or online.
E-mail: puzzles@harpercollins.co.uk

PUZZLES

PUZZLE 1

Across

1 Cipher (4)
3 Waterside area (8)
9 Dark pigment in skin (7)
10 Raises up (5)
11 Friend (Spanish) (5)
12 Rotated quickly (7)
13 Eg Iceland (6)
15 Instrumental piece of music (6)
17 Not in any place (7)
18 ___ Eastwood: US actor (5)
20 Groom's partner (5)
21 Biting sharply (7)
22 Elementary negatively charged particle (8)
23 Matured (4)

Down

1 Friendly (13)
2 New ___ : Indian capital (5)
4 Elaborately adorned (6)
5 Children's toy (12)
6 Leguminous plant also called lucerne (7)
7 Deprived (13)
8 Formal notice (12)
14 Despicable person (7)
16 Temporary shelter (4-2)
19 Cake decoration (5)

PUZZLE 2

Across

1 Forewarning (11)
9 Clean spiritually (5)
10 Seventh Greek letter (3)
11 Greek writer of fables (5)
12 Browned bread (5)
13 Humility (8)
16 Dismiss as unimportant (5,3)
18 Measures duration (5)
21 Path or road (5)
22 Floor mat (3)
23 Handle a tool effectively (5)
24 Having celebrities in attendance (4-7)

Down

2 Male chicken (7)
3 Soaking up (7)
4 These relay bodily messages (6)
5 Special reward (5)
6 Dramatic musical work (5)
7 Consisting of incomplete parts (11)
8 Place where fighting occurs (11)
14 Protected (7)
15 Loquacious (7)
17 Not disposed to cheat (6)
19 Strength (5)
20 Effluent system (5)

PUZZLE 3

1		2		3	■	4		5		6		7
	■		■		■		■		■		■	
8							■	9				
	■		■		■		■		■	■	■	
10				■	11					12		
	■		■	13	■		■		■		■	■
14						■	15					16
■	■		■		■	17	■		■		■	
18								■	19			
	■	■	■		■		■	20	■		■	
21		22			■	23						
	■		■		■		■		■		■	
24							■	25				

Across

1 Implant (5)
4 Eventually (7)
8 Block (7)
9 Strongly advised (5)
10 Lazy (4)
11 Structure giving lift in flight (8)
14 Long-tailed crow (6)
15 Probable (6)
18 Twist together (8)
19 Domesticate (an animal) (4)
21 Chopping (5)
23 Devoted time to learning (7)
24 Very long (7)
25 ___ on : encouraged (5)

Down

1 Selfishness (7)
2 Illuminate from behind (9)
3 Sullen (4)
4 Tentacle (6)
5 Overly anxious and sensitive (8)
6 Limb used for walking (3)
7 Mountain cry (5)
12 Functioning (9)
13 00:00 on a 24-hour clock (8)
16 Gave way to pressure (7)
17 Stylish (6)
18 Electronic message (5)
20 Delude (4)
22 Pub (3)

PUZZLE 4

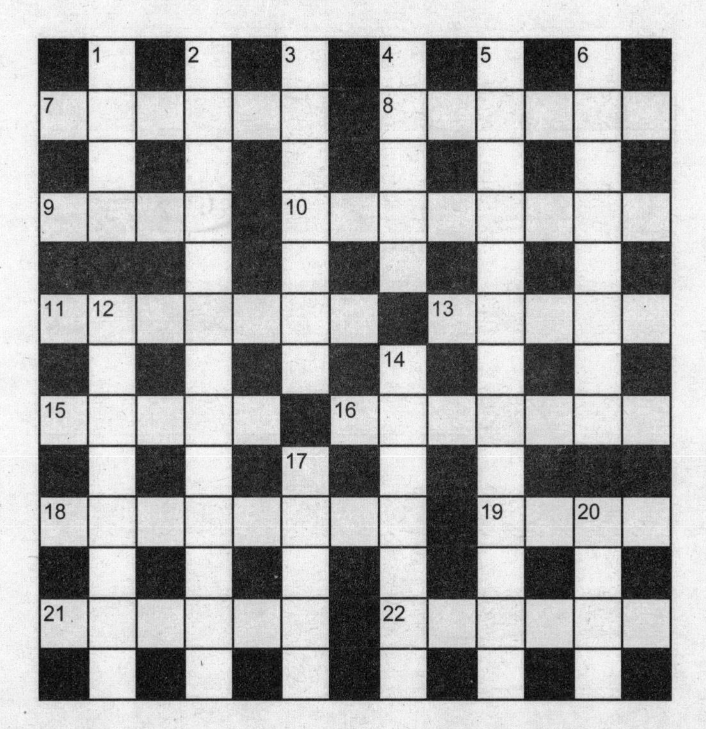

Across

7 Complain about (6)
8 ___ Schwarzenegger: actor (6)
9 Fluent but shallow (of words) (4)
10 Partner (8)
11 See (7)
13 Unconditional love (5)
15 Taut (5)
16 Exploit the power of (7)
18 Form of musical articulation (8)
19 Very small (4)
21 Round caps (6)
22 Rescuing (6)

Down

1 Small room for a prisoner (4)
2 Verified again (6-7)
3 Small fish (7)
4 Drops to the ground (5)
5 Uninventive (13)
6 Egg-laying mammal (8)
12 Stiff coarse hairs (8)
14 Engage in merrymaking (7)
17 Waterlogged area of land (5)
20 One less than ten (4)

PUZZLE 5

Across

1 Craned (anag) (6)
5 Basic metrical unit in a poem (6)
8 Increase in size (4)
9 Military post (8)
10 Rinse out with water (5)
11 Ardent (7)
14 Harmonious; compatible (13)
16 Become more precipitous (7)
18 Existing (5)
20 Inopportune (8)
22 People in general (4)
23 Gaudy (6)
24 Urge (6)

Down

2 Herbaceous Caribbean plant (9)
3 European primula (7)
4 Road ___ : anger when driving (4)
5 Tubes for ejecting liquids (8)
6 Live by (5)
7 Place where one sees animals (3)
12 Watering device (9)
13 Calmly (8)
15 ___ Night: Shakespeare play (7)
17 Leaves (5)
19 Stringed instrument (4)
21 Nothing (3)

PUZZLE 6

Across

1 Wanderer (5)
4 Signs up (7)
8 Of great size (7)
9 Manner of speaking (5)
10 Still to be paid (4)
11 Admired and respected (8)
14 Long-haired breed of dog (6)
15 Wreckage washed ashore (6)
18 Boldly and courageously (8)
19 Mr ___ : Rowan Atkinson character (4)
21 Mythical monster (5)
23 Mythical being (7)
24 Personal belongings (7)
25 Incantation (5)

Down

1 Ideas (7)
2 In bad condition (4-5)
3 Great ___ : breed of dog (4)
4 More than is necessary (6)
5 Heard (8)
6 Utter (3)
7 Warhorse (5)
12 Get up to no good (9)
13 Type of state (8)
16 Solid inorganic substance (7)
17 Pieces of bread (6)
18 Headdress worn by a bishop (5)
20 Nous (anag) (4)
22 Clumsy person (3)

PUZZLE 7

Across

1 Plots; schemes (5)
4 Aquatic creature with prominent barbels (7)
7 Awry; wrong (5)
8 Commonplace (8)
9 Less high (5)
11 Falls back (8)
15 Agreed (8)
17 God (5)
19 Formal meal (8)
20 Preclude (5)
21 Increased efficiency by working together (7)
22 Flowers (5)

Down

1 Check for errors in text (9)
2 Eagerness (7)
3 Slow bowler in cricket (7)
4 Red wine (6)
5 Nuclear reaction; merger (6)
6 Military blockade (5)
10 Preparedness (9)
12 One who hunts illegally (7)
13 Commercials (7)
14 Walk with long steps (6)
16 Eg Hampshire or Surrey (6)
18 Messenger (5)

PUZZLE 8

Across

1 Orchestral piece at the beginning of an opera (8)
5 Symbol (4)
8 Striped animal (5)
9 Joins in matrimony (7)
10 Stealing (7)
12 Fusion chamber (7)
14 Choices (7)
16 Stamped (7)
18 Makes untidy with rubbish (7)
19 Deprive of weapons (5)
20 Ride the waves (4)
21 Whole numbers (8)

Down

1 Greek spirit (4)
2 Set out on a journey (6)
3 Officially registered name (9)
4 Comment (6)
6 Medical treatment centre (6)
7 Bouquets (8)
11 Shed for vessels by a river (9)
12 Expensive fungi (8)
13 Component (6)
14 More likely than not (4-2)
15 Hydrocarbon found in petroleum spirit (6)
17 Flightless birds (4)

PUZZLE 9

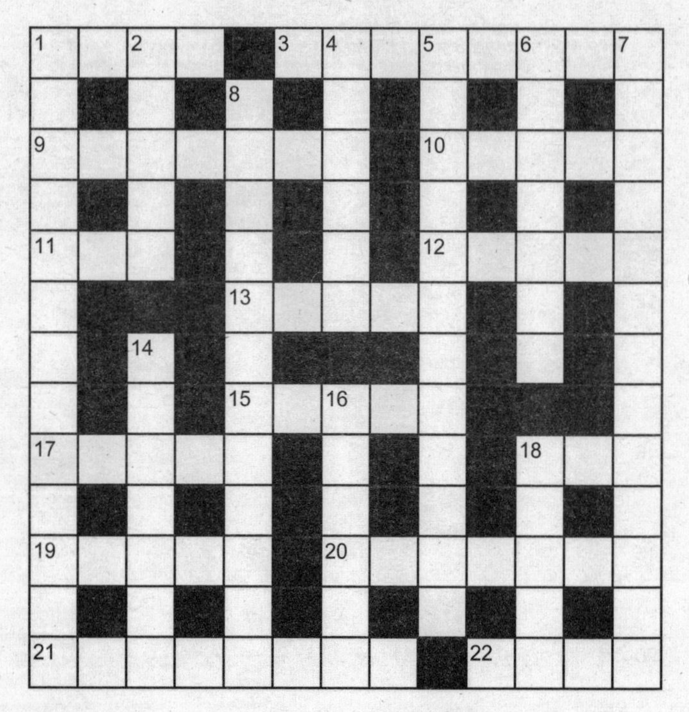

Across

1 Jumble (4)
3 Person or company owed money (8)
9 Caring for (7)
10 Water vapour (5)
11 Propel a boat (3)
12 Allocate money (5)
13 Passenger ship (5)
15 Ethos (anag) (5)
17 Punctuation mark (5)
18 ___ Weasley: friend of Harry Potter (3)
19 Climb onto (5)
20 Fuss and bother (7)
21 Disregards (8)
22 Vale (4)

Down

1 British actress in Goldfinger (5,8)
2 Sharp-pointed metal pin (5)
4 District (6)
5 Unpleasant (12)
6 Comic film with Jim Carrey and Cameron Diaz (3,4)
7 Device for changing TV channel (6,7)
8 Casual chatter (6-6)
14 Port in northern Germany (7)
16 Yield (6)
18 Variety show (5)

PUZZLE 10

Across

1 Person in second place (6-2)
5 ___ Ifans: Welsh actor (4)
9 Imitator (7)
10 Leg bone (5)
11 Way of cooking an egg (4-6)
14 Smear or blur (6)
15 Representatives (6)
17 Region of England (4,6)
20 Pashmina (5)
21 Asserted without proof (7)
22 Fat used to make puddings (4)
23 Reverie (8)

Down

1 Wealthy (4)
2 Bites at (4)
3 Capable of being traded (12)
4 Messy (6)
6 Limping (8)
7 A magical quality (8)
8 Determined (6-6)
12 Evaluates the quality of (8)
13 Parasol (8)
16 Large lizard (6)
18 Look at amorously (4)
19 First man (4)

PUZZLE 11

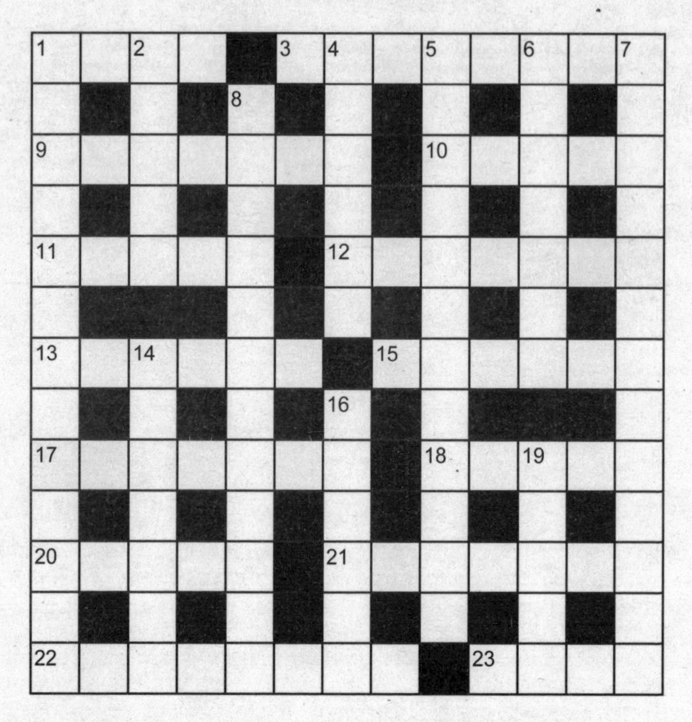

Across

1 ___ Lendl: former tennis star (4)
3 Relating to love (8)
9 Humorous drawing (7)
10 Musical speeds (5)
11 Gena Lee ___ : actress (5)
12 Ugly thing (7)
13 Discharges (6)
15 Make an unusually great effort (6)
17 Thoroughly (2,5)
18 Malediction (5)
20 Makhaya ___ : South African former fast bowler (5)
21 Observes (7)
22 Legal UK drinking age (8)
23 Broken husks of seeds (4)

Down

1 Put to trouble (13)
2 Fourth month (5)
4 16 of these in a pound (6)
5 Establish as genuine (12)
6 Lottery (7)
7 British comedy author (5,8)
8 Compensate for (12)
14 Eternal (7)
16 Possibility (6)
19 Carer (anag) (5)

PUZZLE 12

Across

1 Illuminating (8)
5 Beige colour (4)
8 Thread-weaving machines (5)
9 Connoisseur; gourmet (7)
10 Division of the United Kingdom (7)
12 Feeling guilty (7)
14 Taunting; mocking (7)
16 Italian rice dish (7)
18 Undermine the authority of (7)
19 Drain away from soil (of a chemical) (5)
20 Chopped; cancelled (4)
21 Uses again (8)

Down

1 Scottish singer-songwriter (4)
2 Grumpy person (6)
3 Will (9)
4 Required (6)
6 Puma (6)
7 Incessant (8)
11 Usually (9)
12 Food of the gods (8)
13 Functional (6)
14 Bump against roughly (6)
15 Country in the Middle East (6)
17 Therefore (4)

PUZZLE 13

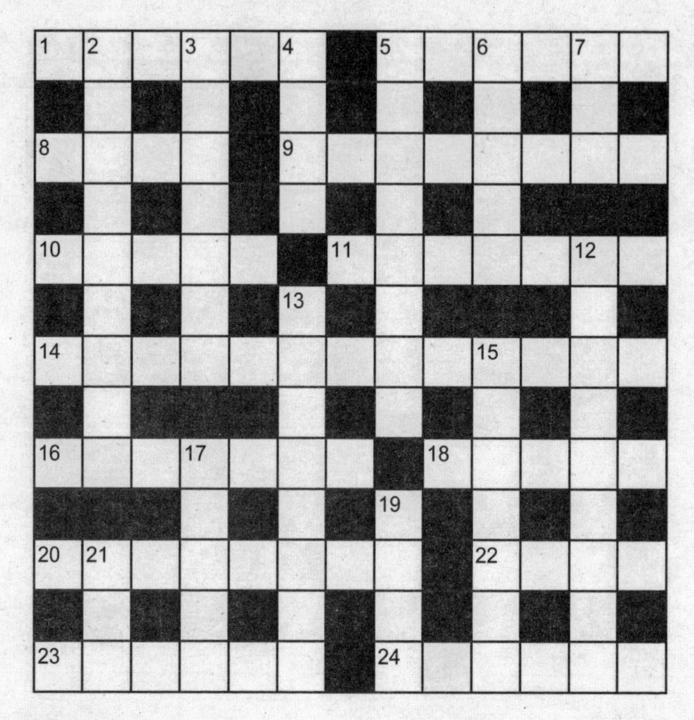

Across

1 Climbed (6)
5 Peevish and annoyed (6)
8 Fertile type of soil (4)
9 Betting (8)
10 Interruption (5)
11 Hiding underground (7)
14 Stoical; patient (13)
16 Rich white cheese (7)
18 British nobles (5)
20 Administrative division (8)
22 Attic (4)
23 Distorts (6)
24 Modernise (6)

Down

2 Tightly bound together (5-4)
3 Back pain (7)
4 Chief magistrate of Venice (4)
5 Shared (8)
6 Narrow passageway (5)
7 Rubbish holder (3)
12 Not commercially motivated (3-6)
13 Assigns a job to (8)
15 Provoked or teased (7)
17 Feels deep affection for (5)
19 Domesticated ox (4)
21 Uncooked (of meat) (3)

PUZZLE 14

Across

1 Metrical foot (6)
7 Became visible (8)
8 Scarf of feathers or fur (3)
9 Prayer book (6)
10 Regretted (4)
11 Small canoe (5)
13 In reality; actually (2,5)
15 Modified (7)
17 Storage place (5)
21 Slightly open (4)
22 Lender (6)
23 ___ Botham: cricketer (3)
24 Plant with decorative leaves (8)
25 Sailing vessels (6)

Down

1 Expose as being false (6)
2 Damp and sticky to touch (6)
3 Slight error; oversight (5)
4 Put to practical use (7)
5 Nobel ___ : winner of a Nobel Prize (8)
6 Bidding (6)
12 Obvious (8)
14 In good physical condition (7)
16 Dispirit (6)
18 Rot or decay (of food) (6)
19 Unspecified objects (6)
20 Small white garden flower (5)

PUZZLE 15

Across

1 Fabricate (11)
9 Climbing shrubs (5)
10 Fish appendage (3)
11 Personnel at work (5)
12 Hank of wool (5)
13 Man who has never married (8)
16 Exaggerated masculinity (8)
18 Individual things (5)
21 Contented cat sounds (5)
22 Louse egg (3)
23 High-pitched tone (5)
24 Devices popular before computers existed (11)

Down

2 With an attitude of suspicion (7)
3 Joined together (7)
4 With hands on the hips (6)
5 Long pointed teeth (5)
6 Firearm (5)
7 Insubordinate (11)
8 Without giving a name (11)
14 Dog bred for racing (7)
15 Pursuer (anag) (7)
17 Seem (6)
19 Act of going in (5)
20 Cavalry sword (5)

PUZZLE 16

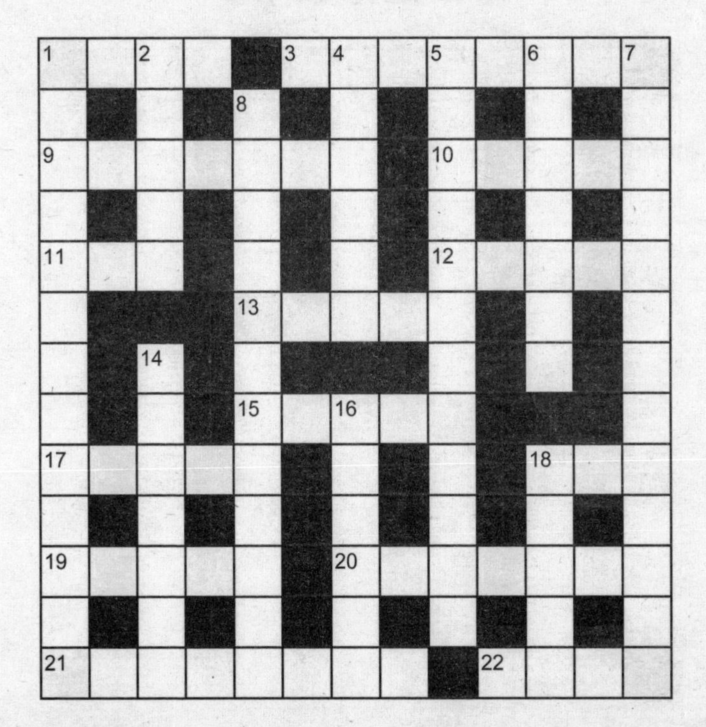

Across

1 Snug (4)
3 Showering with liquid (8)
9 Starting points (7)
10 Precious stone (5)
11 Unit of energy (3)
12 Hang with cloth (5)
13 Tremble (5)
15 Concerning (5)
17 Tree of the birch family (5)
18 Hair style (3)
19 ___ couture: expensive clothes (5)
20 Advocate (7)
21 Held out against (8)
22 Paul ___: former England footballer (4)

Down

1 Musical dance co-ordinator (13)
2 Move back and forth (5)
4 Former Spanish currency (6)
5 Able to use both hands well (12)
6 Intrusions (7)
7 50th anniversary of a major event (6,7)
8 Squint harder (anag) (12)
14 Insects found where you sleep (7)
16 Prophet (6)
18 Subatomic particle such as a photon (5)

PUZZLE 17

Across

1 Final (11)
9 Diacritical mark (5)
10 Flee (3)
11 Crouch down in fear (5)
12 Positive electrode (5)
13 Spanish dance (8)
16 Lays in wait for (8)
18 Risky (5)
21 Weatherproof coat (5)
22 Bite sharply (3)
23 Fill with high spirits (5)
24 Act of publishing in several places (11)

Down

2 Small European thrush (7)
3 Beg (7)
4 Elongated rectangle (6)
5 Stadium (5)
6 In a slow tempo (of music) (5)
7 Gathering information (4-7)
8 Needless (11)
14 Believe tentatively (7)
15 Spicy Spanish sausage (7)
17 Picture produced from many small pieces (6)
19 Idiotic (5)
20 Produce as a fruit (5)

PUZZLE 18

Across

1 Sweet dessert (4)
3 US state (8)
9 Upstart; one who has recently gained wealth (7)
10 Geographical plan (5)
11 In a persuasive manner (12)
14 Twitch (3)
16 Break out with force (5)
17 In favour of (3)
18 Immediately (12)
21 Earthy pigment (5)
22 Portentous (7)
23 Putting into practice (8)
24 Worry about (4)

Down

1 Maximum number a stadium can hold (8)
2 Donna ___ New York: clothing label (5)
4 Flightless bird (3)
5 Build up again from parts (12)
6 Bivalve mollusc (7)
7 Poker stake (4)
8 Intentionally (12)
12 Held on tightly (5)
13 Knowing many languages (8)
15 Get up to speed (5,2)
19 Thin crisp biscuit (5)
20 Closing section of music (4)
22 Wetland (3)

PUZZLE 19

Across

1 Male singer (8)
5 Where darts players throw from (4)
8 Detailed assessment of accounts (5)
9 Takes away (7)
10 Dryness (7)
12 Letter-for-letter; verbatim (7)
14 Imprecise (7)
16 Six-sided shape (7)
18 Lift up (7)
19 Not a winner (5)
20 Clean up (4)
21 Delays it (anag) (8)

Down

1 Undergarments (4)
2 Gnawing animal like a rat (6)
3 Walking unsteadily (9)
4 Standard; usual (6)
6 Collapse (4,2)
7 Writer of literary works (8)
11 Among other things (Latin) (5,4)
12 Least heavy (8)
13 Surpass (6)
14 Arthropod (6)
15 Andre ___ : former US tennis player (6)
17 Make a request to God (4)

PUZZLE 20

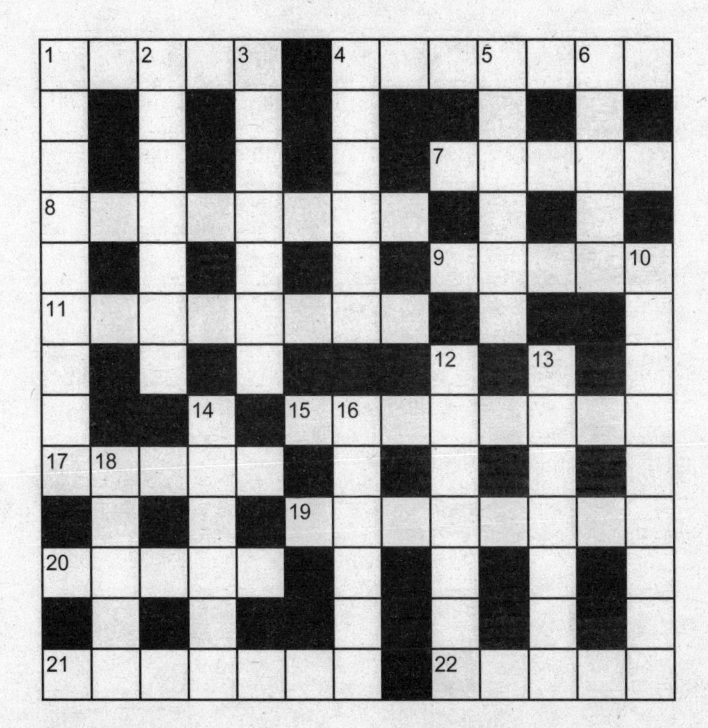

Across

1 Removes the skin from (5)
4 Demilitarises (7)
7 Baked ___ : popular tinned food (5)
8 North African semolina (8)
9 Ringo ___ : one of the Beatles (5)
11 Head of a government department (8)
15 Glass-like volcanic rock (8)
17 Sets of players (5)
19 Block (8)
20 Watched secretly (5)
21 Junction between nerve cells (7)
22 Sense experience (5)

Down

1 Arrangement (9)
2 Following immediately (7)
3 Opposite of failure (7)
4 Deactivate an explosive device (6)
5 Wards off (6)
6 Large residence (5)
10 Restore to use (9)
12 Deform (7)
13 Religious ceremonies (7)
14 Single-celled organism (6)
16 Pocket of air in a sphere of liquid (6)
18 Not containing anything (5)

PUZZLE 21

Across

1 Assists; holds up (8)
5 Rebuff (4)
9 ___ one's nest: enrich oneself (7)
10 Imitative of the past (5)
11 Product of your creative thinking (10)
14 Wildcat (6)
15 Programme (6)
17 Large and heavily armoured vessel (10)
20 Published false statement (5)
21 Existing at the beginning (7)
22 Period of 365 days (4)
23 Reference point; norm (8)

Down

1 Settee (4)
2 Baby carriage (4)
3 Preternatural (12)
4 Dick ___: English highwayman (6)
6 Substance that nourishes (8)
7 Famous street in Manhattan (8)
8 Knowledge of a future event (12)
12 Protruding rotund stomach (8)
13 Segment of the spinal column (8)
16 Lightweight garment (1-5)
18 Unit of type-size (4)
19 Ran away (4)

PUZZLE 22

1		2		3	■	4			5		6	

Across

1 Small streams (5)
4 Augmented (7)
7 Steered a car (5)
8 Study of animal behaviour (8)
9 Large waterbirds (5)
11 Disappears (8)
15 Courgette (US) (8)
17 The ___ Gatsby: novel (5)
19 All-round view (8)
20 Sets of six balls (cricket) (5)
21 Petitions to God (7)
22 Absolute (5)

Down

1 Being presented with (9)
2 Whipping (7)
3 Smart and fashionable (7)
4 Bracelet (6)
5 View in detail (6)
6 ___ Presley: US singer (5)
10 One who approximates (9)
12 Learning institutions (7)
13 Very odd (7)
14 Justly (6)
16 Customary practices (6)
18 Wanderer (5)

PUZZLE 23

Across

1 Dynasty in China (4)
3 SE Asian country (8)
9 Enlarged; puffy (7)
10 Donald ___ : US President (5)
11 Valuable thing or person (5)
12 Pear-shaped fruit (7)
13 Good luck charm (6)
15 Occupation or profession (6)
17 Terrestrial (7)
18 Eighth Greek letter (5)
20 Edward ___ : composer (5)
21 Fragrant gum or spice (7)
22 Walked unsteadily (8)
23 Catch sight of (4)

Down

1 Ineptitude in running a business (13)
2 Crevices (5)
4 Yearly (6)
5 Science of space travel (12)
6 Not a ___ : nothing at all (7)
7 Suitably (13)
8 Framework for washed garments (7,5)
14 Standing erect (7)
16 Piece of text that names the writer of an article (6)
19 Jessica ___-Hill: British former heptathlete (5)

PUZZLE 24

Across

1 Thin layer of sedimentary rock (6)
7 Makes defamatory remarks (8)
8 Towards the stern (3)
9 Raise up (6)
10 Official records (4)
11 Judges (5)
13 Written law (7)
15 Ancient parchment (7)
17 ___ Fury: British boxer (5)
21 Norse god of thunder (4)
22 Ball-shaped object (6)
23 Cry (3)
24 Very small unit of length (8)
25 Look through casually (6)

Down

1 Jumped (6)
2 Develop (6)
3 Put a question to (5)
4 Noisy colourful birds (7)
5 Great adulation (8)
6 Intense feeling of fear (6)
12 Female head of a borough (8)
14 Financial award (7)
16 Feeling a continuous dull pain (6)
18 Change rapidly from one position to another (6)
19 Gnaw (6)
20 Pollex (5)

PUZZLE 25

Across

1 Reverse (4)
3 Eg from Tokyo (8)
9 Day of rest (7)
10 Royal (5)
11 Join together as one (5)
12 Posting (7)
13 Consent to receive (6)
15 Extremely fashionable; scalding (3-3)
17 Person who bargains (7)
18 ___ John: Rocket Man singer (5)
20 Jewelled headdress (5)
21 Reticular (7)
22 Eg rooks and knights (8)
23 Strip of leather worn round the waist (4)

Down

1 Uncaring (13)
2 Suspend; prevent (5)
4 Struck by overwhelming shock (6)
5 Agreements; plans (12)
6 Eg from London (7)
7 The ___ : intellectual movement (13)
8 Butterfly larvae (12)
14 Blood relative (7)
16 Edge (6)
19 Biter (anag) (5)

PUZZLE 26

Across

1 Woodland plant (7)
6 Annoy (3)
8 Blood vessels (5)
9 Offence (7)
10 Small room used as a steam bath (5)
11 Omnipresence (8)
13 Bovine animals (6)
15 Shoe (6)
18 Raging conflagration (8)
19 Mark of insertion (5)
21 Gently (7)
22 Eg radio and television (5)
23 Make a living with difficulty (3)
24 Fall back (7)

Down

2 African country (7)
3 Obscurely (8)
4 Happenings (6)
5 Depressions; brief swims (4)
6 Distributing (7)
7 Form of singing for entertainment (7)
12 Extravagant (8)
13 Succinct (7)
14 Phoenician warship (7)
16 Unfurls (7)
17 Post (6)
20 Periodic movement of the sea (4)

PUZZLE 27

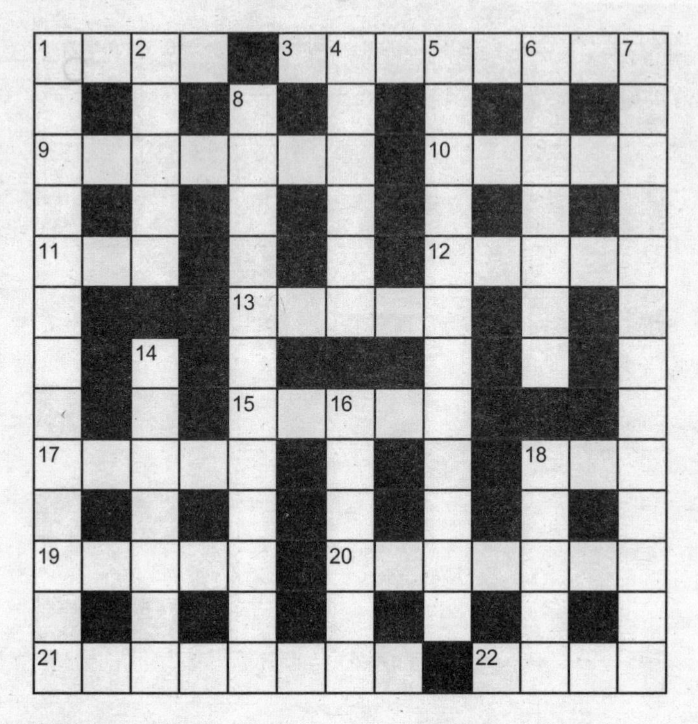

Across

1 Concave roof (4)
3 People who provide massages (8)
9 Reveal (7)
10 Dense ring-shaped bread roll (5)
11 Mauna ___ : Hawaiian volcano (3)
12 Small boat (5)
13 Coming after (5)
15 A woolly ruminant animal (5)
17 Removes the lid (5)
18 Tavern (3)
19 Piece of bread (5)
20 Newtlike salamander (7)
21 Assimilate again (8)
22 Extravagant publicity (4)

Down

1 Betrayer (6-7)
2 Type of coffee drink (5)
4 Bangle worn at the top of the foot (6)
5 Advance payment (12)
6 Necessity (7)
7 25th anniversary celebration (6,7)
8 Vagrancy (12)
14 United States (7)
16 Cream pastry (6)
18 Person acting as a deputy (5)

PUZZLE 28

Across

1 State of being well known (11)
9 Folded back part of a coat (5)
10 Strong drink (3)
11 Spike used by a climber (5)
12 Used up (5)
13 Where tents are pitched (8)
16 Criminal (8)
18 Mexican tortilla wraps (5)
21 Entertain (5)
22 Not on (3)
23 Renowned (5)
24 Founded (11)

Down

2 Study of the body (7)
3 Sickness (7)
4 Deposit knowledge (6)
5 Tumbles (5)
6 Steer (anag) (5)
7 Belief something will happen (11)
8 Small pieces (11)
14 Periods of ten years (7)
15 Declare to be true (7)
17 Conventional (6)
19 Eateries (5)
20 Capital of Bulgaria (5)

PUZZLE 29

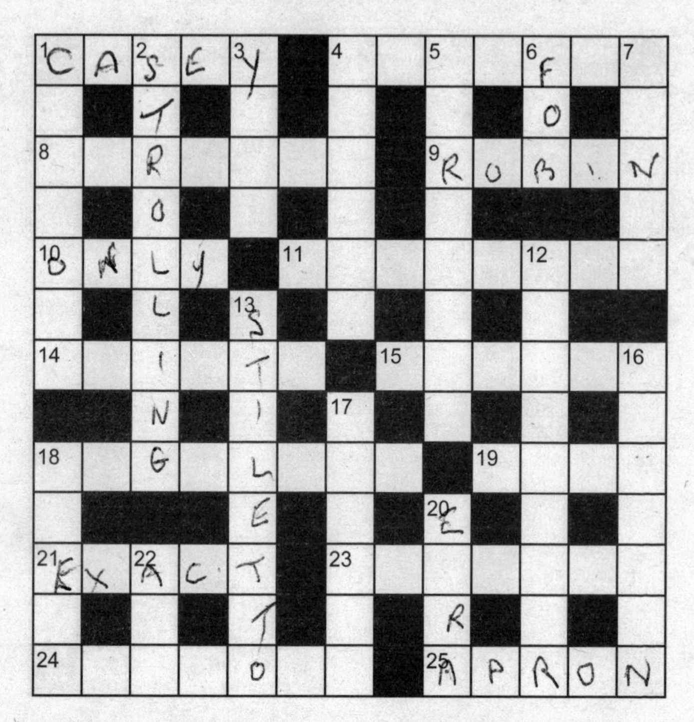

Across

1 ___ Affleck: US actor (5)
4 Handful (7)
8 Distributes around (7)
9 Bird with a red breast (5)
10 Solely (4)
11 Merited (8)
14 Deceives; fakes (6)
15 Affluence (6)
18 Control (8)
19 Black ___ : Colombian bird (4)
21 Precise (5)
23 Most slothful (7)
24 Admirers (7)
25 Protective garment worn in the kitchen (5)

Down

1 Get rid of (4,3)
2 Sauntering (9)
3 Chinese monetary unit (4)
4 Attach firmly (6)
5 Magician (8)
6 Chain attached to a watch (3)
7 Covered the inside of a bin (5)
12 Freely offer to do something (9)
13 Sharp heel (8)
16 Cheer (7)
17 Main plant stems (6)
18 Tall plants of the grass family (5)
20 ___ Pound: US poet (4)
22 Muhammad ___ : boxer (3)

PUZZLE 30

Across

1 Covered walk in a convent (8)
5 Revolve (4)
9 Excuse (7)
10 Find out (5)
11 Increase in value (10)
14 Scoundrel (6)
15 Classifies; sorts (6)
17 Engine part (10)
20 Sequence (5)
21 One of the platinum metals (7)
22 At any time (4)
23 Obviously offensive (of an action) (8)

Down

1 Mimic (4)
2 Cooking appliance (4)
3 Somnambulism (12)
4 Obtain through intimidation (6)
6 Signs for public display (8)
7 Gibberish (8)
8 Very exciting (12)
12 Vehicle with three wheels (8)
13 Increase (8)
16 Cause sudden excitement (6)
18 Capital of Peru (4)
19 Small flake of soot (4)

PUZZLE 31

Across

1 Applaud (4)
3 Move out the way of (8)
9 Capital of Kenya (7)
10 Coarse twilled cotton fabric (5)
11 One who steals (5)
12 Visual display unit (7)
13 Remove from a container (6)
15 Groups of lions (6)
17 Root vegetables (7)
18 Island in the Bay of Naples (5)
20 Eg heart or liver (5)
21 Exceptional; not usual (7)
22 Group of symptoms which occur together (8)
23 Remain (4)

Down

1 Buildings (13)
2 Excuse or pretext (5)
4 Expressions (6)
5 Behavioural peculiarity (12)
6 Distorted (7)
7 Increasingly (13)
8 Someone who makes sweets (12)
14 Model of excellence (7)
16 Greatly respect (6)
19 Double fold in a garment (5)

PUZZLE 32

Across

1 Large US feline (4)
3 Grassy clumps (8)
9 The exposure of bedrock (7)
10 Portion (5)
11 Uncomplimentary (12)
13 Anticipate (6)
15 Coiffure (6)
17 Body of voters in a specified region (12)
20 Port-au-Prince is the capital here (5)
21 A placeholder name (2-3-2)
22 Left one's job (8)
23 Abrupt movement (4)

Down

1 Manufactures (8)
2 Distinctive design (5)
4 Self-important; arrogant (6)
5 Occult (12)
6 Less dirty (7)
7 Wets (anag) (4)
8 Airing a TV program (12)
12 Exterior of a motor vehicle (8)
14 Showy flowers (7)
16 Fine cloth; type of paper (6)
18 Prod with the elbow (5)
19 US pop star (4)

PUZZLE 33

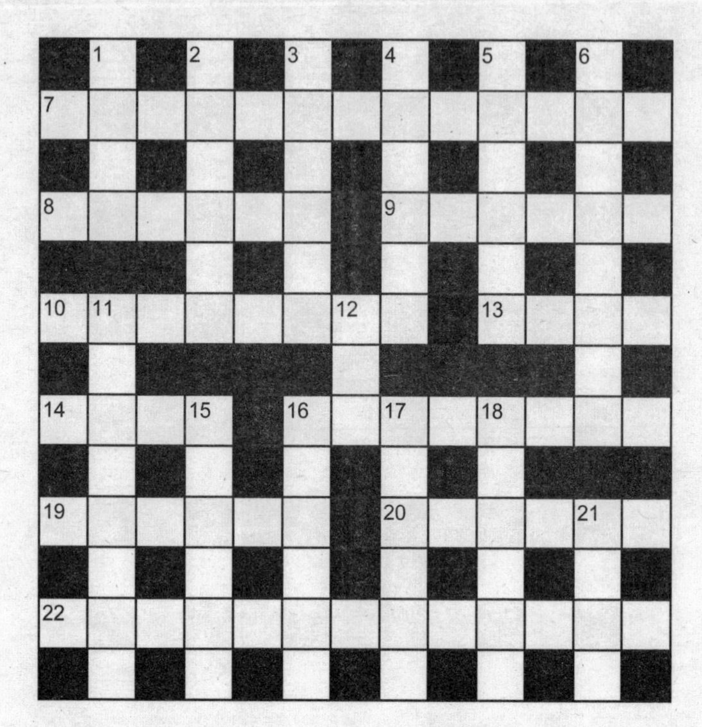

Across

7 Specialist in the care of children (13)
8 Erase (6)
9 Long-legged wading birds (6)
10 Feelings (8)
13 ___ feed: supply bit by bit (4)
14 Sudden quick movement (4)
16 Thinks about something continually (8)
19 Rue doing something (6)
20 Background actors (6)
22 Problem-solving method (5,3,5)

Down

1 Wise man; herb (4)
2 Promotional material (6)
3 Get by with what is available (4,2)
4 Wafer-thin potato slices (6)
5 Reverberated (6)
6 Rump (8)
11 Type of edible fruit (8)
12 Arrest (3)
15 Passage to the lungs and stomach (6)
16 Wanted criminal (6)
17 Travels too quickly (6)
18 Sixth planet from the sun (6)
21 River of central England (4)

PUZZLE 34

Across

7 Garment part that covers an arm (6)
8 Beat with the fists (6)
9 Money paid for a journey (4)
10 Collected or stored (8)
11 Blackberry bush (7)
13 Logical and easy to understand (5)
15 Examines quickly (5)
16 Support (7)
18 Proper; apt (8)
19 Ship's officer; friend (4)
21 Very brave and courageous (6)
22 Mild or kind (6)

Down

1 Prayer (4)
2 Firmness of purpose (13)
3 Aquatic bird (7)
4 Reproductive unit of fungi (5)
5 Ornamentation (13)
6 Use something to maximum advantage (8)
12 Hermits (8)
14 Medicated tablet (7)
17 Taken ___ : surprised (5)
20 Chat (4)

PUZZLE 35

Across

1 Large bag (4)
3 Soft leather shoe (8)
9 Pertaining to the tongue (7)
10 Extreme (5)
11 Sample of a larger group (5,7)
14 Pronoun used to refer to a ship (3)
16 Harsh and grating in sound (5)
17 Eg pecan (3)
18 Marksman (12)
21 Lively; cheerful (5)
22 Stand for small items (7)
23 Stops temporarily (8)
24 Purposes (4)

Down

1 Grammatical mistake (8)
2 Showing a willingness to achieve results (3-2)
4 Viscous liquid (3)
5 Female fellow national (12)
6 Take a seat (3,4)
7 Less than average tide (4)
8 Short tale told to children (7,5)
12 Gets less difficult (5)
13 Utters repeatedly (8)
15 Urges strongly (7)
19 Outdoor shelters (5)
20 Musical composition (4)
22 Marry (3)

PUZZLE 36

Across

1 At a distance (4)
3 Barely adequate (8)
9 Decaying (7)
10 Metal pieces used as money (5)
11 Without parallel (6,2,4)
13 Defame (6)
15 Sheep known for its wool (6)
17 Decisively (12)
20 The Hunter (constellation) (5)
21 Variety of rummy (7)
22 French bread stick (8)
23 Examine by touch (4)

Down

1 Substance used for polishing (8)
2 Loft (5)
4 Fourscore (6)
5 Awkward (12)
6 Dry red table wine of Italy (7)
7 Compass point (4)
8 Importance (12)
12 Hairstyle (8)
14 Circling around (7)
16 Variety of grape (6)
18 Follow on (5)
19 Implement for styling hair (4)

PUZZLE 37

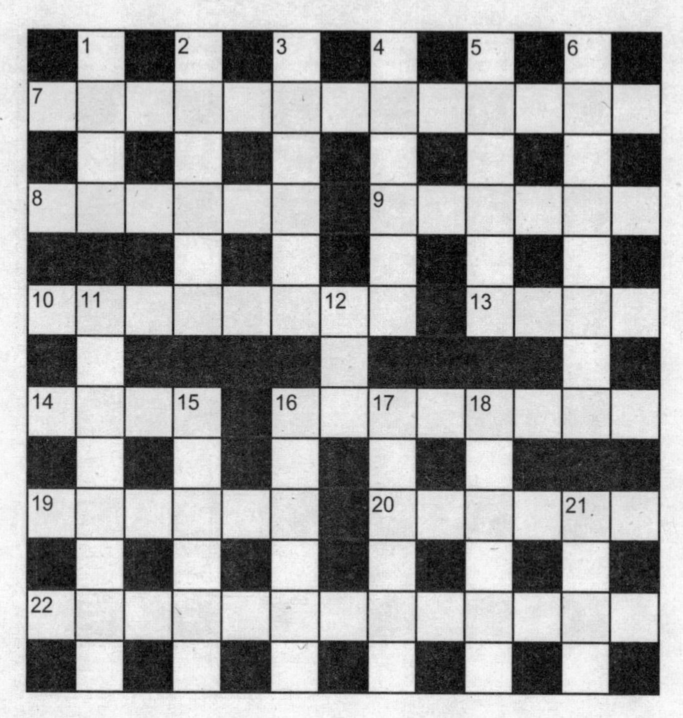

Across

7 US state (13)
8 A size of book page (6)
9 Move or travel hurriedly (6)
10 Go beyond a limit (8)
13 Raise (4)
14 European mountain range (4)
16 Taxonomic group (8)
19 Warning (6)
20 Owning (6)
22 Weather forecaster (13)

Down

1 Capital of Azerbaijan (4)
2 Loan shark (6)
3 Address a person boldly (6)
4 Keep secret (4,2)
5 Snores (anag) (6)
6 Cheapest berth on a ship (8)
11 Small communities (8)
12 ___ de Cologne: perfume (3)
15 Boiled slowly (6)
16 Parody (6)
17 On ___ of: in the interests of (6)
18 Destroy (6)
21 Kate ___ : British singer (4)

PUZZLE 38

Across

1 Estates where crops are grown on a large scale (11)
9 Practice of lending money at high interest rates (5)
10 Dr ___ : US rapper and record producer (3)
11 Bandage that supports an arm (5)
12 Songbirds (5)
13 Best (8)
16 Hypothesise (8)
18 Warming drink (5)
21 Recycle (5)
22 Sphere or globe (3)
23 Monster with nine heads (5)
24 A thing one excels at (6,5)

Down

2 Restricted in use (7)
3 Zeroes (7)
4 Grown-ups (6)
5 Pastoral poem (5)
6 Lowest level (5)
7 Act of giving up one's job (11)
8 Quantification (11)
14 Highest singing voice (7)
15 Tar-like hydrocarbon (7)
17 Sausage in a roll (3,3)
19 First appearance (5)
20 Loutish person (5)

PUZZLE 39

Across

1 Person who receives guests (4)
3 Type of Eurasian carp (8)
9 A bird's feathers collectively (7)
10 Fish basket (5)
11 Tear (3)
12 Horse sound (5)
13 With a forward motion (5)
15 Renown (5)
17 Two times (5)
18 Clothing needed for an activity (3)
19 Major African river (5)
20 ___ oil: product of the flax plant (7)
21 Football official (8)
22 Ruse (4)

Down

1 Excessively negative about (13)
2 Drink noisily (5)
4 Exaggerate (6)
5 Medicine taken when blocked-up (12)
6 Tool for the Arctic (3,4)
7 Unenthusiastically (4-9)
8 Quarrelsome and uncooperative (12)
14 French city (7)
16 Garden flowering plant (6)
18 Genuflect (5)

PUZZLE 40

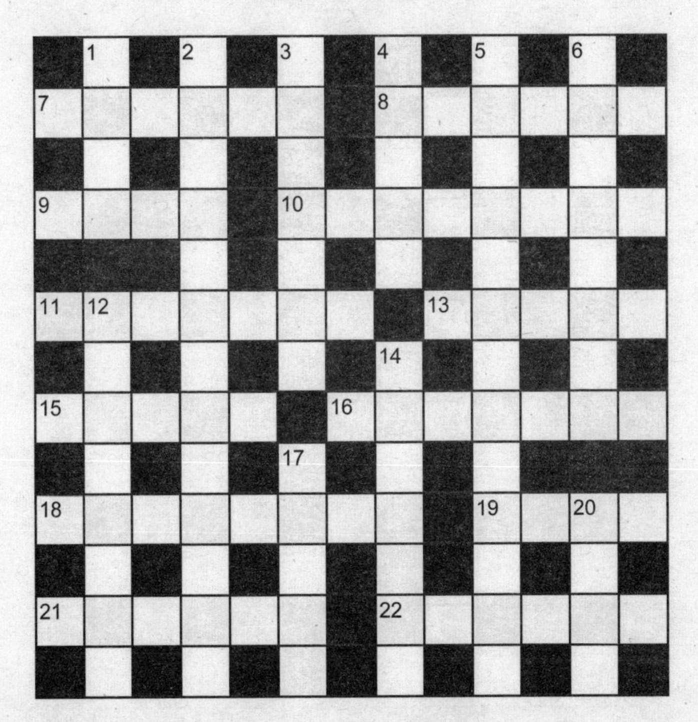

Across

7 Modern ballroom dance (3-3)
8 Experienced sailor (3,3)
9 Game played on horseback (4)
10 Bulbous perennial herb (8)
11 Self-important (7)
13 Cinders (5)
15 Large pebble (5)
16 Increasing rapidly (7)
18 One who travels to work regularly (8)
19 Cereal plant (4)
21 Aromatic plant of the parsley family (6)
22 Type of examination (6)

Down

1 US state (4)
2 Supporting musical part (13)
3 Timid (7)
4 The lion who rules over Narnia (5)
5 Scared (5-8)
6 Opposite of Northern (8)
12 Conclusions (8)
14 Morally depraved (7)
17 Stable compartment (5)
20 Restrain (4)

PUZZLE 41

Across

1 Sends out in the post (5)
4 Trap for the unwary (7)
8 Seats for more than one person (7)
9 Creative thoughts (5)
10 Freezes over (4)
11 User; purchaser (8)
14 Large container (6)
15 Pictures (6)
18 Beauty treatment (8)
19 Dam (4)
21 Drive forward (5)
23 Employment vacancy (7)
24 Uncovers; reveals (7)
25 Card game (5)

Down

1 Powerful dog (7)
2 Not in possession of the facts (2,3,4)
3 Slanting; oblique (4)
4 Points (anag) (6)
5 Arduous (8)
6 Beer (3)
7 Intense light beam (5)
12 Metallic element (9)
13 Single eyeglasses (8)
16 Scrawny (7)
17 Inspirational people (6)
18 Cereal plant (5)
20 Prophet (4)
22 Drivel; nonsense (3)

PUZZLE 42

Across

1 Endorsed (11)
9 Monetary unit of Serbia (5)
10 Obtained (3)
11 Russell ___ : Gladiator actor (5)
12 Vast multitude (5)
13 Unnecessary (8)
16 Person highly skilled in music (8)
18 Assumed proposition (5)
21 Ciphers (5)
22 Pouch; enclosed space (3)
23 Express gratitude (5)
24 Apron cutter (anag) (11)

Down

2 Relished (7)
3 Trying experiences (7)
4 Eg May and June (6)
5 Compass point (5)
6 Gardening tool (5)
7 Type of postage stamp (6-5)
8 Energetically or vigorously (11)
14 Snobbish (5-2)
15 A child beginning to walk (7)
17 Inborn (6)
19 Extremely small (prefix) (5)
20 ___ du Beke: ballroom dancer (5)

PUZZLE 43

1		2		■	3	4		5		6		7
	■		■	8	■		■		■		■	
9							■	10				
	■		■		■		■		■		■	
11					■	12						
	■	■	■		■		■		■		■	
13		14				■	15					
	■		■		■	16	■		■	■	■	
17							■	18		19		
	■		■		■		■		■		■	
20					■	21						
	■		■		■		■		■		■	
22								■	23			

Across

1 Not in favour (4)
3 Assembled (8)
9 Prompting device (7)
10 Short letters (5)
11 Greeting (5)
12 One who breaks the rules (7)
13 Excessively (6)
15 Scandinavian (6)
17 Fit in place (7)
18 Brief smell (5)
20 Religious doctrine (5)
21 Not physically existing (7)
22 Urging on (8)
23 Refuse to admit the truth of (4)

Down

1 Misplaced in time or date (13)
2 Sum; add up (5)
4 Business organisation (6)
5 From this time on (12)
6 Moved round an axis (7)
7 Shamefully (13)
8 Teacher (12)
14 Vital content (7)
16 Ten plus one (6)
19 Accustom (5)

PUZZLE 44

Across

1 Long for (5)
4 Take back (7)
7 Chequered cloth (5)
8 Country in Africa (8)
9 Small hill (5)
11 Musicians who perform alone (8)
15 In spite of the fact (8)
17 Inhales open-mouthed when sleepy (5)
19 Toes vary (anag) (8)
20 Concur (5)
21 Baffling puzzle (7)
22 Person who eats in a restaurant (5)

Down

1 Succinctly (9)
2 Irregularity (7)
3 Entangle (7)
4 Highly seasoned stew (6)
5 Controlling (6)
6 Reduce the temperature of (5)
10 Unit of astronomical length (5,4)
12 Unusually lucky (of a person's life) (7)
13 Instruction (7)
14 Purpose (6)
16 Vivacious (6)
18 Annoyed (5)

PUZZLE 45

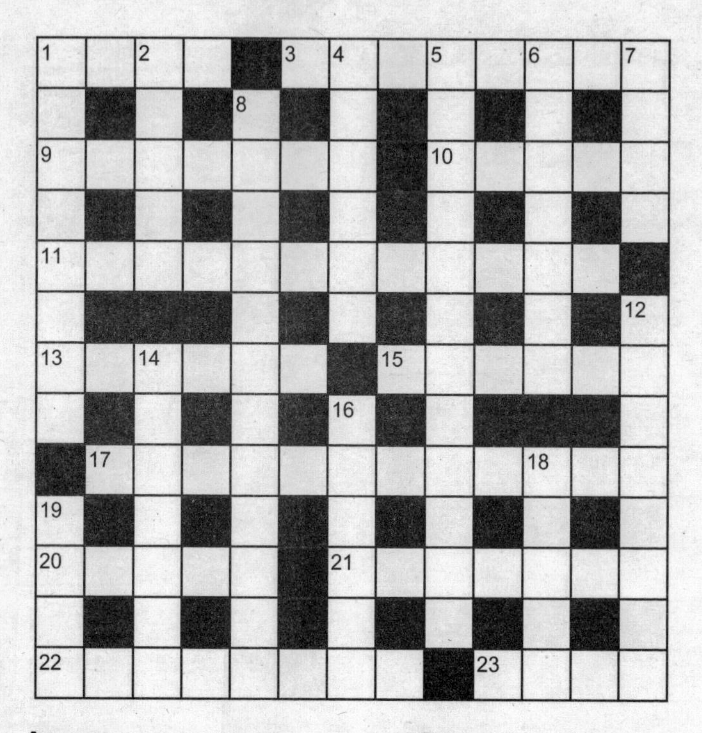

Across

1 Religious group (4)
3 Unrealistic (8)
9 Uncommon (7)
10 Anxious (5)
11 Act of influencing someone deviously (12)
13 Calamitous (6)
15 Mark of disgrace (6)
17 Relating to farming (12)
20 Remove errors from software (5)
21 Viewing (7)
22 Rigorous investigation (8)
23 Opposite of right (4)

Down

1 Extremely compatible partner (8)
2 Machine for making butter (5)
4 Form of a gene (6)
5 Person's physical state (12)
6 220 yards (7)
7 Puts down (4)
8 Shockingly (12)
12 Illumination from the sun (8)
14 Branch of maths (7)
16 Central parts of cells (6)
18 Increment (5)
19 Suggestion (4)

PUZZLE 46

Across

1 Thin fogs (5)
4 The first Gospel (7)
7 Annoy (5)
8 Foot soldiers (8)
9 Belief in a creator (5)
11 Piece of jewellery (8)
15 Alert in advance (8)
17 Melts (5)
19 Ruler who has absolute power (8)
20 Pertaining to birds (5)
21 Correctional institutions (7)
22 Nonsense (5)

Down

1 Malevolent (9)
2 Be adequate (7)
3 Cheat; con (7)
4 A system of measurement (6)
5 Swarmed (6)
6 Sprites (5)
10 Natural charm or appealing quality (9)
12 Enhance a photo (7)
13 Jeer noisily at (7)
14 Pinches sharply (6)
16 Musical works (6)
18 Hang in the air (5)

PUZZLE 47

Across

1 Prefix denoting one thousand (4)
3 White crested parrot (8)
9 Therein (anag) (7)
10 Exposes secret information (5)
11 Dispirited (12)
14 Soil; dirt (3)
16 Arm joint (5)
17 Thee (3)
18 Picture (12)
21 Confuse or obscure (5)
22 Bicycle stunt (7)
23 Forbearing (8)
24 Change (4)

Down

1 Royal domains (8)
2 Dens (5)
4 Belonging to us (3)
5 Orcas (6,6)
6 Ornamental stone openwork (7)
7 Kiln for drying hops (4)
8 Fast food item (12)
12 Automaton (5)
13 Most amusing (8)
15 Mournful (7)
19 Lazed (5)
20 Touch or lean on (4)
22 Finish first (3)

PUZZLE 48

Across

1 Froth of soap and water (4)
3 Transport systems (8)
9 Make a substantial profit (5,2)
10 Sticky (5)
11 Agreed upon by several parties (12)
13 Heading on a document (6)
15 Mexican cloak (6)
17 Considerately (12)
20 Gastropod (5)
21 Small flute (7)
22 Irritating (8)
23 Challenge; openly resist (4)

Down

1 Large Eurasian maple (8)
2 Reside (5)
4 Repeat (6)
5 Unemotional and practical (6-2-4)
6 Old-fashioned (7)
7 Utters (4)
8 Separately (12)
12 Plump (4-4)
14 Sheikdom in the Persian Gulf (7)
16 Frederic ___ : Polish composer (6)
18 Not tight (5)
19 One of the continents (4)

PUZZLE 49

Across

1 The squandering of money (11)
9 Nonsense (5)
10 Policeman (3)
11 Military vehicles (5)
12 Craftsman who uses stone (5)
13 Took a firm stand (8)
16 Progeny (8)
18 Approaches (5)
21 Sense of seeing (5)
22 ___ Barker: former tennis player (3)
23 Opinions (5)
24 Stargazers (11)

Down

2 Coolness (7)
3 Remain alive (7)
4 Courteous (6)
5 Unit of heat (5)
6 Killer whales (5)
7 Lack of being (11)
8 Dogmatic (11)
14 Mass of flowers (7)
15 Part of a gun (7)
17 Within this context (6)
19 Declares (5)
20 Divide by cutting (5)

PUZZLE 50

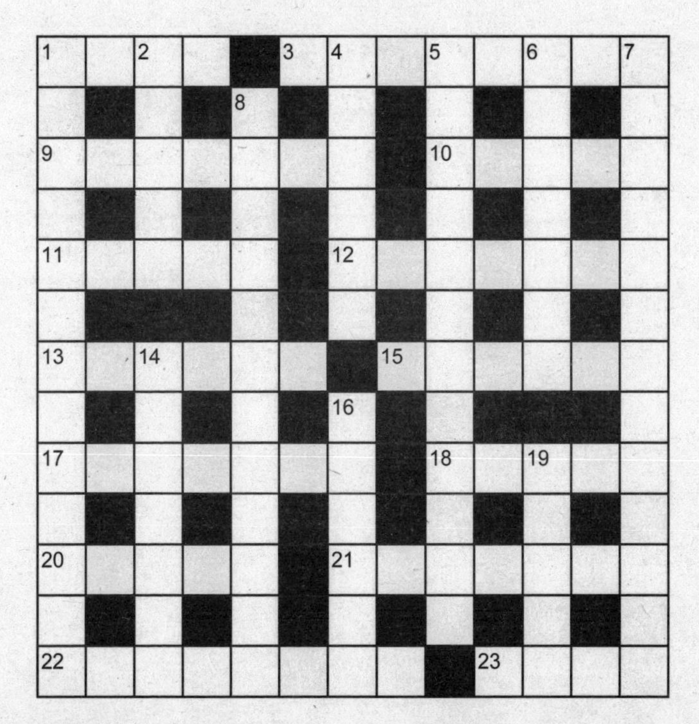

Across

1 Targets (4)
3 Informal term for a feline pet (8)
9 Write music (7)
10 Feudal vassal (5)
11 Pulls along forcefully (5)
12 Things that evoke reactions (7)
13 Most pleasant (6)
15 Narrow passage of water (6)
17 Movable models of people (7)
18 Fissures (5)
20 Circle a planet (5)
21 Pancreatic hormone (7)
22 All people (8)
23 Sector (4)

Down

1 Liable to get injured (8-5)
2 Snake (5)
4 Anxious (6)
5 Narcissism (4-8)
6 Pause in a line of verse (7)
7 Horror film directed by M. Night Shyamalan (3,5,5)
8 Constantly; always (12)
14 Competent (7)
16 Allocate (6)
19 A leaf of paper (5)

PUZZLE 51

Across

1 Search rigorously for (5)
4 Connected by kinship (7)
7 Got to one's feet (5)
8 Sonorous (8)
9 Becomes worn at the edges (5)
11 Put more in a container than it can hold (8)
15 Unable to appreciate music (4-4)
17 Valleys (5)
19 Monument (8)
20 Shyly (5)
21 Formal speech (7)
22 Daniel ___ : James Bond actor (5)

Down

1 Right side of a boat (9)
2 Long wandering journey (7)
3 Reintegrate (7)
4 Nasal (6)
5 Major blood vessel (6)
6 Dark wood (5)
10 Mixing a deck of cards (9)
12 Ordinary colloquial speech (7)
13 ___ Joan Hart: American actress (7)
14 Kitchen tool to remove vegetable skin (6)
16 Musical dramas (6)
18 Girls ___ : pop group (5)

PUZZLE 52

Across

1 Distinguishing characteristic (5)
4 Weighs down (7)
8 Morally right (7)
9 Paved area (5)
10 Mythical giant (4)
11 Give courage (8)
14 Area of flat unforested grassland (6)
15 Moved rhythmically to music (6)
18 Measure of the heat content of a system (8)
19 Opposite of shut (4)
21 Arrive at (5)
23 Passionate (7)
24 Hat with a wide brim (7)
25 Clock pointers (5)

Down

1 Slight earthquakes (7)
2 Loathsome (9)
3 Short nail (4)
4 Sincere; serious (6)
5 International negotiator (8)
6 Auction item (3)
7 Faint (5)
12 Deceit; trickery (9)
13 Spatters with liquid (8)
16 Domestic beasts of burden (7)
17 Abdominal organ (6)
18 Gets through merit (5)
20 ___ Hartnett: actor (4)
22 Consumed food (3)

PUZZLE 53

Across

1 Allot justice (4)
3 School bags (8)
9 Existing solely in name (7)
10 African country whose capital is Niamey (5)
11 Luckily (12)
14 Male aristocrat (3)
16 Top degree mark (5)
17 Asian sauce (3)
18 Unnecessarily careful (12)
21 Speak without preparation (2-3)
22 Distribute illicitly (7)
23 Fully aware (4-4)
24 Facial blemish (4)

Down

1 Clear or obvious (8)
2 Type of stopwatch (5)
4 Trouble in body or mind (3)
5 Act of discussing something; deliberation (12)
6 Envelops (7)
7 One of the Channel Islands (4)
8 Intolerable (12)
12 ___ firma: dry land (5)
13 Vision (8)
15 Reassess financial worth (7)
19 Type of primula (5)
20 Roman censor (4)
22 Farewell remark (3)

PUZZLE 54

Across

7 Unsuitable for living in (13)
8 Youth ___ : accommodation provider (6)
9 Crowd (6)
10 Cold Spanish tomato soup (8)
13 Unpleasant sensation (4)
14 Very short skirt or dress (4)
16 Plan anew (8)
19 Expresses one's opinion (6)
20 Purchased (6)
22 Disreputable (13)

Down

1 Toon (anag) (4)
2 Arch of the foot (6)
3 Strong-smelling bulb (6)
4 Inexpensive restaurant (6)
5 Ancient Persian governor (6)
6 Holding on tightly (8)
11 Female pilot (8)
12 Gradation of colour (3)
15 Whole (6)
16 Uttered coarsely (6)
17 Trash (6)
18 Sharp shrill cry (6)
21 Sacred (4)

PUZZLE 55

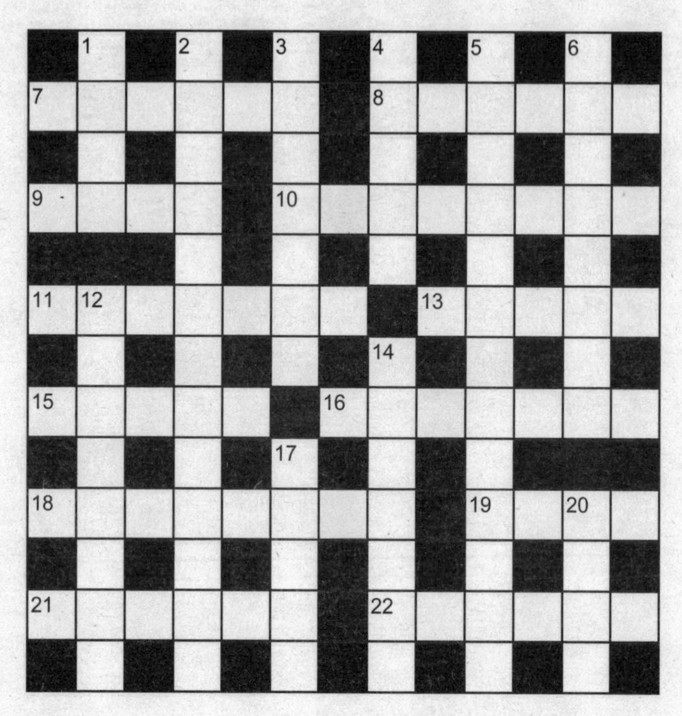

Across

7 Mourn the loss of (6)
8 Title placed before a name (6)
9 Foot of a horse (4)
10 Male riders (8)
11 Eg Evita (7)
13 Select; formally approve (5)
15 Isle of ___ : island near Southampton (5)
16 Small apes (7)
18 Mind reader (8)
19 Tardy (4)
21 Sagacious (6)
22 Bear witness (6)

Down

1 Vigour (4)
2 Sanctimonious (4-9)
3 Person with auburn hair (7)
4 Boxes lightly (5)
5 Reliability (13)
6 Longevity of an individual (8)
12 Cosmos (8)
14 Public road (7)
17 Natural underground chambers (5)
20 Long pointed tooth (4)

PUZZLE 56

Across

1 Group of players (4)
3 Clergyman (8)
9 Newspaper audience (7)
10 Large spoon with a long handle (5)
11 Practice of mentioning famous people one knows (4-8)
14 Excavate (3)
16 Individual things (5)
17 Chopping tool (3)
18 Terrified or extremely shocked (6-6)
21 Eg taste or touch (5)
22 Farewell remark (7)
23 Of striking appropriateness (8)
24 Goes wrong (4)

Down

1 Lamentation (8)
2 Warning of danger (5)
4 Belonging to him (3)
5 Best starting placement in a motor race (4,8)
6 Written additions (7)
7 Negative votes (4)
8 Main premises of a company (12)
12 Willow twig (5)
13 Irresponsible (8)
15 Adult (5-2)
19 Brown earth pigment (5)
20 ___ Fisher: actress (4)
22 Tug (anag) (3)

PUZZLE 57

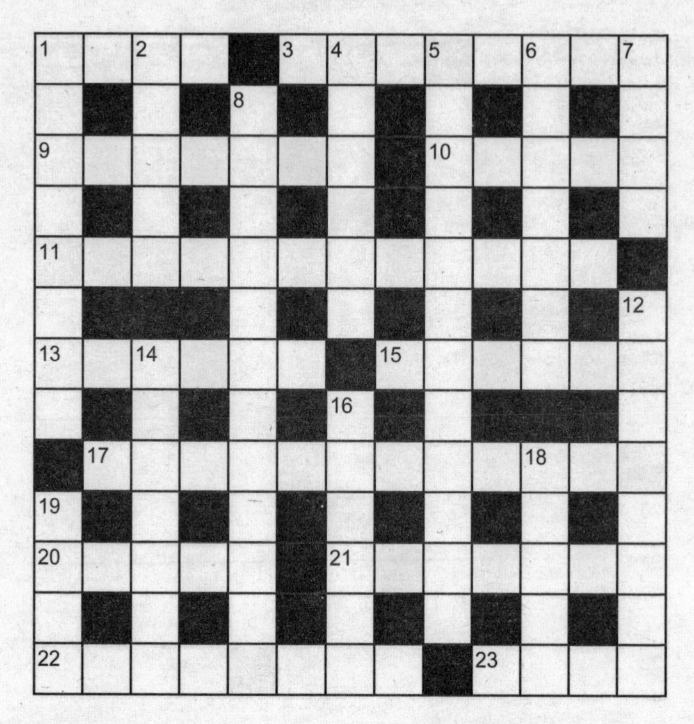

Across

1 Remedy (4)
3 Fearless and brave (8)
9 ___ Down the Wind: musical (7)
10 Outstanding (of a debt) (5)
11 Repository for misplaced items (4,8)
13 Appease (6)
15 Shrub with glossy leaves (6)
17 Unhappy (12)
20 Seemingly (combining form) (5)
21 Extraordinary occurrence (7)
22 Inattentively; vaguely (8)
23 English public school (4)

Down

1 European primulas (8)
2 Causes great damage (5)
4 Liam ___ : Irish actor (6)
5 Large Brazilian city (3,2,7)
6 Artist (7)
7 Canines (4)
8 Bewilderment (12)
12 Short heavy club (8)
14 Medieval body armour (7)
16 Type of living organism (6)
18 Implied without being stated (5)
19 Greenish blue colour (4)

PUZZLE 58

Across

1 Contaminate (6)
4 State of matter (6)
9 Speak haltingly (7)
10 Edible marine molluscs (7)
11 Simple song (5)
12 Conventions (5)
14 Cuts slightly (5)
15 Doctrine; system of beliefs (5)
17 Decrease; lessen (5)
18 Able to pay one's debts (7)
20 Cost (7)
21 Gets to one's feet (6)
22 Composite of different species (6)

Down

1 Situated within the confines of (6)
2 Break (8)
3 Snug and nice to wear (5)
5 Periods of instruction (7)
6 Tender to the touch (4)
7 Comes up (6)
8 Company that transmits TV shows (11)
13 Rain tree (anag) (8)
14 Collection of sheets of paper (7)
15 Universe (6)
16 Myth (6)
17 Put into use (5)
19 Tibetan Buddhist monk (4)

PUZZLE 59

Across

1 Take a breath owing to astonishment (4)
3 Not genuine (8)
9 Rowers (7)
10 Bore into (5)
11 Senseless (5)
12 Eyelash cosmetic (7)
13 Mischievous (6)
15 Russian carriage (6)
17 Contrary to (7)
18 Lump or bump (5)
20 Clumsy (5)
21 Unusually large (7)
22 Impartial parties (8)
23 Increases; sums up (4)

Down

1 Exaltation (13)
2 Country in the Middle East (5)
4 Country in Central America; wide-brimmed hat (6)
5 Reallocate (12)
6 Paper folding (7)
7 Conscious knowledge of oneself (4-9)
8 Imitator (12)
14 Flat highland (7)
16 Walk casually (6)
19 Scottish landholder (5)

PUZZLE 60

Across

1 Barber's tools (6)
7 Consisting of fine particles (8)
8 Item constructed by a spider (3)
9 Recover (6)
10 Silly person (4)
11 Strong currents of air (5)
13 Permitted (7)
15 Flowed (of liquid) (7)
17 Grave and serious (5)
21 Breezy (4)
22 Followed (6)
23 Large deer (3)
24 Old toll road (8)
25 Invalidate (6)

Down

1 Arguing (6)
2 Striped animals (6)
3 Lance (5)
4 Diminish (7)
5 Moderately rich (4-2-2)
6 Remove from office (6)
12 Delaying (8)
14 Advantage gained from something (7)
16 Repulsive (6)
18 A wine shop (6)
19 Novice (6)
20 Trembling poplar (5)

PUZZLE 61

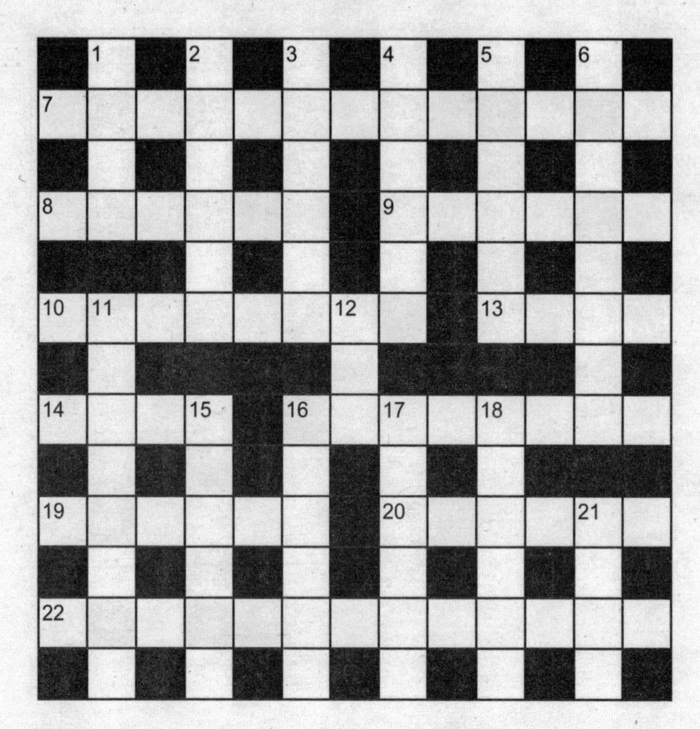

Across

7 Amiably (4-9)
8 Grunts (anag) (6)
9 ___ Dorries: Conservative MP (6)
10 Upset; hurt (8)
13 Close by (4)
14 Young sheep (4)
16 Put back (8)
19 Love affairs (6)
20 Shackle (6)
22 Harmlessly (13)

Down

1 Bird of the rail family (4)
2 Advance evidence for (6)
3 Tattered (6)
4 Flipped (6)
5 Connective tissue (6)
6 Lengthen (8)
11 Break into pieces (8)
12 Female sheep (3)
15 Feigns (6)
16 Hurries (6)
17 Most secure (6)
18 Series of eight notes (6)
21 ___ Fitzgerald: famous jazz singer (4)

PUZZLE 62

Across

1 Killer whale (4)
3 Instalments of a TV series (8)
9 Medieval cell (7)
10 Animal that uses two legs for walking (5)
11 Convalescence (12)
14 Annoy continuously (3)
16 Noble gas (5)
17 Much ___ About Nothing: play (3)
18 What p.m. stands for (4,8)
21 Prophet (5)
22 Reduced in scope or length (3-4)
23 Strip of land by a highway (8)
24 Arthur ___ : former US tennis player (4)

Down

1 Sorting (8)
2 Sceptic (5)
4 Joke (3)
5 Strengthen; confirm (12)
6 Certificate (7)
7 Team (4)
8 Peruse matter (anag) (12)
12 Natural elevation (5)
13 Start (8)
15 US state (7)
19 People who are greatly admired (5)
20 Couple (4)
22 Fish often eaten with chips (3)

PUZZLE 63

Across

1 Poisonous green gas (8)
5 The wise men (4)
8 Throw forcefully (5)
9 Expression of blame (7)
10 Country whose capital is Tirana (7)
12 Primarily (7)
14 Painters (7)
16 Type of cell division (7)
18 One of the planets (7)
19 Adult insect stage (5)
20 Egg-shaped (4)
21 Franking (8)

Down

1 Part of a sleeve (4)
2 Linger aimlessly (6)
3 Official lists or records (9)
4 Where one finds Oslo (6)
6 Exist in great numbers (6)
7 Pumps air into (8)
11 Microorganism (9)
12 Spanish dance (8)
13 Ideally perfect state (6)
14 Agreement (6)
15 Expedition to see animals (6)
17 Tune (4)

PUZZLE 64

Across

1 Gelatinous substance (4)
3 Showing embarrassment (8)
9 Light fabric often made of silk (7)
10 Period of keeping awake to pray (5)
11 Very cold (3)
12 ___ Coogan: English comedian (5)
13 Swift (5)
15 West Indian dance (5)
17 Store of hoarded wealth (5)
18 Very small (3)
19 Submerged ridges of rock (5)
20 Cigar (7)
21 Campaigner (8)
22 Ale (4)

Down

1 Pertaining to building design (13)
2 Friendship (5)
4 Finish a telephone call (4,2)
5 Person who listens into conversations (12)
6 Act of entering (7)
7 Fairground ride (6-7)
8 Easily (12)
14 Saying (7)
16 Cuts up meat very finely (6)
18 Tower (anag) (5)

PUZZLE 65

Across

1 Captivates (5)
4 Deity (7)
8 Time off (7)
9 Confess to (5)
10 Fancy (4)
11 Unknown person (8)
14 Annually (6)
15 Comfort in a time of misfortune (6)
18 Feigns (8)
19 Quantity of bread (4)
21 Business proposal; playing field (5)
23 Make loud demands (7)
24 Film or play texts (7)
25 Takes a break (5)

Down

1 Corridor (7)
2 Arise; start (9)
3 Surprise; amaze (4)
4 In the ___ : Elvis Presley song (6)
5 Organ stop (8)
6 Tree (3)
7 Discourage (5)
12 Alluring (9)
13 Reliable stock market company (4,4)
16 Exertions (7)
17 Proclamations (6)
18 Long tubes (5)
20 Equitable (4)
22 Rocky hill (3)

PUZZLE 66

Across

1 Long walk (4)
3 Manufacturer (8)
9 Ricochet (7)
10 Scorch (5)
11 Skilled joiner (12)
14 Animal enclosure (3)
16 Fault (5)
17 Piece of pasture (3)
18 Penny-pinching (12)
21 Hymn of thanksgiving (5)
22 Vending (7)
23 Establish firmly (8)
24 Writing fluids (4)

Down

1 Printed version of data on a computer (4,4)
2 Skewered meat (5)
4 Relieve or free from (3)
5 Hopelessly (12)
6 Curdle (7)
7 Roll of photographic film (4)
8 Most perfect example of a quality (12)
12 Monotonous hum (5)
13 Minced meat products (8)
15 Most tidy (7)
19 Edible pungent bulb (5)
20 Church recess (4)
22 Dry (of wine) (3)

PUZZLE 67

Across

1 Sheer dress fabric (7)
6 Curved shape (3)
8 Violent weather (5)
9 Momentum (7)
10 Pains (5)
11 Defeat (8)
13 Season before Christmas (6)
15 Oppose a plan successfully (6)
18 Giving off (8)
19 Half of six (5)
21 Move apart (7)
22 Titles (5)
23 Consume a meal (3)
24 Sully (7)

Down

2 Took away (7)
3 Observing (8)
4 Take as being true (6)
5 Brown carbonated drink (4)
6 Ancient large storage jar (7)
7 Be composed of (7)
12 At all; of any kind (8)
13 Organic solvent (7)
14 Bright and striking (7)
16 Goes back on a promise (7)
17 Among (6)
20 Prestigious TV award (4)

PUZZLE 68

Across

1 Square measure (4)
3 ___ Verdi: composer (8)
9 Restores honour (7)
10 Variety of chalcedony (5)
11 Cameraman (12)
13 Unrefined (6)
15 Pygmy chimpanzee (6)
17 Myopic (5-7)
20 Not concealed (5)
21 Foot pedal (7)
22 Scottish seaport (8)
23 Exercise venues (4)

Down

1 Area an aeroplane can fly in (8)
2 Wireless (5)
4 Place inside something else (6)
5 Having an acrid wit (5-7)
6 Inactive pill (7)
7 Saw; observed (4)
8 Showed (12)
12 Children who are beginning to walk (8)
14 Eg Paula Radcliffe (7)
16 African bloodsucking insect (6)
18 Toy bear (5)
19 System of contemplation (4)

PUZZLE 69

Across

1 Otherwise (4)
3 Military units (8)
9 Primarily (7)
10 Rise (3,2)
11 Destruction (12)
14 Domestic bovine animal (3)
16 Large bird of prey (5)
17 Also (3)
18 Not guided by good sense (12)
21 Camera image (abbrev) (5)
22 Sudden increase (7)
23 Remaining (8)
24 Close (4)

Down

1 Make gradual inroads (8)
2 Flow with a whirling motion (5)
4 Put down (3)
5 Fellowship (12)
6 Distant settlement (7)
7 Exhausts; pass (anag) (4)
8 Unofficially (3,3,6)
12 Fits of violent anger (5)
13 Anticlimax (8)
15 Transparent envelope panels (7)
19 Mooring for a ship (5)
20 Strong pole on a ship (4)
22 ___ Thurman: Hollywood star (3)

PUZZLE 70

Across

1 Deep regret (11)
9 Ire (5)
10 Very small child (3)
11 Walk with an affected gait (5)
12 Electrician (5)
13 Struggle helplessly (8)
16 Creature that eats both meat and plants (8)
18 Four-wheeled vehicle (5)
21 Coral reef (5)
22 Umpire (abbrev) (3)
23 Epic poem ascribed to Homer (5)
24 Celebrity (11)

Down

2 Elate (7)
3 Thin coating of metal (7)
4 Small worry; irritate (6)
5 Hurled away (5)
6 Semiaquatic mammal (5)
7 Advance quickly (4-7)
8 Narrator (11)
14 Stronghold (7)
15 Small crown (7)
17 Slander (6)
19 Blunder (5)
20 Snail (anag) (5)

PUZZLE 71

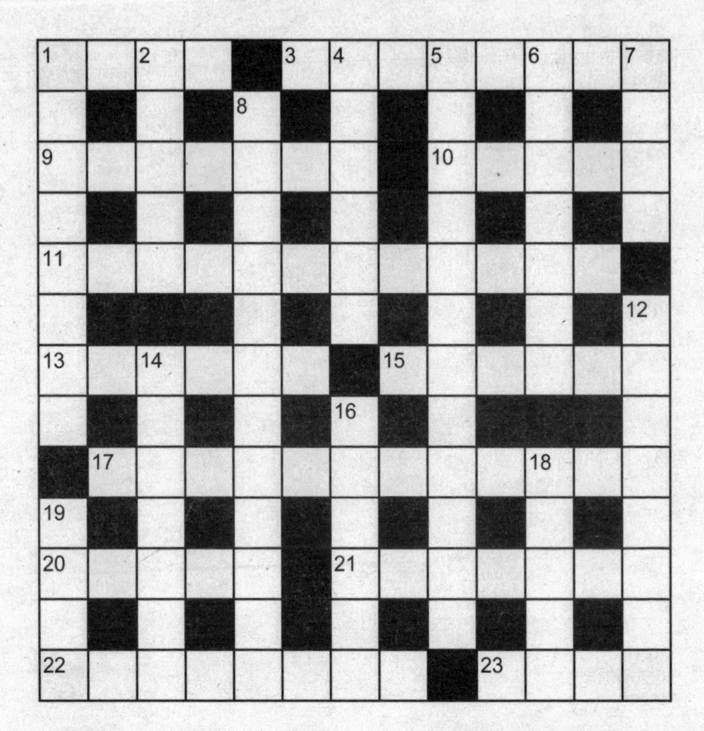

Across

1 Price (4)
3 The scholastic world (8)
9 Collided with another vehicle (7)
10 Denim (anag) (5)
11 Knowing more than one language (12)
13 Thrill (6)
15 Brought about (6)
17 Not intoxicating (of a drink) (12)
20 Subject of a talk (5)
21 Coat with precious gems (7)
22 People in hospital (8)
23 Singe; burn (4)

Down

1 Long green vegetable (8)
2 Growl with bare teeth (of dogs) (5)
4 One who carries golf clubs (6)
5 Data about a population (12)
6 Handbooks (7)
7 German car manufacturer (4)
8 24th December (9,3)
12 Teacher (8)
14 Nearest (7)
16 Stress mark (6)
18 Giggle (5)
19 Finish (4)

PUZZLE 72

Across

1 Smudge (4)
3 Street closed at one end (3-2-3)
9 Water-bearing rock (7)
10 Radiancy; gloss (5)
11 Come to a point (5)
12 Temporary measure (7)
13 Spanish festival (6)
15 One who judges a literary work (6)
17 Imaginary creature (7)
18 Enthusiasm (5)
20 Performing a deed (5)
21 Book of the Bible (7)
22 Drink consumed before bed (8)
23 Pottery material (4)

Down

1 Animal used for heavy work (5,2,6)
2 Take the place of (5)
4 Turbulence (6)
5 Disheartening (12)
6 Cunning (7)
7 Prominently (13)
8 Malice ___ : intention to harm (12)
14 Going out (7)
16 Complex problem (6)
19 Mexican plant fibre (5)

PUZZLE 73

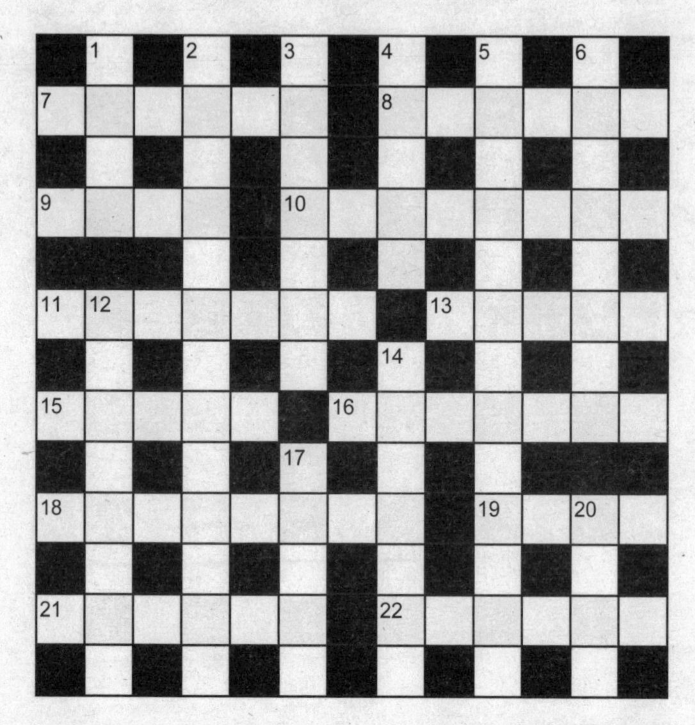

Across

7 Apprehend someone (6)
8 Bowed string instruments (6)
9 Charges (4)
10 Preserve (8)
11 Examines in detail (7)
13 Extra advantage (5)
15 Organ situated in the skull (5)
16 Armoury (7)
18 Frozen dessert (3,5)
19 Absorbent pad (4)
21 Maxim (6)
22 Stopped (6)

Down

1 Centre (4)
2 Type of surveillance system (6-7)
3 First in importance (7)
4 Use to one's advantage (5)
5 Contentious (13)
6 A Roman emperor (8)
12 Traitor (8)
14 Facial expression showing disgust (7)
17 Chunk (5)
20 Inspires fear and wonder (4)

PUZZLE 74

Across

1 Limitation (11)
9 Postpone (5)
10 What our planet orbits (3)
11 Faint bird cry (5)
12 Speed (5)
13 Wheeled supermarket vehicles (8)
16 Standards (8)
18 Under (5)
21 Japanese mattress (5)
22 Small social insect (3)
23 Cram (5)
24 Going on and on (5-6)

Down

2 Surround entirely (7)
3 Larval frog (7)
4 State of dishonour (6)
5 Portable source of light (5)
6 Drives out from a place (5)
7 Disturb the status quo (4,3,4)
8 Performer (11)
14 Manned (7)
15 Formal speech (7)
17 Decline to do something; rubbish (6)
19 Machine for shaping wood or metal (5)
20 Use inefficiently; rubbish (5)

PUZZLE 75

Across

1 Does the same thing again (7)
6 Container for a drink (3)
8 US state (5)
9 Come out on top (7)
10 Despised (5)
11 Porcelain (8)
13 Upward slope (6)
15 Nastily (6)
18 Neutral particle with negligible mass (8)
19 Rope used to catch cattle (5)
21 Quivering singing effect (7)
22 Unwarranted (5)
23 Plant fluid (3)
24 Abounding (7)

Down

2 People who make money (7)
3 Frightening (8)
4 Sandstone constituent (6)
5 Hasty or reckless (4)
6 Have within (7)
7 Resembling dust (7)
12 Person with an appreciation of beauty (8)
13 Having no purpose at all (7)
14 Tightly framed camera shot (5-2)
16 Fatty substance (7)
17 Group of six (6)
20 Chances of winning (4)

PUZZLE 76

Across

1 Exist permanently in (6)
4 Walk laboriously (6)
9 Mixed up (7)
10 Endure (7)
11 Enclosed (5)
12 Big cats (5)
14 Soft paste (5)
15 Mammal that eats bamboo (5)
17 Smooth; groom (5)
18 Twisting force (7)
20 Finished (3,4)
21 Well-being (6)
22 Stagnation or inactivity (6)

Down

1 Force fluid into (6)
2 Simple and unsophisticated (8)
3 Governed (5)
5 Willingly (7)
6 Barrier between rooms (4)
7 Raise in relief (6)
8 Serving to enlighten; instructive (11)
13 Notes; sees (8)
14 Not in a hurry (7)
15 Violent uprising (6)
16 Accustoms to something (6)
17 Person who flies an aircraft (5)
19 Roster (4)

PUZZLE 77

Across

1 Greek wine (7)
6 Female kangaroo (3)
8 Find the solution (5)
9 Eg from Madrid (7)
10 Remain very close to (5)
11 Chiropody (8)
13 London suburb (6)
15 Sagacity (6)
18 Gratification (8)
19 Colossus (5)
21 Scent; smell (7)
22 Golf clubs (5)
23 Snake-like fish (3)
24 Graceful in form (7)

Down

2 Look into (7)
3 Copycat (8)
4 Hoarse (anag) (6)
5 Coalition of countries (4)
6 Stated the meaning of (7)
7 Witty saying (7)
12 Have a different opinion (8)
13 Unit of square measure (7)
14 Nasal opening (7)
16 Rower (7)
17 Pass (of time) (6)
20 Noble gas (4)

PUZZLE 78

Across

1 Low value US coins (5)
4 Largest planet (7)
8 Trucks (7)
9 Send money in payment (5)
10 Alcoholic drink (4)
11 Narrow street or passage (8)
14 This Is ___ Tap: film (6)
15 Less warm (6)
18 Occurring regularly (8)
19 The southern part of France (4)
21 Donor (5)
23 Angers (7)
24 Most profound (7)
25 Herb (5)

Down

1 Upright pillars (7)
2 Royal mint (anag) (9)
3 Mix; agitate (4)
4 Fairly (6)
5 Supplier (8)
6 ___ Thumb: folklore character (3)
7 Irritable (5)
12 Readily (9)
13 Veteran of battle (8)
16 Print anew (7)
17 Broadest (6)
18 Stiff (5)
20 Backbone; fortitude (4)
22 Compete (3)

PUZZLE 79

Across

1 Send down a ball in cricket (4)
3 Lower jaw (8)
9 Coarsen (anag) (7)
10 Book (5)
11 Ill-mannered (12)
13 Gossip or idle talk (6)
15 Expels (6)
17 Restrict within limits (12)
20 Capital of Vietnam (5)
21 Mournful (7)
22 Solidity (8)
23 Hair colourants (4)

Down

1 Make valid retrospectively (8)
2 Internal parasites (5)
4 Classify (6)
5 Evening dress for men (6,6)
6 Temporary camp (7)
7 Jellied ___ : English dish (4)
8 Remembrance (12)
12 Fragrant toiletries (8)
14 Narrower (7)
16 Urges to act (6)
18 Coldly (5)
19 Cook (4)

PUZZLE 80

Across

7 Noteworthy and rare (13)
8 What a spider spins (6)
9 Son of Daedalus in Greek mythology (6)
10 Garment worn after a shower (8)
13 Paradise garden (4)
14 Flag lily (4)
16 Facing (8)
19 Furthest; extreme (6)
20 Relations by marriage (2-4)
22 In memory of something (13)

Down

1 International exhibition (4)
2 Process of increasing in size (6)
3 Embarrassing mistake (3-3)
4 Value; respect (6)
5 Enter a country by force (6)
6 Altercation (8)
11 Process of adding air (8)
12 Dance (3)
15 Tempestuous (6)
16 Top aim (anag) (6)
17 Small monastery (6)
18 Breaks apart forcibly (6)
21 Slightly curling lock of hair (4)

PUZZLE 81

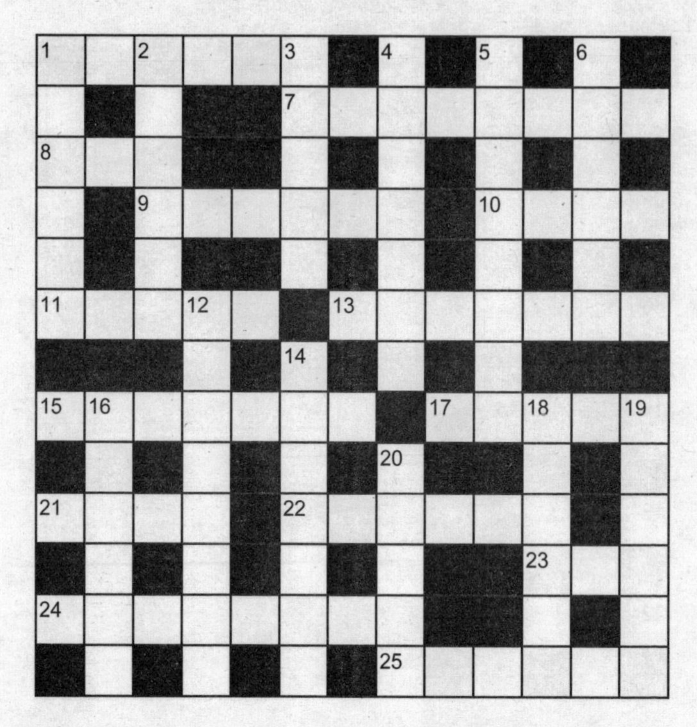

Across

1 Relating to wolves (6)
7 Easily evaporated (of a substance) (8)
8 Court (3)
9 Celestial body (6)
10 Geek (4)
11 Threads or fibres (5)
13 Relaxes (7)
15 Stored away (7)
17 Active cause (5)
21 Ill-mannered person (4)
22 With great effort (3,3)
23 Rodent (3)
24 Dancing hall (8)
25 Exceptionally successful (6)

Down

1 Restrained and subtle (3-3)
2 Suitable; apt (6)
3 Levels out (5)
4 Brazenly obvious (7)
5 Rank or status (8)
6 Made a loud and harsh sound (6)
12 Channels of the nose (8)
14 Treason (anag) (7)
16 Chest (6)
18 Catch or snare (6)
19 Stifled laugh (6)
20 Ball of lead (5)

PUZZLE 82

Across

1 Jobs (11)
9 Nearby (5)
10 Religious sister (3)
11 Trite (anag) (5)
12 Stinging insects (5)
13 Febrile (8)
16 Food poisoning (8)
18 Beneath (5)
21 Small firework (5)
22 Performed an action (3)
23 Holding or grasping device (5)
24 Eg Huw Edwards and Fiona Bruce (11)

Down

2 Prisoner (7)
3 Discard from memory (7)
4 Right to enter (6)
5 Relation by marriage (2-3)
6 Dressed to the ___: elaborately clothed (5)
7 Beyond acceptability (3,2,6)
8 Incalculable (11)
14 Decided based on little evidence (7)
15 Sweet alcoholic spirit (7)
17 Juicy citrus fruit (6)
19 Evade (5)
20 Religious acts (5)

PUZZLE 83

Across

1 Piece of evidence (4)
3 White flakes in the hair (8)
9 Chemical element (7)
10 European country (5)
11 Relit (anag) (5)
12 Small-scale model (7)
13 Motor vehicle storage building (6)
15 Characteristic (6)
17 Someone who studies data (7)
18 Good sense; reasoned judgement (5)
20 Emerge from an egg (5)
21 Seven-a-side game (7)
22 Make fun of (8)
23 In an inactive way; with no particular purpose (4)

Down

1 Code-breaker (13)
2 Up to the time when (5)
4 Fleet of ships (6)
5 Very sad (12)
6 Ignorant of something (7)
7 Tremendously (13)
8 Written in pictorial symbols (12)
14 Cooked meat in the oven (7)
16 Not written in any key (of music) (6)
19 Impressive in appearance (5)

PUZZLE 84

Across

1 Visage (4)
3 Geniality (8)
9 Not varying (7)
10 Chooses (5)
11 Long essay (12)
14 Title of a married woman (3)
16 ___ Cable: leader of the Liberal Democrats (5)
17 Long period of time (3)
18 Skilfully prepared refined food (5,7)
21 Capital of Japan (5)
22 An acted riddle (7)
23 Agreeable (8)
24 Stained a fabric or hair (4)

Down

1 Domains (8)
2 Friends (5)
4 Lyric poem (3)
5 Conjectural (12)
6 Microorganism (7)
7 Freedom from difficulty or hardship (4)
8 Perceptions (12)
12 Invigorating medicine (5)
13 Note (4,4)
15 Restrain; limit (7)
19 European country (5)
20 Pace (4)
22 Metal container (3)

PUZZLE 85

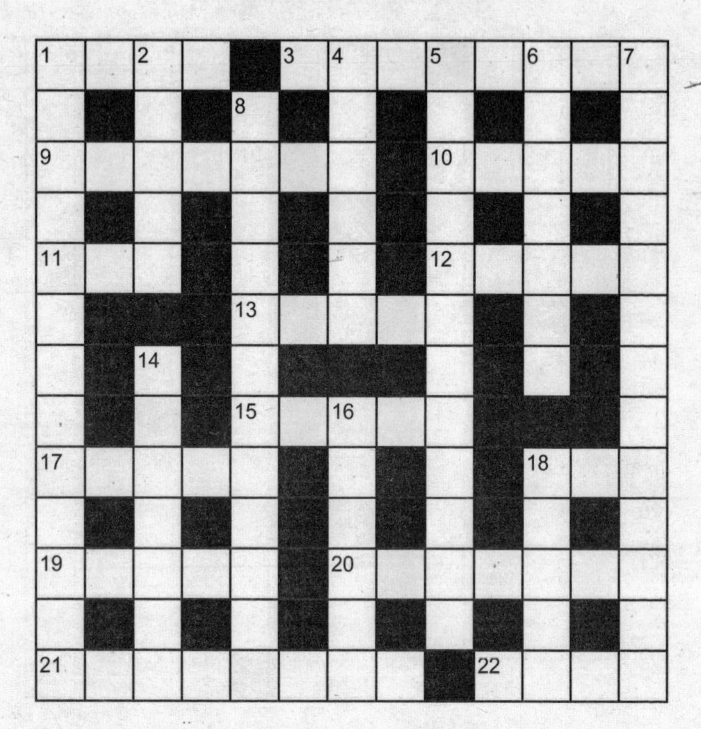

Across

1 Stirling ___ : racing driver (4)
3 Person who writes music (8)
9 Apprehensive (7)
10 Kick out (5)
11 Cook in hot oil (3)
12 Run away with a lover (5)
13 Finished (5)
15 One side of a gem (5)
17 Customary (5)
18 Bleat of a sheep (3)
19 Sea duck (5)
20 Rupert ___ : English actor (7)
21 Accented (8)
22 Cry of derision (4)

Down

1 Makers (13)
2 Penitent (5)
4 Expelled from office (6)
5 Planned in advance (12)
6 Assume (7)
7 Amusement park ride (6,7)
8 Upper chamber in Parliament (5,2,5)
14 Quiver (7)
16 Dairy product (6)
18 Musical note (5)

PUZZLE 86

Across

1 Paying out money to buy goods (8)
5 Dutch cheese (4)
9 Assumed identities (7)
10 Words that identify things (5)
11 Propitious (10)
14 Introduction (4-2)
15 Historical records (6)
17 US state (10)
20 Sandy fawn colour (5)
21 Aseptic (7)
22 Therefore (Latin) (4)
23 Bite (8)

Down

1 Crush with a sharp blow (4)
2 Wicked (4)
3 Displeased (12)
4 Person who fails to turn up (2-4)
6 Percussion sound (8)
7 Uses seam (anag) (8)
8 Inflexible (12)
12 Easily calmed (8)
13 Leaping up or over (8)
16 Wall painting; mural (6)
18 Piece of land under the feudal system (4)
19 Distribute playing cards (4)

PUZZLE 87

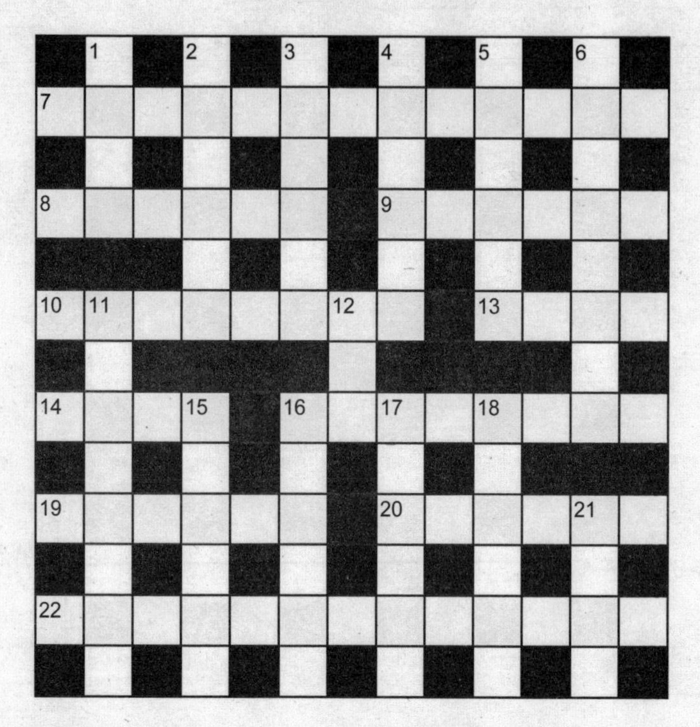

Across

7 Group of stars (13)
8 Lapis ___ : blue gemstone (6)
9 Plan; strategy (6)
10 Undomesticated animals (8)
13 Spheres (4)
14 ___ Sharif: Egyptian actor (4)
16 Complains (8)
19 Breathe in (6)
20 Meal eaten in the fresh air (6)
22 Amusement (13)

Down

1 Garment of ancient Rome (4)
2 Distributed (6)
3 Third sign of the zodiac (6)
4 Happy; carefree (6)
5 Plaster for coating walls (6)
6 Friendly and outgoing (8)
11 Impending (8)
12 Coniferous tree (3)
15 Raised (6)
16 Welcomes (6)
17 Not yet settled (of a bill) (6)
18 Develop into (6)
21 Pubs (4)

PUZZLE 88

Across

1 Have faith in (5)
4 Eg Rebecca Adlington (7)
8 Cattle herders (US) (7)
9 Songbird (5)
10 Extreme anger (4)
11 Translucently clear (8)
14 Book of accounts (6)
15 Opposite of fast forward (6)
18 Designers of trendy clothes (8)
19 Lead singer of U2 (4)
21 Supple (5)
23 Used for the storage of fat (of tissue) (7)
24 Tapering stone pillar (7)
25 Type of verse (5)

Down

1 Considerate; diplomatic (7)
2 Strange (9)
3 Snatched (4)
4 Long strips of cloth (6)
5 Driven to action (8)
6 Soak up; wipe away (3)
7 Judged; ranked (5)
12 Treatment of the feet (9)
13 Disease (8)
16 Bishop's jurisdiction (7)
17 Seek to hurt (6)
18 Group of shots (5)
20 Row or level of a structure (4)
22 Draw (3)

PUZZLE 89

Across

1 Functioned (8)
5 ___ Khan: British boxer (4)
8 Franz ___ : novelist (5)
9 Time between events (7)
10 Made bare (7)
12 Trimmed (anag) (7)
14 Spring locks for doors (7)
16 Molasses (7)
18 Arc of coloured light (7)
19 Small house (5)
20 Profound (4)
21 Words with similar meanings (8)

Down

1 Trees that bear acorns (4)
2 Envelop (6)
3 Acting to relieve pain (of a drug) (9)
4 US rapper (6)
6 Large saltwater game fish (6)
7 Curative medicines (8)
11 Case (9)
12 Overcame (8)
13 City in NE Italy (6)
14 Margin of safety (6)
15 Period of prosperity (6)
17 Disorder; confused situation (4)

PUZZLE 90

Across

1 Large barrel (4)
3 Medicine (8)
9 More than enough (7)
10 More pleasant (5)
11 Intense (12)
14 17th Greek letter (3)
16 Mosquito (5)
17 ___ Ferdinand: England footballer (3)
18 Form of deception (12)
21 Andrew Lloyd Webber musical (5)
22 Gather (7)
23 An indirect and sometimes snide implication (8)
24 Individual article or unit (4)

Down

1 Lord Chancellor's Court (8)
2 Reception room in a large house (5)
4 Climbing shrub (3)
5 Person recovering from an illness (12)
6 Uncertain (7)
7 Currency of Spain and Holland (4)
8 Coming between two things in time (12)
12 English royal house (5)
13 Tree of the birch family (8)
15 Point of view (7)
19 Inactive (5)
20 Round before the final (abbrev) (4)
22 Dishonourable person (3)

PUZZLE 91

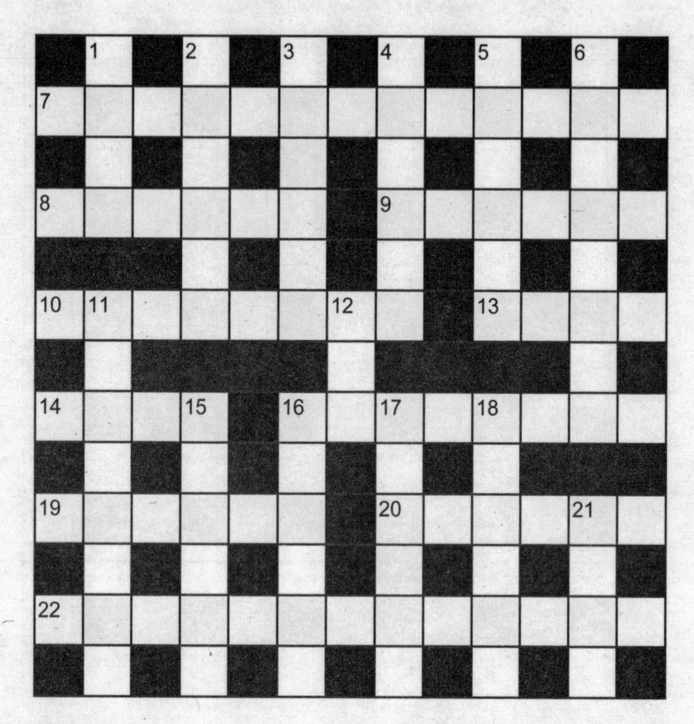

Across

7 Congratulations (13)
8 Instrument panel (6)
9 Exemplify (6)
10 Musical composition (8)
13 School bedroom (abbrev) (4)
14 Tehran is the capital here (4)
16 Least old (8)
19 Not singular (6)
20 Band of colour (6)
22 Irretrievable (13)

Down

1 Second Greek letter (4)
2 Involuntary spasm (6)
3 Alyssa ___ : US actress and producer (6)
4 Type of dough (6)
5 Moved at high speed (6)
6 Specified work clothes (8)
11 Pageantry (8)
12 Pair of performers (3)
15 Hospital carers (6)
16 Colour of a lemon (6)
17 Not noticed (6)
18 Language spoken in Berlin (6)
21 Animal skin (4)

PUZZLE 92

Across

1 Come into view (6)
4 Removed the skin (6)
9 Raging fire (7)
10 Tell a story (7)
11 Severe (5)
12 Noble gas (5)
14 Scale representation (5)
15 Fight (3-2)
17 Rupture (5)
18 A very long time ago (4,3)
20 ___ Lohan: actress (7)
21 Indicate (6)
22 Took part in a game (6)

Down

1 ___ Wood: US actor (6)
2 Liquid waste discharged into the sea (8)
3 Spiny yellow-flowered shrub (5)
5 Endless (7)
6 Molten rock (4)
7 Lower someone's dignity (6)
8 Assuredly (11)
13 One of the Channel Islands (8)
14 Biting (7)
15 Fashioned (6)
16 Steady (anag) (6)
17 Hackneyed (5)
19 Very long period of time (4)

PUZZLE 93

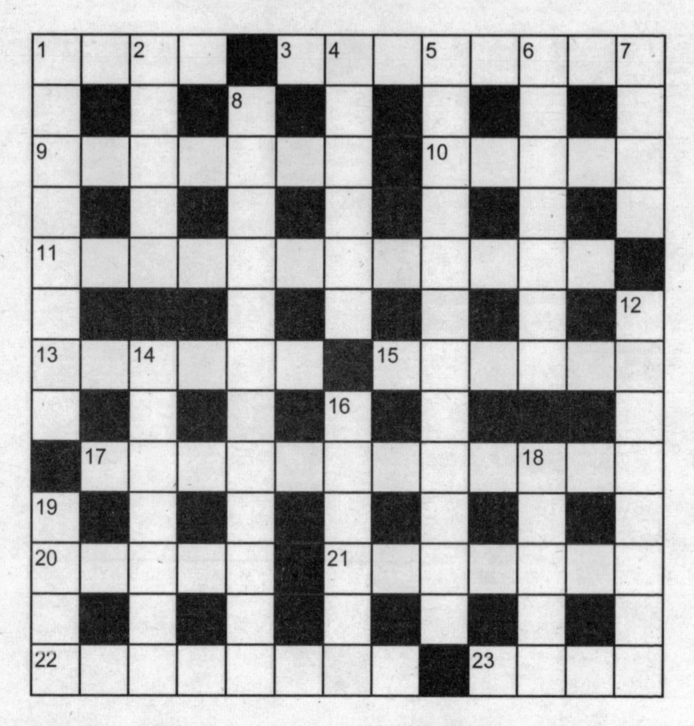

Across

1 Identical; unchanged (4)
3 Events that hinder progress (8)
9 Located in the fresh air (7)
10 Enlighten (5)
11 Awe-inspiring (12)
13 French museum (6)
15 Modify (6)
17 Bride's primary attendant (4,2,6)
20 ___ Dushku: actress (5)
21 Great suffering (7)
22 Battered (8)
23 Fight off (4)

Down

1 Increase rapidly (8)
2 Mound that forms the site of a castle (5)
4 Printed mistakes (6)
5 Productive insight (12)
6 Sophisticated hair style (7)
7 Plant of the pea family (4)
8 Person studying after a first degree (12)
12 Looked for (8)
14 Radioactive element (7)
16 Ablaze (6)
18 Small fruit used for oil (5)
19 Wire lattice (4)

PUZZLE 94

Across

1 Character in the musical Oliver! (5)
4 Error (7)
7 Show pleasure facially (5)
8 Prevent heat loss (8)
9 Brag (5)
11 Permitting (8)
15 Creator (8)
17 Tool used for digging (5)
19 Adversary (8)
20 Musical toy (5)
21 Use again (7)
22 Impudent (5)

Down

1 Proposes a candidate for office (9)
2 Loudly (7)
3 Eg primrose and lemon (7)
4 Liquefied by heat (6)
5 Cylindrical drum (3-3)
6 Ovens (5)
10 Geographical region (9)
12 Refuses to acknowledge (7)
13 Plans to do something (7)
14 Stupidity (6)
16 Show up; reveal (6)
18 Flat surface (5)

PUZZLE 95

Across

1 Female horse (4)
3 Eg London and Paris (8)
9 Containerful (7)
10 Red cosmetic powder (5)
11 Precondition (12)
14 Monstrous humanoid creature (3)
16 Follows closely (5)
17 Argument against something (3)
18 Insubordination (12)
21 Sharp-pointed organ of a bee (5)
22 Make more entertaining (7)
23 Protects from the elements (8)
24 Parched (4)

Down

1 Figure of speech (8)
2 Extent or limit (5)
4 Every (3)
5 Overwhelmingly compelling (12)
6 Living in water (7)
7 Perceives (4)
8 An idea that is added later (12)
12 Join together (5)
13 Confined as a prisoner (8)
15 Style of cooking (7)
19 At no time (5)
20 Poses a question (4)
22 Make a mistake (3)

PUZZLE 96

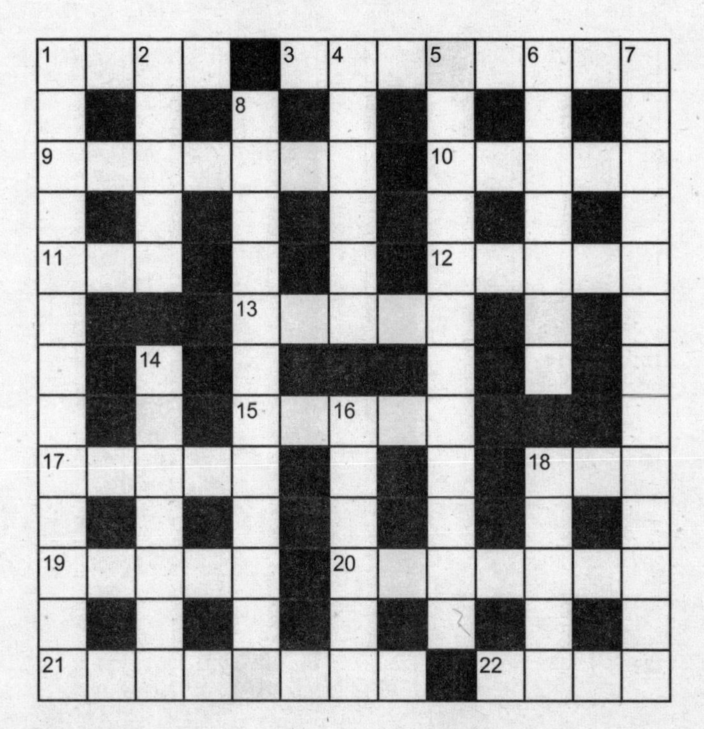

Across

1 Talon (4)
3 Fortify against attack (8)
9 Render utterly perplexed (7)
10 Ape (abbrev) (5)
11 Person who steers a boat (3)
12 Backless sofa (5)
13 Debate in a heated manner (5)
15 Not in good physical condition (5)
17 Play a guitar (5)
18 Fish eggs (3)
19 Town in Surrey; sheer (anag) (5)
20 Surpass (7)
21 Chosen (8)
22 Areas of ground for growing plants (4)

Down

1 Awareness (13)
2 Attach to (5)
4 Pondering (6)
5 Not on purpose; inadvertently (12)
6 Robbers (7)
7 Ebullience (13)
8 Using both letters and numerals (12)
14 Officer in the armed forces (7)
16 Turn to ice (6)
18 Indian monetary unit (5)

PUZZLE 97

Across

1 Fine soft thread (4)
3 Assumed (8)
9 Litter (7)
10 Assesses performance (5)
11 Walk heavily and firmly (5)
12 Walker without a fixed route (7)
13 Worldwide (6)
15 Expert in a particular subject (6)
17 Mild (of weather) (7)
18 The reproduction of sound (5)
20 Let (5)
21 Proportionately (3,4)
22 Christmas season (8)
23 Wet with condensation (4)

Down

1 Tactically (13)
2 Country whose capital is Tripoli (5)
4 Wedding officials (6)
5 Pram (12)
6 Paid a debt (7)
7 Tidier crayons (anag) (13)
8 Action of moving a thing from its position (12)
14 Taken as a whole (7)
16 Unintelligent (6)
19 Male duck (5)

PUZZLE 98

Across

1 Midwestern US state (8)
5 Plant used for flavouring (4)
8 Form of oxygen found in the atmosphere (5)
9 Type of respiration (7)
10 Slender stemlike plant appendage (7)
12 Acknowledgements (7)
14 Abandoned (7)
16 One who holds property for another (7)
18 Wavering vocal quality (7)
19 Dessert dish (5)
20 Travelled too quickly (4)
21 Reasonable and judicious (8)

Down

1 Bleak upland (4)
2 Absorbent material (6)
3 Between sunset and sunrise (9)
4 Responds to (6)
6 Stefan ___ : Swedish tennis player (6)
7 Made still (8)
11 Bothersome people (9)
12 Hostages (8)
13 Topple (6)
14 Reduce to a lower grade (6)
15 Residential district (6)
17 ___ Campbell: Canadian actress (4)

PUZZLE 99

Across

1 Insects with brightly coloured wings (11)
9 Crucial person or point (5)
10 Kind or sort (3)
11 Attacks without warning (5)
12 Models for a photograph (5)
13 Short joke (3-5)
16 US state (8)
18 Device used to connect to the internet (5)
21 Form of identification (5)
22 Command to a horse (3)
23 Fairy (5)
24 Meaningless (11)

Down

2 Single-handed (7)
3 Nip spot (anag) (7)
4 Bring back to life (6)
5 Abatement (5)
6 Gives off (5)
7 Person who looks identical to another (6,5)
8 Very tall buildings (11)
14 River in Africa (7)
15 Venetian boat (7)
17 Horn (6)
19 ___ Maradona: footballer (5)
20 Sulks (5)

PUZZLE 100

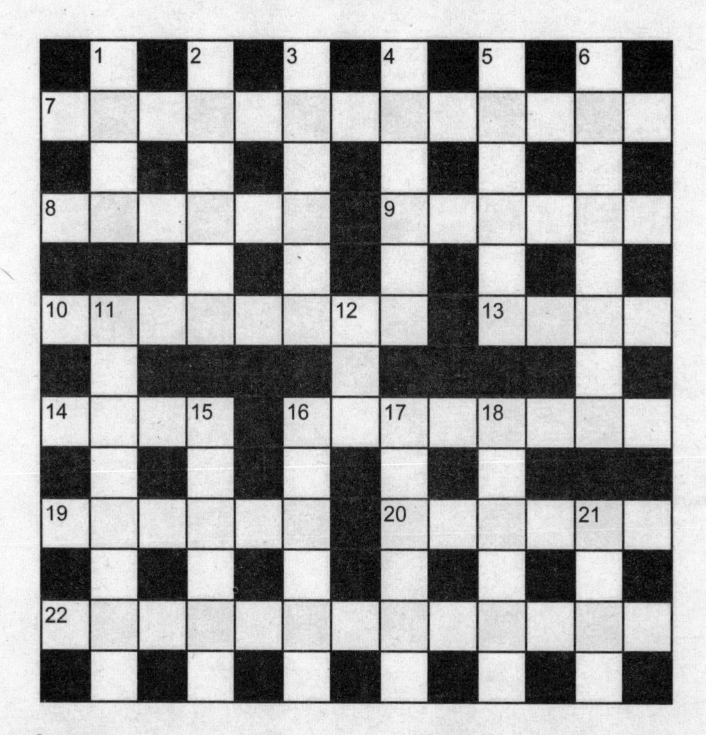

Across

7 Unbelievably (13)
8 Boredom (6)
9 Fashionable; exciting (6)
10 Individuality (8)
13 Skirt worn by ballerinas (4)
14 Compassionate (4)
16 Opposite of a pessimist (8)
19 Type of rhododendron (6)
20 Opposite of passive (6)
22 Process of transformation (of an insect) (13)

Down

1 Leg joint (4)
2 Pertaining to Jupiter (6)
3 Norway lobsters (6)
4 Regal (6)
5 Prance around (6)
6 Lifts up (8)
11 Rained gently (8)
12 Touch gently (3)
15 US monetary unit (6)
16 Public speaker (6)
17 Walks heavily and firmly (6)
18 Woman in charge of nursing (6)
21 Empty space (4)

PUZZLE 101

Across

1 Raise to the third power (4)
3 Food enhancer (8)
9 Cues given to performers (7)
10 Hidden storage space (5)
11 Teach to accept a belief uncritically (12)
13 Cause to fall from a horse (6)
15 Breed of dog (6)
17 Nursery school (12)
20 Pancake sweetener (5)
21 Weasel-like animal (7)
22 Grew in size (8)
23 Pass (anag) (4)

Down

1 Pepper plant (8)
2 Wide (5)
4 Wish for (6)
5 Heartbroken (12)
6 Provoked; encouraged (7)
7 For Your ___ Only: Bond film (4)
8 Spotless (5-3-4)
12 Newborn children (8)
14 Foot support for a rider (7)
16 Multiply by three (6)
18 Folds close together (5)
19 Small island (4)

PUZZLE 102

Across

1 Solid; not soft (4)
3 Yellow flower (8)
9 Courteously (7)
10 Eg performs karaoke (5)
11 Lavish event (12)
14 Small amount of something (3)
16 ___ with: supported (5)
17 Boolean operator (3)
18 Reckless; ready to react violently (7-5)
21 Middle of the body (5)
22 Apprehend (7)
23 Bulbous plant (8)
24 ___ sail: begins a voyage (4)

Down

1 Large Spanish estate (8)
2 Short bolt or pin (5)
4 ___ Winehouse: singer (3)
5 Popular takeaway food (4,3,5)
6 Resident (7)
7 Young woman (4)
8 Having keen vision (5-7)
12 Mix up or confuse (5)
13 Dreariness (8)
15 Tortilla rolled around a filling (7)
19 Temporary stop (5)
20 Is indebted to pay (4)
22 Sound of a dove (3)

PUZZLE 103

Across

1 ___ Major: the Great Bear (4)
3 Friendly (8)
9 Typewriter rollers (7)
10 Longest river in Europe (5)
11 Drink a little (3)
12 Reclining (5)
13 ___ Piper: potato (5)
15 Rescuer (5)
17 Refute by evidence (5)
18 Large vessel (3)
19 Soar; rush (5)
20 Caused to burn (7)
21 Catastrophe (8)
22 Associate (4)

Down

1 Not heat-treated (of milk) (13)
2 Impress a pattern on (5)
4 Gain control of; overcome (6)
5 Public official (5,7)
6 Optimistic about something (7)
7 In an inflated manner (13)
8 Female school boss (12)
14 Residential areas (7)
16 Manly (6)
18 Essential (5)

PUZZLE 104

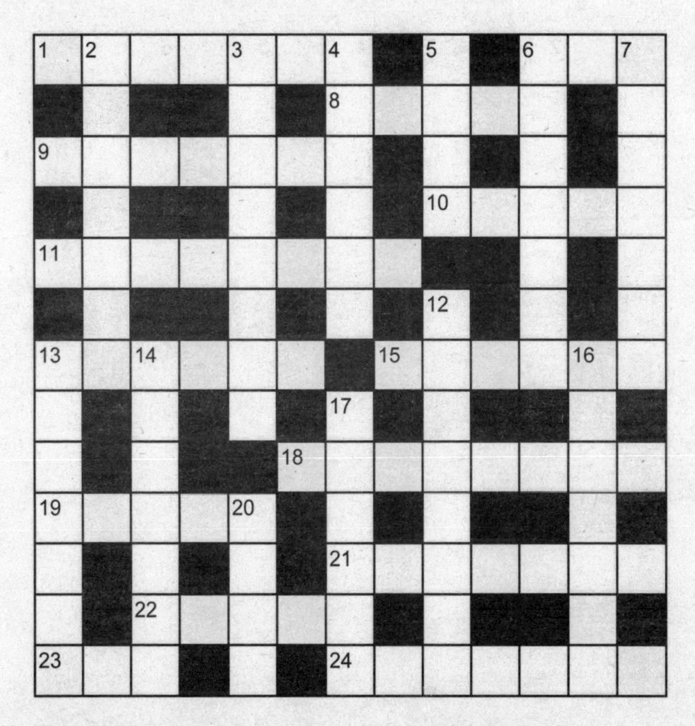

Across

1 Characteristics (7)
6 Cup (3)
8 ___ Klum: supermodel (5)
9 Bison (7)
10 Ascend (5)
11 Yearly (8)
13 Mixes up or confuses (6)
15 Occupant (6)
18 Device that tests for the presence of something (8)
19 Proceeding from the pope (5)
21 Laughable (7)
22 Spread out (5)
23 Stimulus (3)
24 Rayon fabric (7)

Down

2 Rendered senseless (7)
3 Popular party game (8)
4 Ought to (6)
5 Silvery-white metallic element (4)
6 Force of civilians trained as soldiers (7)
7 Small fast ship (7)
12 Goes backwards (8)
13 Sterile (7)
14 Get rid of (7)
16 Pasta strips (7)
17 History play by Shakespeare (5,1)
20 Quieten down (4)

PUZZLE 105

Across

1 Desperate Housewives actress (3,8)
9 Piece of code to automate a task (5)
10 At this moment (3)
11 Decline sharply (5)
12 A gold coin (5)
13 Courteously (8)
16 Lover (8)
18 Kind of wheat (5)
21 Plants of a region (5)
22 Weep (3)
23 Ousel (anag) (5)
24 Restrained (11)

Down

2 Uncertainly; not clearly (7)
3 Clinging shellfish (7)
4 Five cent coin (US) (6)
5 Egg-shaped solid (5)
6 Type of chemical bond (5)
7 Make in bulk (4-7)
8 European country (11)
14 Crisp plain fabric (7)
15 Large German city (7)
17 Collections of photos (6)
19 Smooth textile fibre (5)
20 Skirmish (5)

PUZZLE 106

1	2		3		4	■	5		6		7	
■		■		■		■		■		■		■
8				■	9							
■		■		■		■		■		■	■	■
10					■	11					12	
■		■		■	13	■		■	■	■		■
14									15			
■		■	■	■		■		■		■		■
16			17				■	18				
■	■	■		■		■	19	■		■		■
20	21							■	22			
■		■		■		■		■		■		■
23						■	24					

Across

1 Stops (6)
5 Inside information (3-3)
8 Fish (4)
9 Leaving out (8)
10 Technical problem (5)
11 Accidents (7)
14 Fitness to fly (13)
16 Contemptuously (7)
18 Assists in a crime (5)
20 Participant in a meeting (8)
22 Direct one's gaze at (4)
23 Has objective reality (6)
24 Least young (6)

Down

2 Imitation (9)
3 Swift-flying songbird (7)
4 Hard hit cricket shot (4)
5 Gloaming (8)
6 Piece of land (5)
7 Enjoyable (3)
12 Places carefully (9)
13 Introductory pieces of music (8)
15 Took small bites out of (7)
17 Put clothes on (5)
19 Nought (4)
21 A man's dinner jacket (abbrev) (3)

PUZZLE 107

Across

1 Sporting venues (6)
7 Food storerooms (8)
8 For each (3)
9 Confer holy orders on (6)
10 Narrow opening (4)
11 Microscopic fungus (5)
13 Snarled (anag) (7)
15 A Roman Catholic devotion (7)
17 Large wading bird (5)
21 Corrode (4)
22 Figure of speech (6)
23 Partly digested animal food (3)
24 Capital of Finland (8)
25 Outer parts of bread loaves (6)

Down

1 Provide (6)
2 ___ borealis: Northern Lights (6)
3 Pertaining to bees (5)
4 Fatuously (7)
5 Captive (8)
6 Far away (6)
12 Most saccharine (8)
14 Making the sound of a bee (7)
16 Not masculine or feminine (6)
18 Calculating machine (6)
19 Book of the Old Testament (6)
20 Agreeable sound or tune (5)

PUZZLE 108

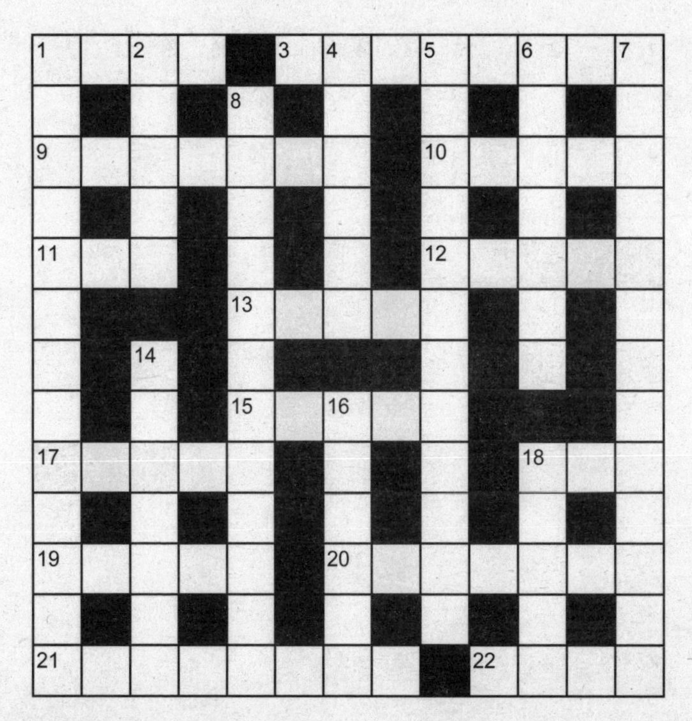

Across

1 Widespread (4)
3 Two-wheeled vehicles (8)
9 Warship (7)
10 Go in (5)
11 Writing fluid (3)
12 Lifting device (5)
13 Recently made (5)
15 Polite and courteous (5)
17 Wide-awake (5)
18 Hairpiece (3)
19 Command (5)
20 Plants that live a year or less (7)
21 Finely chopped (8)
22 Plant with fronds (4)

Down

1 Cooling devices (13)
2 Sudden jerk (5)
4 Break apart (6)
5 Irresistible (12)
6 No longer in existence (7)
7 The Duchess of York (5,8)
8 Made (12)
14 Slim (7)
16 Make empty (6)
18 Large marine mammal (5)

PUZZLE 109

Across

1 Make something look more attractive (8)
5 Award (informal) (4)
9 One more (7)
10 ___ Nash: writer of light verse (5)
11 Destroy (10)
14 Far away from home (6)
15 Writing implement (6)
17 Gasping for air (10)
20 Cook meat in the oven (5)
21 Not level (7)
22 Song for a solo voice (4)
23 Seahorse (anag) (8)

Down

1 Beloved; expensive (4)
2 Dove sounds (4)
3 Restore to good condition (12)
4 Murky (6)
6 Mounted guns (8)
7 Warily (8)
8 Total despair (12)
12 Capital of Australia (8)
13 Intelligentsia (8)
16 Refer to indirectly (6)
18 Popular martial art (4)
19 Primary colour (4)

PUZZLE 110

Across

1 Very small amount (4)
3 Young (8)
9 Teemed (7)
10 Small island (5)
11 In accordance with general custom (12)
14 Regret with sadness (3)
16 Trunk of the body (5)
17 Nevertheless (3)
18 Generally accepted (12)
21 Once more (5)
22 Fear of heights (7)
23 Recently (8)
24 Precious stones; outstanding people or things (4)

Down

1 Lacking confidence (8)
2 Mark ___ : Samuel Langhorne Clemens (5)
4 Not new (3)
5 Mathematics of triangles (12)
6 Misconception (7)
7 Allows (4)
8 Impudence (12)
12 Lose a contest intentionally (5)
13 Scholarly (8)
15 Bewitch (7)
19 Objection; minor complaint (5)
20 ___ Daniels: magician (4)
22 ___ Kilmer: famous actor (3)

PUZZLE 111

Across

1 Soft fruit (5)
4 TV audience (7)
8 People in jail (7)
9 Call forth or cause (5)
10 Electrical safety device (4)
11 Loose-fitting protective garment (8)
14 Landowners (6)
15 One's environment (6)
18 Deplorably (8)
19 Garden implement (4)
21 Country whose capital is Valletta (5)
23 Traditional piano keys (7)
24 Makes ineffective (7)
25 Drawing making up part of a cartoon strip (5)

Down

1 Hurtful (7)
2 Truce (9)
3 Smacks (4)
4 Sight (6)
5 Relating to critical explanation (8)
6 Self-esteem (3)
7 A sense (5)
12 State of nervous excitement (9)
13 ___ stork: large bird (8)
16 Domestic implement (7)
17 Spinal (anag) (6)
18 Ladies (5)
20 Substance used for washing (4)
22 Piece of wood (3)

PUZZLE 112

Across

1 Cry out (4)
3 Relating to sound (8)
9 ___ power: energy source (7)
10 Stage play (5)
11 Surpass (5)
12 Film directed by Stephen Gaghan (7)
13 Treeless Arctic region (6)
15 Create by carving (6)
17 Most favourable (7)
18 Layabout (5)
20 Tines (anag) (5)
21 Preventing success; unfavourable (7)
22 Margaret ___ : former Prime Minister (8)
23 Playing cards (4)

Down

1 Acrobat who twists and bends their body (13)
2 Lawful (5)
4 Light red colour (6)
5 Perform below expectation (12)
6 Burdensome work (7)
7 Bland and dull (13)
8 Histrionic (12)
14 ___ Bedingfield: musician (7)
16 Region of France (6)
19 Expressing emotions (of poetry) (5)

PUZZLE 113

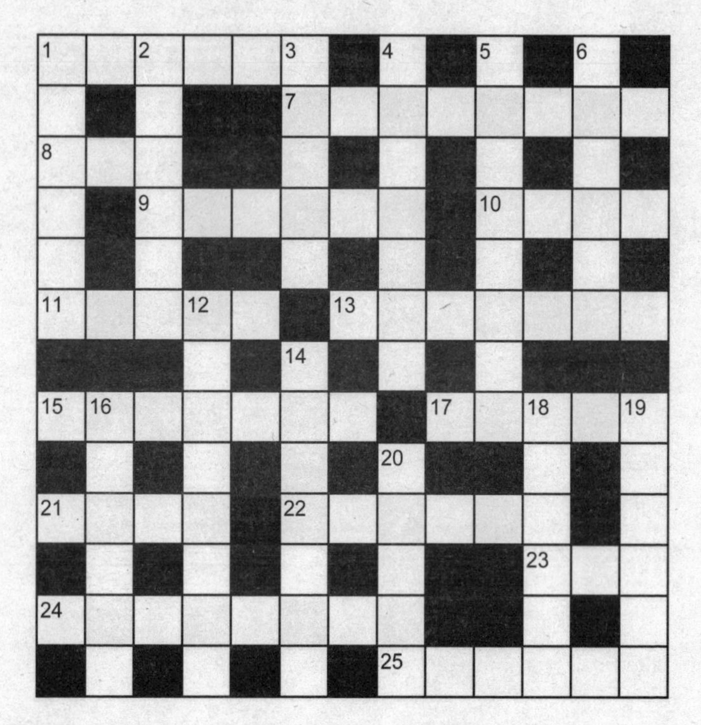

Across

1 True skin (6)
7 Running out (8)
8 Assist (3)
9 Make worse (6)
10 Vessel (4)
11 Impersonator (5)
13 Impressed a pattern on (7)
15 Gambling houses (7)
17 Ring solemnly (5)
21 Opposite of pass (4)
22 Sumptuous and large (of a meal) (4-2)
23 Beam of light (3)
24 Musical pieces for solo instruments (8)
25 Outer layer of the cerebrum (6)

Down

1 Crown (6)
2 Element discovered by Marie and Pierre Curie (6)
3 Danes (anag) (5)
4 Alcoholic drinks (7)
5 First-year university student (US) (8)
6 Machine that produces motion (6)
12 Language used by an individual (8)
14 Shaving of the crown of head (7)
16 River in South America (6)
18 Sprightliness (6)
19 Voice box (6)
20 Frenzied (5)

PUZZLE 114

Across

1 Lower in rank (11)
9 Spread by scattering (5)
10 Division of a play (3)
11 Where tennis is played (5)
12 Piece of paper (5)
13 Relight a fire (8)
16 Daring (8)
18 Needing to be scratched (5)
21 Mark of repetition (5)
22 Bat (anag) (3)
23 ___ acid: protein building block (5)
24 Done with great care (11)

Down

2 Ill-fated (7)
3 Driving out (7)
4 Come off the tracks (6)
5 Pond-dwelling amphibians (5)
6 Poke fun at (5)
7 Doubt (11)
8 Aristocratic mansion (7,4)
14 Small field (7)
15 Type of heron (7)
17 Raise (6)
19 Venomous snake (5)
20 Long for (5)

PUZZLE 115

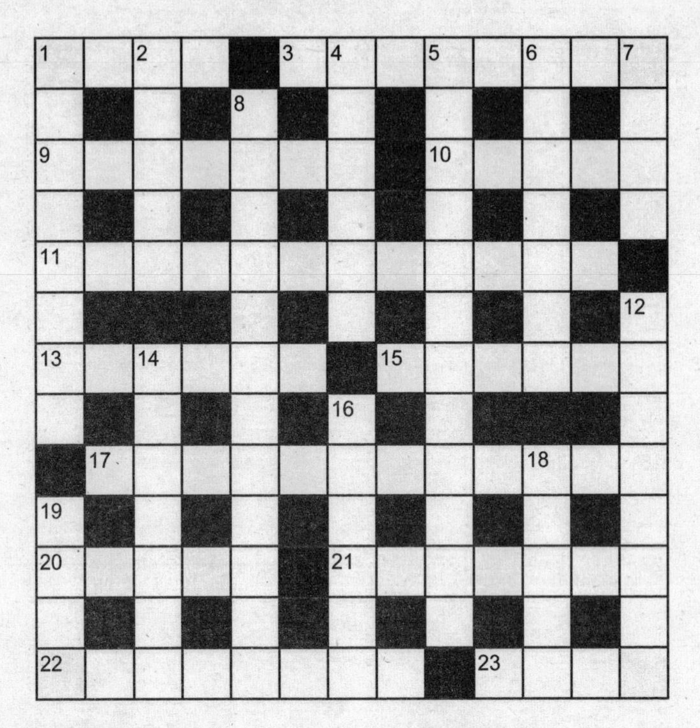

Across

1 Trees of the genus Ulmus (4)
3 Liar (8)
9 Rich fish soup (7)
10 Fists (5)
11 Prerequisite (12)
13 Duplicity (6)
15 Representation of a plan or theory (6)
17 Eager (12)
20 English singer-songwriter (5)
21 Soft-bodied invertebrate (7)
22 Beneficial (8)
23 Become healthy again (4)

Down

1 Wild prank (8)
2 Large deer (5)
4 Wear away (6)
5 Not discernible (12)
6 Annoying (7)
7 ___ Daly: TV presenter (4)
8 Firm rebuke (12)
12 Absurd (8)
14 Hide (7)
16 Moires (anag) (6)
18 Armistice (5)
19 Spielberg thriller about a shark (4)

PUZZLE 116

Across

1 Lowest adult male singing voice (4)
3 Yellowish edible seed (8)
9 Act of awakening from sleep (7)
10 ___ Milan: Italian football club (5)
11 Conclude (5)
12 Shut in (7)
13 Resistant to something (6)
15 Word that qualifies another (6)
17 Stern (7)
18 Flaring stars (5)
20 Angry (5)
21 Ascertain dimensions (7)
22 Working against (8)
23 ___ and wherefores: reasons for something (4)

Down

1 Step towards canonisation (13)
2 Parody (5)
4 Divides in two (6)
5 Occurring at the same time (12)
6 Stalk joining a leaf to a stem (7)
7 Pleasantness (13)
8 Separation; alienation (12)
14 Small hardy range horse (7)
16 Sailor (6)
19 Pledge (5)

PUZZLE 117

Across

1 Edible bivalve (6)
7 Safety restraint in a car (4,4)
8 Belgian town (3)
9 Be aggrieved by (6)
10 Hollow cylinder (4)
11 Tearful (5)
13 Steep in; engross (7)
15 Precede (7)
17 Hurt by an insect like a wasp (5)
21 Where you are (4)
22 Reduces to shreds (6)
23 Anger (3)
24 Highly seasoned smoked beef (8)
25 Weird (6)

Down

1 Type of nut (6)
2 Accuse; run at (6)
3 County in E England (5)
4 Kind of music (7)
5 Point of contact; masonry support (8)
6 Excuses of any kind (6)
12 Moral instructions (8)
14 Thief (7)
16 Unidirectional (3-3)
18 Bearlike (6)
19 Avaricious (6)
20 Simple (5)

PUZZLE 118

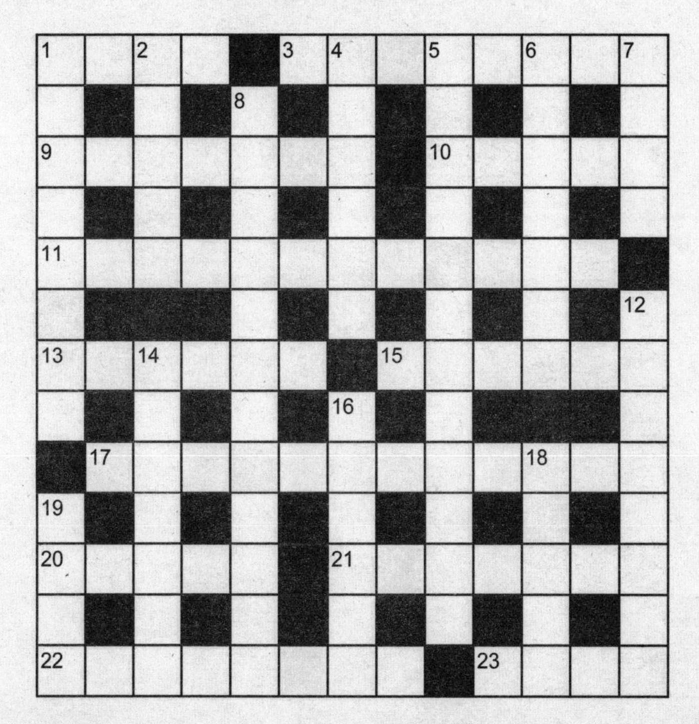

Across

1 Dandies (4)
3 Official orders (8)
9 Tearing (7)
10 Temporary lodgings (5)
11 Pertaining to letters (12)
13 Leave a ship (6)
15 Improve the quality of (6)
17 Disturbance; act of meddling (12)
20 Game similar to bowls (5)
21 Freezing (3-4)
22 Ultimate (8)
23 Impose a tax (4)

Down

1 Opposite of backwards (8)
2 Appear suddenly (3,2)
4 Fishes (6)
5 Lexicons (12)
6 Kettledrums (7)
7 Cloth worn around the waist (4)
8 Conflict of opinion (12)
12 Astutely (8)
14 Juliette ___ : French actress (7)
16 Continent (6)
18 Loop with a running knot (5)
19 Double-reed instrument (4)

PUZZLE 119

Across

1 Clergyman (5)
4 Grandeur (7)
8 Whispers (7)
9 Intended (5)
10 Type of golf club (4)
11 Easily frightened (8)
14 Fences made of bushes (6)
15 Wrote (6)
18 Rural (8)
19 Depart (4)
21 Russian country house (5)
23 Kind of breakfast cereal (7)
24 Small toothed whale (7)
25 Suggest (5)

Down

1 Gloss (7)
2 Recording device (9)
3 Destroy (4)
4 Believer in the occult (6)
5 Large celebration (8)
6 Large body of water (3)
7 Abominable snowmen (5)
12 Very unpleasant (9)
13 Rebuke (8)
16 Diminish the worth of (7)
17 Edge (6)
18 Assisted (5)
20 Grating noise; coarse file (4)
22 Mountain pass (3)

PUZZLE 120

Across

1 Bothers (8)
5 Domestic felines (4)
9 Mental collapse (7)
10 Water lily (5)
11 Variable (10)
14 Very milky (6)
15 Homes (6)
17 Occurring periodically (10)
20 Belonging to them (5)
21 Insignificant (7)
22 Apex or peak (4)
23 Fence formed by bushes (8)

Down

1 Brass instrument (4)
2 Belonging to us (4)
3 Science of biological processes (12)
4 Scope (6)
6 Protein that neutralises an antigen (8)
7 Anxious uncertainty (8)
8 Comprehensive (3-9)
12 Type of puzzle (8)
13 Educators (8)
16 Type of beard (6)
18 Fibber (4)
19 Exhaled air (4)

PUZZLE 121

Across

1 Be foolishly fond of (4)
3 Not in a specific location (8)
9 SI unit of electric charge (7)
10 Nick ___ : former Deputy Prime Minister (5)
11 Metal device for removing tops (6,6)
14 Untruth (3)
16 Ruin (5)
17 One and one (3)
18 Type of bus (6-6)
21 Artificial waterway (5)
22 Eg iron or oxygen (7)
23 Finance department (8)
24 Egyptian goddess of fertility (4)

Down

1 Sound units (8)
2 Tease or pester (5)
4 Crux of a matter (3)
5 Specialist cricketing position (12)
6 Mountain in the Himalayas (7)
7 Verge (4)
8 Intense anxiety (12)
12 Corpulent (5)
13 Greek philosopher (8)
15 Enunciate (7)
19 Retains (5)
20 Short tail (4)
22 What one hears with (3)

PUZZLE 122

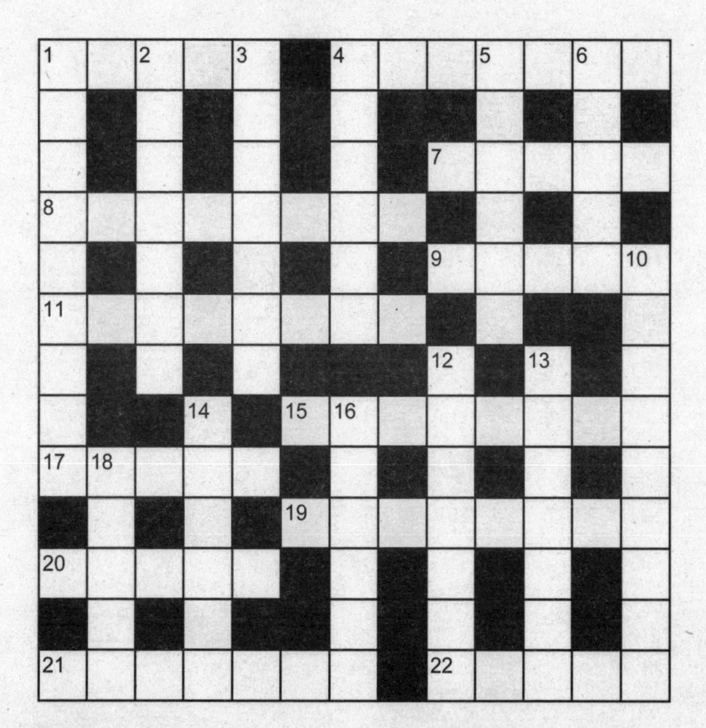

Across

1 Very informal phrases (5)
4 European country (7)
7 Rigid (5)
8 Grinding machine with sails (8)
9 Remains (5)
11 Reserved (8)
15 Lacking knowledge (8)
17 Old silver coin (5)
19 Text of an opera (8)
20 Currently in progress (5)
21 Receptacle for cigarette residue (7)
22 Teacher (5)

Down

1 Spraying with water (9)
2 Useful feature of a place (7)
3 Novelty (7)
4 Bad-tempered mythical creature (6)
5 Short choral compositions (6)
6 Attractively stylish (5)
10 Merchant who sells writing materials (9)
12 Make right (7)
13 Most obese (7)
14 Very unconventional (3-3)
16 Graceful; pleasing (6)
18 Floating platforms (5)

PUZZLE 123

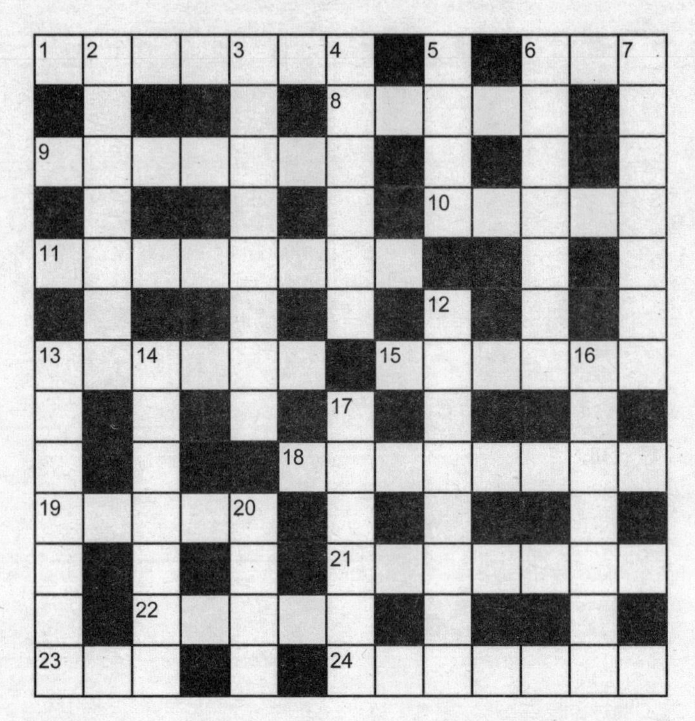

Across

1 Hot wind blowing from North Africa (7)
6 Seed of an apple (3)
8 Freight (5)
9 Japanese massage technique (7)
10 Nocturnal insects (5)
11 Relating to trees (8)
13 Way of standing; posture (6)
15 Soft felt hat (6)
18 Recognise (8)
19 Edits (anag) (5)
21 Finery (7)
22 Body of rules (5)
23 Before the present (of time) (3)
24 Attendant (7)

Down

2 Acquire as an heir (7)
3 Large waterfall (8)
4 Of the eye (6)
5 Public transport vehicle (4)
6 Type of porch (7)
7 Individual character (7)
12 Person aged 13 - 19 (8)
13 Seedless raisin (7)
14 Decorative style of the 1920s and 1930s (3,4)
16 Violent and lawless person (7)
17 Decorates (6)
20 Without (literary) (4)

PUZZLE 124

Across

1 Small bunch of flowers (4)
3 Teaches (8)
9 Free from doubt (7)
10 Suffuse with colour (5)
11 Antique; not modern (3-9)
13 Fly an aircraft (6)
15 Emotional shock (6)
17 Distinctive behavioural attribute (12)
20 Slender woman or girl (5)
21 Uncomplaining (7)
22 Defeated (8)
23 Inflammation of an eyelid (4)

Down

1 Pertaining to the chest (8)
2 Very small amount (5)
4 Small inflatable boat (6)
5 Chair proctor (anag) (12)
6 Group of figures representing a scene (7)
7 Noticed (4)
8 Extremely harmful (12)
12 Dark colour that is virtually black (4,4)
14 Satisfy a desire (7)
16 Mineral used to make plaster of Paris (6)
18 English racetrack (5)
19 Capital of Norway (4)

PUZZLE 125

Across

1 Gambling house (6)
7 Apartment cohabitant (8)
8 Large dark antelope (3)
9 Jumped up (6)
10 Break suddenly (4)
11 Vault under a church (5)
13 Walk aimlessly (7)
15 Ancient wise king (7)
17 Cairo is in this country (5)
21 Strand; lock (4)
22 Having been defeated (6)
23 Ground condensation (3)
24 Most foolish (8)
25 Helix (6)

Down

1 Brandy (6)
2 Sloppy (6)
3 Bits of meat of low value (5)
4 Sausages (informal) (7)
5 Wonderful (8)
6 Sprats (anag) (6)
12 Immediately (8)
14 Moved unsteadily from side to side (7)
16 Starting point (6)
18 Over there (6)
19 Small gardening tool with a curved scoop (6)
20 Game involving pointed projectiles (5)

PUZZLE 126

Across

1 Brightly coloured parrot (5)
4 Stirring (7)
8 Sum of money paid to someone regularly (7)
9 In what place (5)
10 Mend with rows of stitches (4)
11 Small turtle (8)
14 Formal assessment (6)
15 Trousers that end above the knee (6)
18 Method and practice of teaching (8)
19 ___ vera: plant (4)
21 Loose outer garments (5)
23 Put in order (7)
24 Breastbone (7)
25 Senior figure in a tribe (5)

Down

1 Follow a winding course (of a river) (7)
2 Artificial; strained (9)
3 Abandoned person (4)
4 Had corresponding sounds (6)
5 Undeserving (8)
6 Frozen water (3)
7 Colour of grass (5)
12 Bewildered (9)
13 Alex ___ : former football manager (8)
16 Big ___ : song sung by Shirley Bassey (7)
17 Selfishness (6)
18 Components (5)
20 Axelike tool (4)
22 Insect that can sting (3)

PUZZLE 127

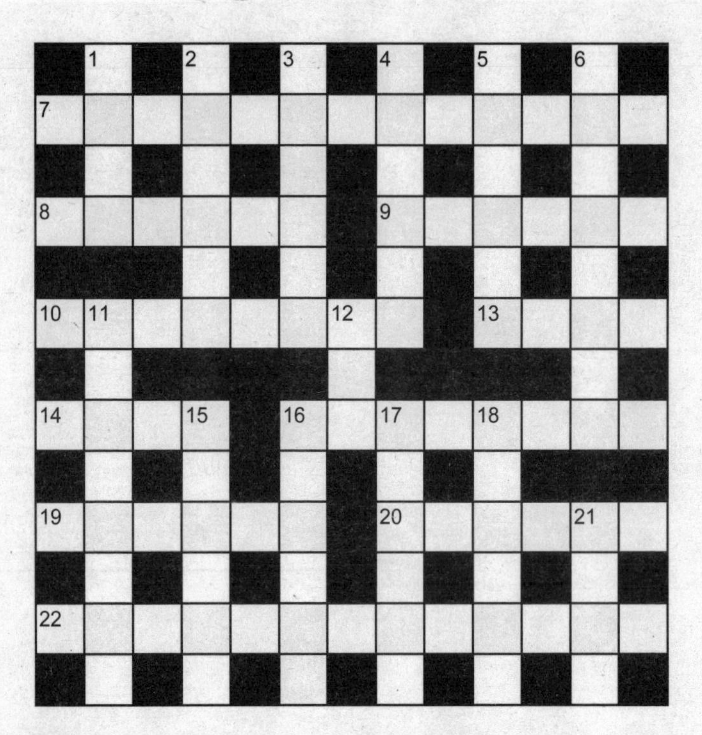

Across

7 Dictatorially (13)
8 Steal (6)
9 Terminate (6)
10 Short musical compositions (8)
13 Ridge of rock (4)
14 Moat (anag) (4)
16 Structured set of information (8)
19 Covered with a shiny coating (6)
20 Child (6)
22 Relevance (13)

Down

1 Run quickly (4)
2 Soundless (6)
3 Thoroughfare (6)
4 Arts and ___ : decorative design (6)
5 Large sign (6)
6 These protect small wounds (8)
11 Eland (8)
12 Military commander or official (3)
15 Light rain (6)
16 Take away (6)
17 Type of hat (6)
18 Confuse (6)
21 Eg pecan and cashew (4)

PUZZLE 128

Across

1 Of inferior quality (6)
4 Pertaining to vinegar (6)
9 Worker who supervises others (7)
10 Eg Edam and Cheddar (7)
11 Consumer of food (5)
12 ___ Valletta: actress (5)
14 Rocky; harsh (5)
15 Acer tree (5)
17 A Fish Called ___ : film (5)
18 Japanese warrior (7)
20 Innocently (7)
21 Plump up (6)
22 Inferior (6)

Down

1 Firm or hard sweet (6)
2 Landing and take-off area (8)
3 Bart's father in the Simpsons (5)
5 Fastest animal on land (7)
6 Young children (4)
7 Nearer (6)
8 Very happy (2,5,4)
13 Bed covers (8)
14 Go back over a route (7)
15 Compact group of mountains (6)
16 Woodcutter (6)
17 Produce a literary work (5)
19 Trade centre (4)

PUZZLE 129

Across

- **1** Type of diving (4,3)
- **6** Unwell (3)
- **8** Moved by air (5)
- **9** Long-bladed hand tools (7)
- **10** Less (5)
- **11** Vivid and brilliant (of a colour) (8)
- **13** Mean (6)
- **15** Holds and uses a tool (6)
- **18** Carve words on something (8)
- **19** Softly radiant (5)
- **21** Harsh; corrosive (7)
- **22** Period of darkness (5)
- **23** Embrace (3)
- **24** Fulfil a desire (7)

Down

- **2** Formation of troops (7)
- **3** Falling heavily (of rain) (8)
- **4** Descend down a rock face (6)
- **5** Predatory canine mammal (4)
- **6** Writing fluid holder (7)
- **7** Catholic shrine in France (7)
- **12** Reduction in price (8)
- **13** Dig out of the ground (7)
- **14** Rudyard ___ : novelist (7)
- **16** Question after a mission (7)
- **17** Makes a bill law (6)
- **20** Money paid for work (4)

PUZZLE 130

Across

8 Itemise (9)
9 Precious stone (3)
10 Research deeply (5)
11 Country in Africa (7)
12 Freedom from intrusion (7)
13 Hunted animal (4)
17 Sheet of paper in a book (4)
18 Due to the fact that (7)
22 Agreement (7)
24 Allotted quantity (5)
25 Gave a meal to (3)
26 Without fixed limits (4-5)

Down

1 Small and round and shiny (of eyes) (5)
2 Large amphibian (8)
3 Keep for future use (7)
4 Unit of astronomical length (6)
5 Tactical manoeuvre (5)
6 Highly excited (4)
7 Hires a new member of staff (7)
14 Replies to a query (8)
15 Define clearly (7)
16 Car makes (7)
19 Small whirlpools (6)
20 Thing that imparts motion (5)
21 Tea container (5)
23 Moves the head to show agreement (4)

PUZZLE 131

Across

7 Complacent and happy with oneself (4-9)
8 Long-legged rodent (6)
9 Gets together (6)
10 Exceptional (8)
13 Person who will inherit (4)
14 Run at moderate pace (4)
16 Choosing (8)
19 Turn down (6)
20 Stinging plant (6)
22 Wide-ranging (13)

Down

1 Mass of floating ice (4)
2 Exude (6)
3 Type of sandwich (6)
4 Habitual practice (6)
5 Aloof (6)
6 Act of removal (8)
11 Building examiner (8)
12 Mock (3)
15 Hits hard (6)
16 Holds out against (6)
17 Bit of partly burnt wood (6)
18 Hate (6)
21 ___ in hope: be optimistic about (4)

PUZZLE 132

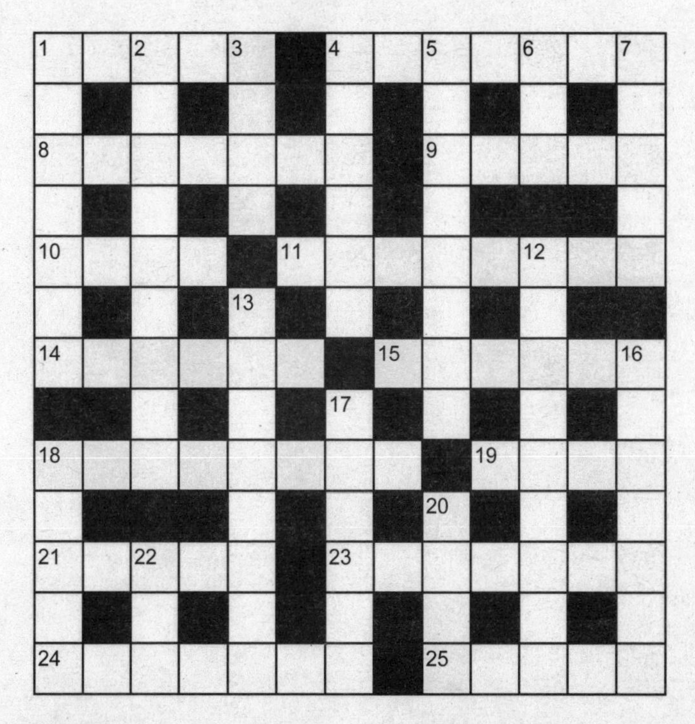

Across

1 Money (5)
4 Noisiest (7)
8 Containing no water at all (4,3)
9 Humid (5)
10 Area of a house (4)
11 Put into action (5,3)
14 Immature insects (6)
15 Device for warming the air (6)
18 Coerce into doing something (8)
19 Slide; lose grip (4)
21 Show indifference with the shoulders (5)
23 Capital of Indonesia (7)
24 Substitute (5-2)
25 Passageway (5)

Down

1 Given generously (7)
2 Large gathering of people (9)
3 Small whirlpool (4)
4 Non-ordained Church member (6)
5 Unidentified (8)
6 Food item from a hen (3)
7 Secret rendezvous (5)
12 Fringes of a city (9)
13 Rubbed with the hands (8)
16 Excessive bureaucracy (3,4)
17 ___ horse: hollow wooden statue in Greek mythology (6)
18 Sends through the mail (5)
20 Gull-like bird (4)
22 Long and narrow inlet (3)

PUZZLE 133

Across

1 A time-consuming flight (4,4)
5 Tailless amphibian (4)
8 Unit of light (5)
9 Teller (7)
10 Disturbance; commotion (7)
12 ___ ball: item used by clairvoyants (7)
14 Mercury alloy (7)
16 Liberty (7)
18 Adhesive label (7)
19 Capital of Ghana (5)
20 Takes to court (4)
21 Story with a symbolic message (8)

Down

1 Bell-shaped flower (4)
2 That is to say (6)
3 Gymnastic exercise (9)
4 Straighten out (6)
6 Dried grape (6)
7 Popular flowering plant (8)
11 Formal procession (9)
12 Befuddles (8)
13 Go to bed (6)
14 Without ethics (6)
15 South American cowboy (6)
17 Change (4)

PUZZLE 134

Across

1 Measure of effectiveness (8)
5 Having inherent ability (4)
9 Sugar heated until it turns brown (7)
10 Sky-blue colour (5)
11 Likely to decay (of food) (10)
14 Special ___ : film illusion (6)
15 Small flower (6)
17 Gathering of people (10)
20 Oak tree nut (5)
21 Isolate (7)
22 Female sheep (pl) (4)
23 They compete in the Olympic Games (8)

Down

1 Every (4)
2 A strengthened and defended building (4)
3 Beginning (12)
4 Port in N France (6)
6 Small N American avian (8)
7 ___ hour: the latest possible moment (8)
8 Caused by disease (12)
12 Discrete; distinct (8)
13 Away from land (8)
16 Enclosed recess (6)
18 Uncle's wife (4)
19 Opposite of more (4)

PUZZLE 135

Across

1 Woody perennial plant (4)
3 Photograph (8)
9 Take out (7)
10 U-shaped curve in a river (5)
11 Gossip (12)
13 Dish served at a formal dinner (6)
15 Part of a motor (6)
17 Scientific research rooms (12)
20 Chessmen (5)
21 Become husky (7)
22 Light brown cane sugar (8)
23 Marries (4)

Down

1 Quivered (8)
2 Additional; excess (5)
4 Innate character of a person (6)
5 Commensurate (12)
6 Natural environment (7)
7 Settlement smaller than a city (4)
8 Troublemaker (6-6)
12 Gifts (8)
14 Small restaurant or cafe (7)
16 Assemble (6)
18 A point in question (5)
19 Walked or stepped (4)

PUZZLE 136

Across

1 Extreme confusion (6)
5 Arrange laws systematically (6)
8 ___ Flynn Boyle: actress (4)
9 Of striking beauty (8)
10 Cloud (anag) (5)
11 Diffusion of molecules through a membrane (7)
14 Quality of being individual (13)
16 Chain of flowers (7)
18 Alter (5)
20 Rucksack (8)
22 Metal fastener (4)
23 Odour-releasing animals (6)
24 Strong ringing sounds (6)

Down

2 Ornate (9)
3 Pamphlet (7)
4 Thin fog (4)
5 Awkwardly (8)
6 Wild dog of Australia (5)
7 Cooling tool (3)
12 Planning to do something (9)
13 Learned people (8)
15 European country (7)
17 Symbol (5)
19 Comedy sketch (4)
21 Ancient boat (3)

PUZZLE 137

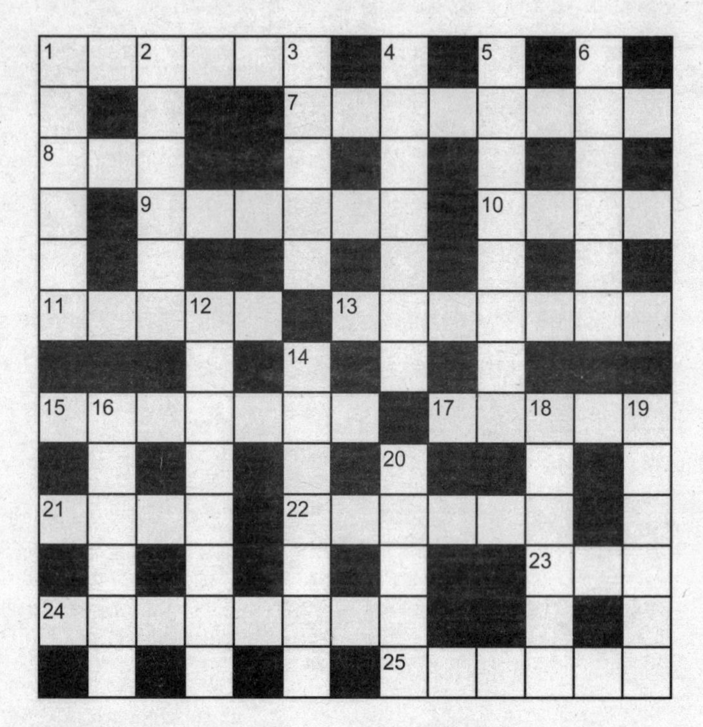

Across

1 Country where one finds Warsaw (6)
7 Act of moving around an axis (8)
8 Coniferous tree (3)
9 Approval (6)
10 Standard regarded as typical (4)
11 Records on tape (5)
13 Formally endorses (7)
15 Having a large belly (7)
17 Burning (5)
21 Deliberately taunt (4)
22 Melodious (6)
23 Top (anag) (3)
24 War memorial (8)
25 Attach (6)

Down

1 Bribe (6)
2 Legitimate (6)
3 Sag (5)
4 Works of fiction (7)
5 Deadlock (5-3)
6 Made bitter (6)
12 Warning of impending danger (8)
14 Type of cheese (7)
16 Astonished (6)
18 Chant; speak solemnly (6)
19 Left (6)
20 Hawaiian greeting (5)

PUZZLE 138

Across

1 Climber (11)
9 Permit (5)
10 Cereal plant (3)
11 Less moist (5)
12 Traveller on horseback (5)
13 Re-evaluate (8)
16 Not appropriate (8)
18 Tool for boring holes (5)
21 Hoarse sound made by a frog (5)
22 Greyish-brown colour (3)
23 Embarrass (5)
24 Holland (11)

Down

2 Relating to sight (7)
3 Closest (7)
4 Lanes (6)
5 More recent (5)
6 Long-___ owl: bird (5)
7 Comprehends (11)
8 Crushed with sorrow (11)
14 Former Greek monetary unit (7)
15 Against (7)
17 Fibre from the angora goat (6)
19 Spirit in a bottle (5)
20 Freshwater fish (5)

PUZZLE 139

Across

1 Device for inflating tyres (4)
3 Partially hidden (8)
9 Mythical stories (7)
10 Ancient object (5)
11 Working for oneself (4-8)
14 Ant and ___ : TV presenters (3)
16 Remove wool from sheep (5)
17 Measure of length (3)
18 Baked product containing seasoned meat (7,5)
21 Promotional wording (5)
22 A very skilled performer (7)
23 The bones of the body (8)
24 Fill to capacity (4)

Down

1 Fence of stakes (8)
2 Tycoon (5)
4 Form of public transport (3)
5 Mapmaker (12)
6 Release someone from duty (7)
7 Passage (4)
8 Untimely (12)
12 Earnest appeals (5)
13 Recreational area for children (8)
15 Sense of resolution (7)
19 Woodland god (5)
20 Falls back (4)
22 Sound that a cow makes (3)

PUZZLE 140

Across

1 Goes through in detail; filters (5)
4 Scuffles (7)
8 Long distance postal service (7)
9 Push back (5)
10 Wild mountain goat (4)
11 With undiminished force (8)
14 Blunders (6)
15 Have a bad posture (6)
18 A desert in south-western Africa (8)
19 Pal (4)
21 Became less intense (5)
23 Honesty (7)
24 Worked out logically (7)
25 Closes and opens an eye (5)

Down

1 Trembling (7)
2 Absent-minded (9)
3 Moved through water (4)
4 Natural skill (6)
5 Scrawl (8)
6 Impertinence (slang) (3)
7 Of definite shape (5)
12 Score in American football (9)
13 Deliberate (8)
16 Upper arm bone (7)
17 Red cab (anag) (6)
18 Manipulate dough (5)
20 Understand (4)
22 Unhappy (3)

PUZZLE 141

Across

1 Charge with a crime (6)
4 Talk idly (6)
9 Film about a magical board game (7)
10 Decorate food (7)
11 Cattle-breeding farm (5)
12 Relay (anag) (5)
14 Ordered arrangement (5)
15 Summed together (5)
17 Vigour and spirit (5)
18 Guglielmo ___ : radio pioneer (7)
20 Mean; dishonourable (3-4)
21 Slacken (6)
22 Small pieces; slivers (6)

Down

1 Damage (6)
2 Insisted upon (8)
3 An easy task (5)
5 In an annoyed manner (7)
6 Cab (4)
7 Slice of bacon (6)
8 Prominent (4,7)
13 Annual (8)
14 Postpone (7)
15 Protective covering (6)
16 Living things (6)
17 Speech sound (5)
19 Move by rotating (4)

PUZZLE 142

Across

7 In a disbelieving manner (13)
8 Not genuine (6)
9 Poor handwriting (6)
10 Gathering (8)
13 Bark of a dog (4)
14 Sailing ship (4)
16 Science of soil management (8)
19 ___ Bocelli: Italian operatic singer (6)
20 Grouchy (6)
22 Person performing official duties (13)

Down

1 Finishes (4)
2 Bird of the pheasant family (6)
3 Boards (anag) (6)
4 Slick and shiny (6)
5 Dig a hole (of an animal) (6)
6 Soft-bodied beetle (4-4)
11 Love song (8)
12 Carry a heavy object (3)
15 Small pet rodent (6)
16 In slow tempo (of music) (6)
17 Legal entitlements (6)
18 Type of sweet (6)
21 Formal ball (4)

PUZZLE 143

Across

1 Unpleasant (11)
9 Slender freshwater fish (5)
10 Superhuman being (3)
11 Type of leather (5)
12 Ascended (5)
13 Disloyal people (8)
16 Loss of importance or status (8)
18 Uneven (of a surface) (5)
21 Pick out; choose (5)
22 Bashful; reluctant to give details (3)
23 A thing that measures (5)
24 Depletion of bodily fluids (11)

Down

2 Forbidden by law (7)
3 Skills (7)
4 Having only magnitude (6)
5 Nice-smelling colourless volatile liquid (5)
6 Strong desires (5)
7 Transfer responsibility elsewhere (4,3,4)
8 Forever (2,9)
14 Young hare (7)
15 Sour cherry (7)
17 Bivalve mollusc (6)
19 Perhaps (5)
20 Delicious (5)

PUZZLE 144

1	2			3		4	■	5	■	6		7

Across

1 Hair-cleansing product (7)
6 Haul (3)
8 Thick; heavy (5)
9 Commanded (7)
10 Vaulted (5)
11 Brilliant musical performers (8)
13 Move back (6)
15 Doing nothing (6)
18 Small pieces; bits (8)
19 Cherished (5)
21 Symbols of disgrace (7)
22 Japanese form of fencing (5)
23 Mature (3)
24 Children's carers (7)

Down

2 Courageous woman (7)
3 Convince (8)
4 Strangest (6)
5 ___ Blyton: writer (4)
6 Stations at the ends of routes (7)
7 Twisting; meandering (7)
12 Take up of a practice (8)
13 Copy (7)
14 Call together (7)
16 Nattier (anag) (7)
17 Agreement or concord (6)
20 Finished; complete (4)

PUZZLE 145

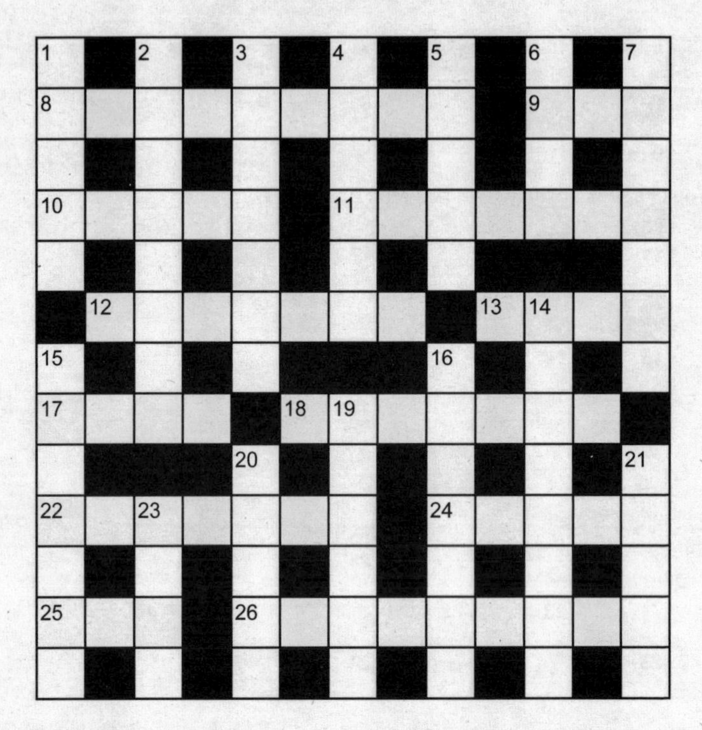

Across

8 Femur (5,4)
9 Put a question to (3)
10 Edge (5)
11 Period of prolonged dryness (7)
12 Break rules (7)
13 Total spread of a bridge (4)
17 Inspired by reverence (4)
18 Overturn (7)
22 Quantity of food (7)
24 Greenish-bronze fish (5)
25 Intentionally so written (3)
26 As likely to succeed as to fail (3-2-4)

Down

1 Heating apparatus (5)
2 Severe headache (8)
3 Four-wheeled carriage (7)
4 Pasta strip (6)
5 Mortise partner (5)
6 Loud noise (4)
7 Moving on ice (7)
14 Type of restaurant (8)
15 Player of an instrument that is low in pitch (7)
16 Lines of equal pressure on maps (7)
19 Mineral of the pyroxene group (6)
20 Dubious (5)
21 Accumulate (5)
23 A swamp grass (4)

PUZZLE 146

1		2		■	3	4		5		6		7
	■		■	8	■		■		■		■	
9							■	10				
	■		■		■		■		■		■	
11					■	12						
	■	■	■		■		■		■		■	
13		14				■	15					
	■		■		■	16	■		■	■	■	
17							■	18		19		
	■		■		■		■		■		■	
20					■	21						
	■		■		■		■		■		■	
22								■	23			

Across

1 ___ Ellington: US musician (4)
3 Of extreme thinness (of china) (8)
9 Kitchen implement (7)
10 Relating to vision (5)
11 Not suitable (5)
12 Aerial (7)
13 ___ mundum: defying everyone (6)
15 Large insect (6)
17 Granite (anag) (7)
18 Bags (5)
20 Strange and mysterious (5)
21 Of enormous effect (7)
22 Longing (8)
23 Shopping centre (US) (4)

Down

1 Characteristically (13)
2 Australian marsupial (5)
4 ___ Norton: Irish comic presenter (6)
5 Malfunction or fail (of an electrical device) (5-7)
6 Baltic country (7)
7 Lazy (13)
8 Underground (12)
14 Country in W Africa (7)
16 Eg spring or winter (6)
19 Brazilian dance (5)

PUZZLE 147

1		2		■	3	4		5		6		7
	■		■	8	■		■		■		■	
9							■	10				
	■		■		■	■	■		■		■	
11						12						■
	■	■	■		■		■		■		■	13
14		15	■	16					■	17		
	■		■		■		■		■	■	■	
■	18									19		
20	■		■		■	■	■		■		■	
21					■	22						
	■		■		■		■		■		■	
23								■	24			

Across

1 Opposite of fail (4)
3 Recent arrival (8)
9 Serious (7)
10 Place where something happens (5)
11 Accepted behaviour whilst dining (5,7)
14 Sticky substance (3)
16 Making a knot in (5)
17 Female pronoun (3)
18 Clearly evident (12)
21 Service colour of the army (5)
22 Giving food to (7)
23 The act of swimming (8)
24 Brave person; idol (4)

Down

1 Repute; standing (8)
2 Clean thoroughly (5)
4 Newt (3)
5 Popular district in London (6,6)
6 Sovereign (7)
7 Ostrichlike bird (4)
8 Person who receives office visitors (12)
12 Assumed name (5)
13 Notes of a chord played in rapid succession (8)
15 Ham it up (7)
19 Inducement (5)
20 This covers your body (4)
22 ___ Rida: American rapper (3)

PUZZLE 148

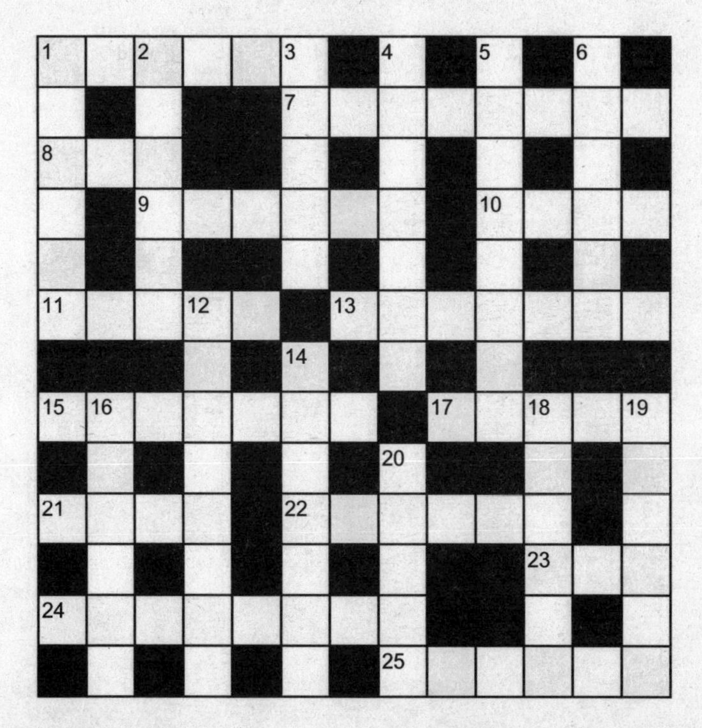

Across

1 Leguminous tree (6)
7 Male siblings (8)
8 21st Greek letter (3)
9 Title of Roman emperors (6)
10 Large deer (pl) (4)
11 Avoid (5)
13 Food pantries (7)
15 ___ seat: aircraft safety device (7)
17 Equipped (5)
21 Plant yield (4)
22 Fairness (6)
23 Head covering (3)
24 Monstrous creature (8)
25 Servant in a royal household (6)

Down

1 Measure of electrical current (6)
2 ___ Keys: US singer (6)
3 Humiliate (5)
4 Periodical (7)
5 Device that chops up documents (8)
6 Buyer and seller (6)
12 Interpret the meaning of (8)
14 Tedium (7)
16 Jolted (6)
18 Chaos (6)
19 Timothy ___ : James Bond actor (6)
20 Growing thickly (of a beard) (5)

PUZZLE 149

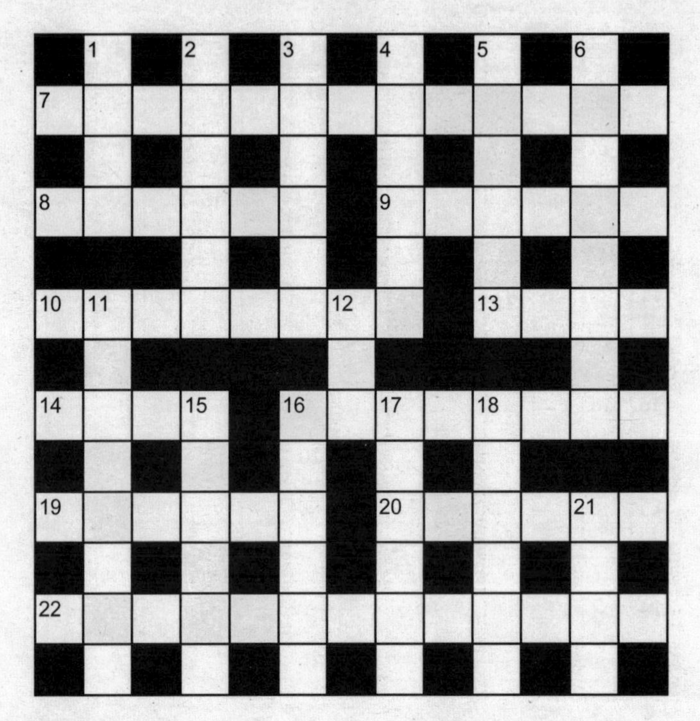

Across

7 Rebirth in a new body (13)
8 Make beloved (6)
9 Developed into (6)
10 Make more concentrated (8)
13 Having a sound mind (4)
14 US state (4)
16 Small stall at an exhibition (8)
19 Easily handled (6)
20 Decorative ornament (6)
22 Process of worsening (13)

Down

1 Average value (4)
2 Straighten out (6)
3 Unproductive (of land) (6)
4 Nebula (anag) (6)
5 Adheres to; fastens (6)
6 Soldier (8)
11 Person not accepted by society (8)
12 Snow runner (3)
15 Protective headgear (6)
16 Hinder the progress of (6)
17 Suspends; prevents (6)
18 Not rough (6)
21 Poultry enclosure (4)

PUZZLE 150

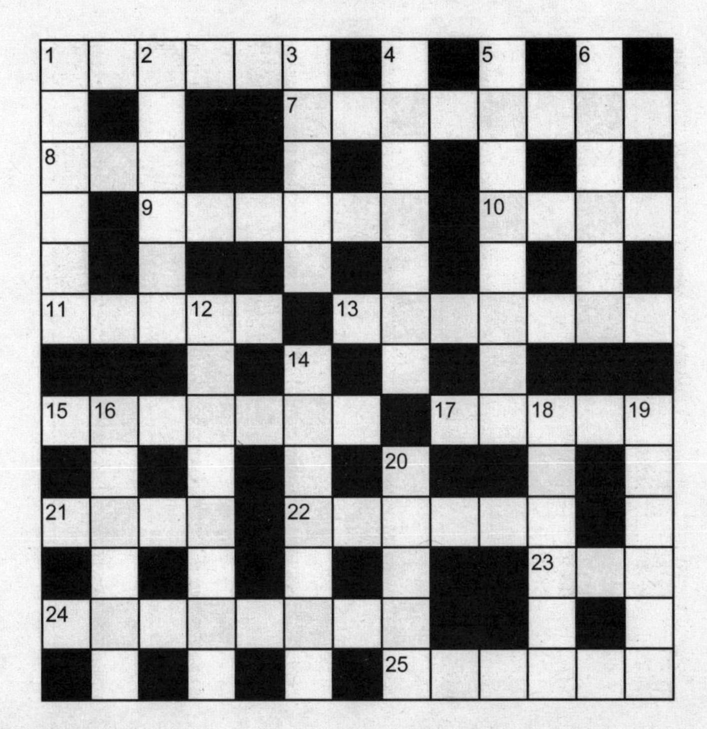

Across

1 Bone in the forearm (6)
7 Amount (8)
8 Surpass (3)
9 Intending (6)
10 Told an untruth (4)
11 Stage performer (5)
13 Most unattractive (7)
15 Summit (7)
17 Cancel (5)
21 Open tart (4)
22 Show servile deference (6)
23 Burdensome charge (3)
24 Greek dish (8)
25 Pollutes (6)

Down

1 Part of the eye (6)
2 Leave (6)
3 Elongated cephalopod mollusc (5)
4 Luggage (7)
5 Adult male horse (8)
6 Guides a vehicle (6)
12 Greasiness (8)
14 Male labourer (7)
16 Ice homes (6)
18 Isaac ___ : physicist (6)
19 Wildcats (6)
20 Perspire (5)

PUZZLE 151

Across

1 Fit for cultivation (of land) (6)
4 Sour to the taste (6)
9 Root vegetable (7)
10 Piece of jewellery (7)
11 Care for; look after (5)
12 Small seat (5)
14 Drenches (5)
15 Floral leaf (5)
17 Nationality of Charlotte Church (5)
18 Far-reaching; thorough (7)
20 Word opposite in meaning to another (7)
21 Pressing keys (6)
22 Deletes (6)

Down

1 Relating to high mountains (6)
2 Flying machine (8)
3 Type of spear (5)
5 Evergreen conifer (7)
6 ___ Moore: Hollywood actress (4)
7 Club (6)
8 Extremely impressive (11)
13 Rough drafts of a plan (8)
14 Make less taut (7)
15 Erupts (anag) (6)
16 Lymphoid organ (6)
17 Liquid essential for life (5)
19 Put down a catch (4)

PUZZLE 152

Across

1 Type of tooth (8)
5 Country bordered by Libya and Sudan (4)
9 Large cushion for sitting on (7)
10 Slopes (5)
11 Sensible and fair (10)
14 Batting order (4-2)
15 Loose protective garments (6)
17 Glass building (10)
20 Small crude shelter (5)
21 Bring to life (7)
22 Dark cloud of smoke (4)
23 Understate (8)

Down

1 Young child (4)
2 Steep and rugged rock (4)
3 Next (12)
4 Take into the body (of food) (6)
6 Type of whale (8)
7 Spread out (8)
8 Act of sending a message (12)
12 Top boat in a fleet (8)
13 Break in activity (8)
16 Trinidad and ___ : country (6)
18 Cry with sorrow or grief (4)
19 Depend upon (4)

PUZZLE 153

Across

1 Bone of the forearm (4)
3 US state (8)
9 Marked by prosperity (of a past time) (7)
10 A sum owed (5)
11 Total destruction (12)
14 Unit of current (3)
16 Foreign language (informal) (5)
17 ___ Tyler: US actress (3)
18 Gathering of people (12)
21 Sweet-scented shrub (5)
22 Sets free or releases (7)
23 Thoroughly conversant with (8)
24 Soft cheese (4)

Down

1 Commotion (8)
2 Synthetic fabric (5)
4 Hurried (3)
5 And also (12)
6 Layer of earth (7)
7 Takes an exam (4)
8 Based on legend (12)
12 Sudden movement (5)
13 Fade away (8)
15 Dilemma (7)
19 Bring on oneself (5)
20 Musical staff sign (4)
22 North American nation (abbrev) (3)

PUZZLE 154

Across

1 Truly (8)
5 Welsh emblem (4)
8 Quantitative relation between two amounts (5)
9 Tall quadruped (7)
10 Distant runner-up (4-3)
12 Domain (7)
14 Gestures that convey meaning (7)
16 Coincide partially (7)
18 Make progress (7)
19 Speed music is played at (5)
20 Becomes brown in the sun (4)
21 Looking up to (8)

Down

1 Fling (4)
2 Concept (6)
3 Rogue (9)
4 Situation that appears irresolvable (6)
6 Exertion (6)
7 Enthusiasm (8)
11 Type of pasta (9)
12 Unit of power (8)
13 Opposite of hell (6)
14 Move apart; open out (6)
15 Former pupils (6)
17 Opposite of short (4)

PUZZLE 155

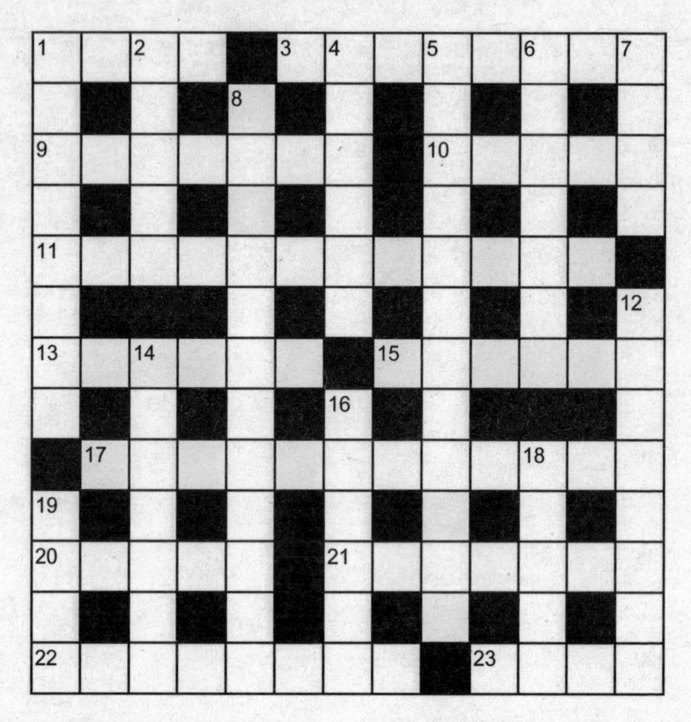

Across

1 Country whose capital is Havana (4)
3 Insincere and dishonest (3-5)
9 Shackle (7)
10 ___ Newton: scientist (5)
11 Clarity (12)
13 Sad pot (anag) (6)
15 ___ Cuthbert: Canadian actress (6)
17 Very upsetting (5-7)
20 Damien ___ : modern English artist (5)
21 Large fortified buildings (7)
22 Opposite in meaning (8)
23 Speck (4)

Down

1 Joke-telling entertainer (8)
2 Shelf-like beds (5)
4 Twist suddenly (6)
5 Amiability (12)
6 Categories (7)
7 Slender freshwater fish (4)
8 Author of screenplays (12)
12 Gift of money (8)
14 Conquer by force (7)
16 Food merchant (6)
18 Ice dwelling (5)
19 Stylish and fashionable (4)

PUZZLE 156

Across

1 Leaping over a rope (8)
5 Leave out (4)
8 Type of tooth (5)
9 Exercise for building arm muscles (5-2)
10 Not outside (7)
12 20th letter of the Greek alphabet (7)
14 Insurance calculator (7)
16 Lead batsmen (cricket) (7)
18 Instruct (7)
19 Praise highly (5)
20 Ooze or leak slowly (4)
21 Choosing to take up or follow (8)

Down

1 Unspecified in number (4)
2 Fillings (6)
3 Permeate (9)
4 Table linen (6)
6 Thing that brings good luck (6)
7 Hand-woven pictorial design (8)
11 Very inexpensive (4,5)
12 Exposes (8)
13 Reserved and coy (6)
14 Go up (6)
15 Opposite of an acid (6)
17 Male deer (4)

PUZZLE 157

Across

1 Memorial (8)
5 ___ Simone: US singer (4)
9 Inclination (7)
10 Cruel or severe (5)
11 Metric unit of length (10)
14 Smells (6)
15 Moral excellence (6)
17 Repot (10)
20 Clear and apparent; obvious (5)
21 Planned one's actions (7)
22 Rouse from sleep (4)
23 Compassion (8)

Down

1 Communicate through gestures (4)
2 Religious sisters (4)
3 Give a false account of (12)
4 Write a music score (6)
6 Annoy (8)
7 Successful person (8)
8 Type of contest (12)
12 Left-handed boxer (8)
13 Light axe (8)
16 Vitreous (6)
18 Release; give out (4)
19 In a tense state (4)

PUZZLE 158

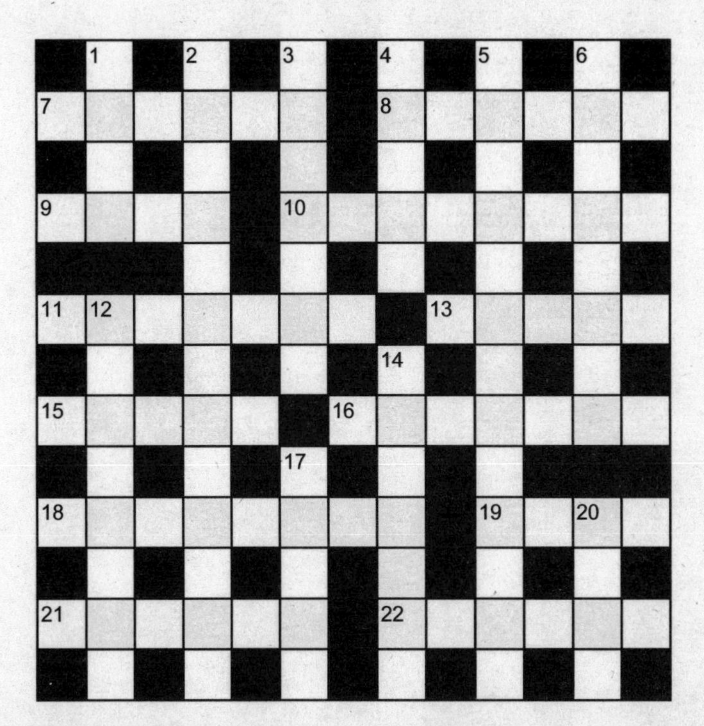

Across

- **7** Former female pupil (6)
- **8** Removes from one's property (6)
- **9** Rip up (4)
- **10** Lazy person (8)
- **11** Distinct sort or kind (7)
- **13** Public announcement officer (5)
- **15** Certain to fail (2-3)
- **16** Paper tokens (7)
- **18** Visionary; utopian (8)
- **19** Furnace (4)
- **21** Small hills (6)
- **22** Mistakes (6)

Down

- **1** Adhesive (4)
- **2** Unfeasible (13)
- **3** Flowers with white petals (7)
- **4** Lists of restaurants dishes (5)
- **5** Trickery (13)
- **6** Large fish (8)
- **12** Trudging (8)
- **14** Male servants (7)
- **17** In the middle of (literary) (5)
- **20** Lie in ambush (4)

PUZZLE 159

Across

1 Stride; rate of moving (4)
3 Surpass in excellence (8)
9 Perfect example of a quality (7)
10 Expect; think that (5)
11 Foreboding (12)
14 Long period of time (3)
16 Avoided by social custom (5)
17 Pointed tool (3)
18 Obfuscation (12)
21 Dole out (5)
22 ___ Monroe: famous actress (7)
23 A reduction in price (8)
24 Extras (cricket) (4)

Down

1 Gets ready (8)
2 Bend or curl (5)
4 Utilise (3)
5 Long athletics race (5-7)
6 US state (7)
7 Grain that grows into a new plant (4)
8 Tamed (12)
12 Remnant of a dying fire (5)
13 Component parts (8)
15 One who eats a bit at a time (7)
19 Embed; type of filling (5)
20 Soothe (4)
22 Cut grass (3)

PUZZLE 160

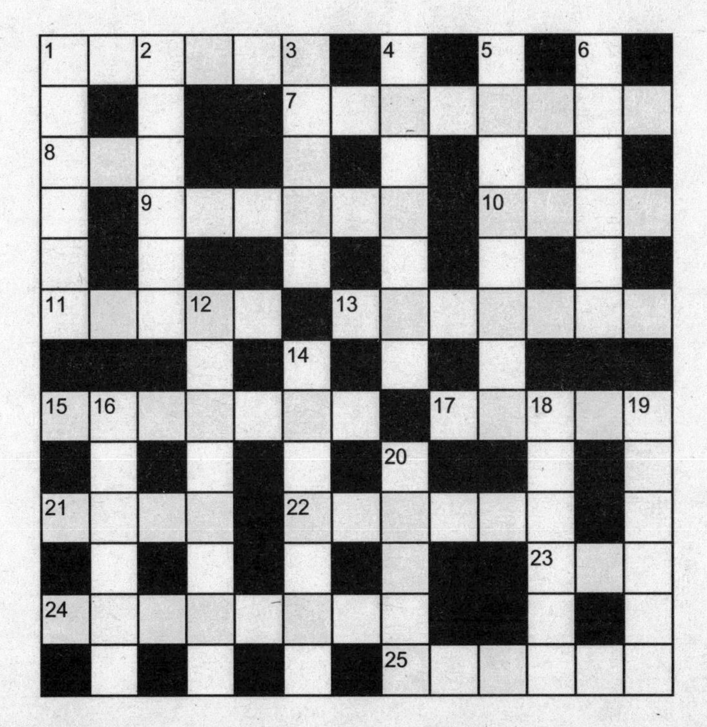

Across

1 Immature (6)
7 Living thing (8)
8 Meat from a pig (3)
9 Quickly (6)
10 Correct; accurate (4)
11 ___ Andronicus: Shakespeare play (5)
13 Approve or support (7)
15 Capital of Iraq (7)
17 Try (5)
21 Complain bitterly (4)
22 Dual audio (6)
23 Friend (3)
24 Exclamation of joy (8)
25 Entreated; beseeched (6)

Down

1 Roman military unit (6)
2 Marine gastropod (6)
3 Injure (5)
4 Stuck on the bottom (of a ship) (7)
5 Oily (8)
6 Important topics for debate (6)
12 Dour help (anag) (8)
14 Highly reactive metal (7)
16 Helps; benefits (6)
18 Excessively casual (6)
19 Shouted out (6)
20 Repeat something once more (5)

PUZZLE 161

Across

1 US space probe to Jupiter (7)
6 Deranged (3)
8 Underwater breathing device (5)
9 Huge wave (7)
10 Authoritative proclamation (5)
11 Plantation producing grapes (8)
13 Line of equal pressure on a map (6)
15 Royal house (6)
18 Nitrogenous organic compounds (8)
19 Broadcast again (5)
21 No longer existing (7)
22 Ride a bike (5)
23 Fire residue (3)
24 Firmly (7)

Down

2 Attacks (7)
3 A period of 366 days (4,4)
4 Willow twigs (6)
5 The Christmas festival (4)
6 Musical instrument (7)
7 Period between sunrise and sunset (7)
12 Loyal (8)
13 Resistance to change (7)
14 Large flightless bird (7)
16 Distrustful of sincerity (7)
17 Buys and sells goods (6)
20 ___ Grimshaw: DJ (4)

PUZZLE 162

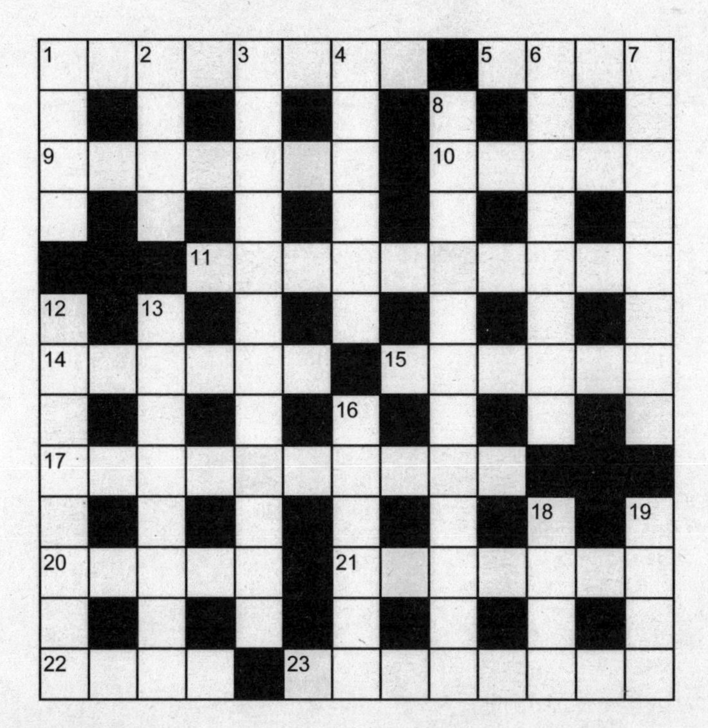

Across

1 Sports grounds (8)
5 Arrive (4)
9 Squash (7)
10 Join together; merge (5)
11 Disloyalty (10)
14 Sell to the public (6)
15 Yellowish-brown pigment (6)
17 Very lucrative endeavour (5,5)
20 Attractive flower (5)
21 Friendly goodbye (7)
22 Part of a pedestal (4)
23 Naive or sentimental (4-4)

Down

1 Strongbox (4)
2 Not at home (4)
3 Growing stronger (12)
4 Praying ___ : insect (6)
6 Views about something (8)
7 Commonplace (8)
8 Monotonously (12)
12 Squirmed (8)
13 ___ for cash: short of money (8)
16 Type of nursery (6)
18 Salver (4)
19 Bend over on itself (4)

PUZZLE 163

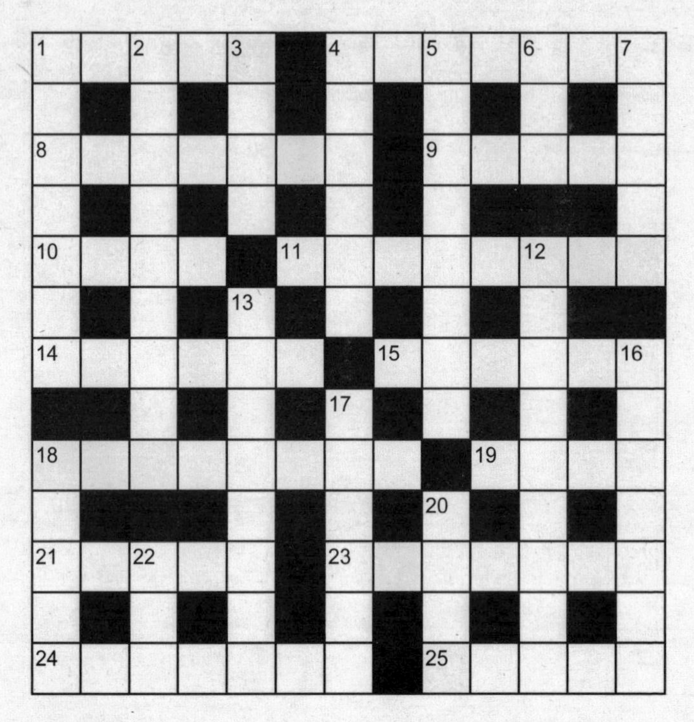

Across

1 ___ Redmayne: English actor (5)
4 Food eaten at a cinema (7)
8 Antlers (anag) (7)
9 Baking appliances (5)
10 Really big (4)
11 Represents in a faithful way (8)
14 River in England (6)
15 Eastern high official (6)
18 Moving slowly (8)
19 Plant stalk (4)
21 Water container (5)
23 The Netherlands (7)
24 This starts on 1st January (3,4)
25 Waggish (5)

Down

1 Hearing range (7)
2 Disparage (9)
3 School test (4)
4 Opposite of pulled (6)
5 Announce publicly (8)
6 Be in debt (3)
7 Facial protuberances (5)
12 ___ Ronaldo: Portuguese footballer (9)
13 Retort (8)
16 Reconstruct (7)
17 Heavy metal weight used by a ship (6)
18 Private room on a ship (5)
20 Delighted (4)
22 Fasten with stitches (3)

PUZZLE 164

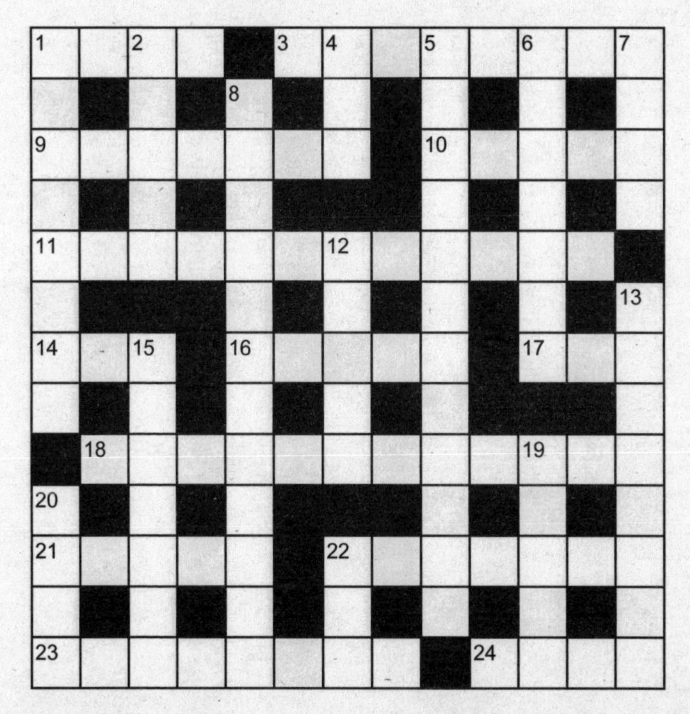

Across

1 Annoy (4)
3 Obscures the light from a celestial body (8)
9 Cleaning item (7)
10 Crustacean like a shrimp (5)
11 Brusque and surly (12)
14 Type of viper (3)
16 Customary practice (5)
17 Used to be (3)
18 Explanatory (12)
21 Unabridged (5)
22 Tentacled cephalopod (7)
23 Broad and strongly built (8)
24 Heavenly body (4)

Down

1 Eg a trumpeter or pianist (8)
2 Fine powdery foodstuff (5)
4 Four-wheeled road vehicle (3)
5 Enhancements (12)
6 Lacking depth (7)
7 Fall slowly downwards in water (4)
8 Deceitfully (12)
12 Seize firmly (5)
13 Appraiser; valuer (8)
15 Remedy for everything (7)
19 Enter data into a computer (5)
20 Of like kind (4)
22 Material from which metal is extracted (3)

PUZZLE 165

Across

1 Shoe ties (5)
4 Small pools of rainwater (7)
7 Church building (5)
8 Prison term (8)
9 Type of plastic (5)
11 Usually (8)
15 Hot pepper (8)
17 Retail stores (5)
19 Legendary island (8)
20 Guide a vehicle (5)
21 Sailing ship (7)
22 View; picture (5)

Down

1 Awfulness (9)
2 Points where edges meet (7)
3 At an unspecified future time (7)
4 Package (6)
5 Capital of the Republic of Ireland (6)
6 All (5)
10 Flatfish of the plaice family (5,4)
12 Destroys (7)
13 Trace of something (7)
14 Support (6)
16 Part of a stamen (6)
18 Place providing accommodation (5)

PUZZLE 166

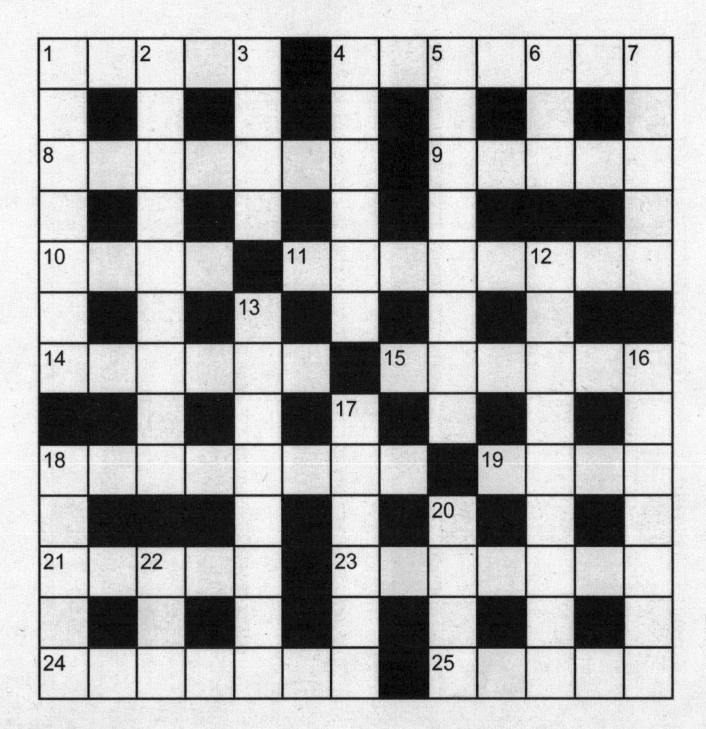

Across

1 Mournful poem (5)
4 Nestled together (7)
8 Ship worker (7)
9 Diving waterbird (5)
10 Dull heavy sound (4)
11 Expanded (8)
14 Highly motivated (6)
15 Throw in the towel (4,2)
18 Ability to act as one wishes (4,4)
19 Catherine ___ : British comedienne (4)
21 Phantasm (5)
23 Pulls back from (7)
24 Digit (7)
25 Made a mistake (5)

Down

1 Exhilarated (7)
2 Senior manager (9)
3 Mays (anag) (4)
4 Sharpening (6)
5 Opinionated and inflexible (8)
6 Brett ___ : Australian fast bowler (3)
7 Extreme fear (5)
12 Type of soldier (9)
13 Contents of the Mediterranean (8)
16 Exerted force upon (7)
17 Consisting of flowers (6)
18 Character in Oliver Twist (5)
20 Throb (4)
22 Unit of resistance (3)

PUZZLE 167

Across

1 Ice cream flavour (7)
6 Range of knowledge (3)
8 One of the United Arab Emirates (5)
9 Bridge above another road (7)
10 Connection; link (3-2)
11 Make less complex (8)
13 Glasses contain these (6)
15 Constructs (6)
18 Ruled with authority (8)
19 Widespread dislike (5)
21 Lie (7)
22 Nosed (anag) (5)
23 Long-leaved lettuce (3)
24 Very small fish (7)

Down

2 Unsurpassed (3-4)
3 Made flat (8)
4 Afloat (6)
5 Encourage in wrongdoing (4)
6 Relating to motion (7)
7 Freshness (7)
12 Apprehended (8)
13 Terse (7)
14 Countries (7)
16 Table support (7)
17 Vigorous; strong and healthy (6)
20 Method; fashion (4)

PUZZLE 168

Across

1 Water-filled ditches around castles (5)
4 Dense masses of vegetation (7)
8 In a relaxed manner (7)
9 Shadow (5)
10 Indication (4)
11 Rebellious (8)
14 Valued highly (6)
15 Portable computer (6)
18 Precise and clear (8)
19 Small fight (4)
21 Turn inside out (5)
23 Land retained by a lord (7)
24 Flavouring from a crocus (7)
25 Beastly (5)

Down

1 Coward (7)
2 Next to (9)
3 Look for (4)
4 Full of happiness (6)
5 Maritime (8)
6 Research place (abbrev) (3)
7 Absorbent pads (5)
12 Cephalopod molluscs (9)
13 Sorriest (anag) (8)
16 Items made from fired clay (7)
17 Concealed from view (6)
18 Paces (5)
20 Portent (4)
22 Mischievous sprite (3)

PUZZLE 169

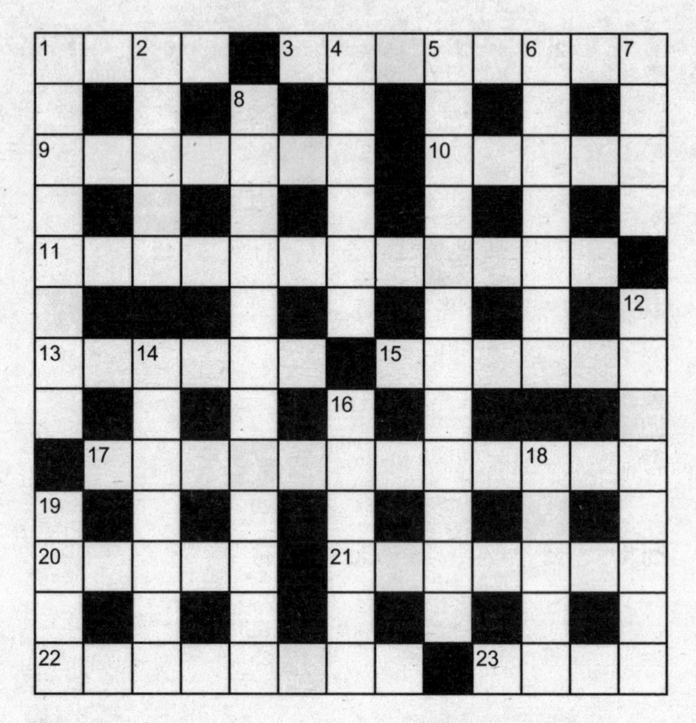

Across

1 Group of actors in a show (4)
3 Boldly (8)
9 Having solidified from lava (of rock) (7)
10 Young bird (5)
11 Total confusion (12)
13 Small summerhouse (6)
15 Indulge a person (6)
17 Effective working together of parts (12)
20 Turf out (5)
21 Roars (7)
22 Statuette (8)
23 ___ Gosling: actor (4)

Down

1 Card game (8)
2 Strong fibrous tissue (5)
4 Reply (6)
5 Immeasurably (12)
6 Smiled broadly (7)
7 Ox-like mammals (4)
8 Fellow plotter (12)
12 Male relation (8)
14 Travelling very quickly (7)
16 Decorative strip of fabric (6)
18 Form of humour (5)
19 Feudal labourer (4)

PUZZLE 170

Across

1 Calmness under pressure (8)
5 Extent of a surface (4)
8 Group of bees (5)
9 Vivid purplish-red colour (7)
10 Meaninglessness (7)
12 Geoffrey ___ : former England cricketer (7)
14 Rebuffed; spurned (7)
16 Sum of money put in the bank (7)
18 Do repeatedly (7)
19 Sound (5)
20 Locate or place (4)
21 Starlike symbol (8)

Down

1 Portfolio (4)
2 By word of mouth (6)
3 Worms used to control pests (9)
4 Underside of an arch (6)
6 World's largest country (6)
7 Examined in detail (8)
11 Emergency vehicle (9)
12 Bedrooms (8)
13 Positive and happy (6)
14 Spirited horses (6)
15 Minimal bathing suit (6)
17 Eat like a bird (4)

PUZZLE 171

Across

1 Ludicrous failure (6)
7 Old World monkeys (8)
8 Disapproving sound (3)
9 Flock of geese (6)
10 Feeling of resentment or jealousy (4)
11 Charming and endearing (5)
13 Need (7)
15 Destructive (7)
17 Long-legged wading bird (5)
21 Foolish person (informal) (4)
22 Mineral form of silica (6)
23 Sprite (3)
24 Commotion (8)
25 Cattle trough (6)

Down

1 Legendary tales (6)
2 Climax or culmination (6)
3 24th Greek letter (5)
4 Plotter (7)
5 Artificial water channel (8)
6 Reveal (anag) (6)
12 Full of interesting happenings (8)
14 Small orange-like citrus fruit (7)
16 Entice or attract (6)
18 Seeping (6)
19 Guardian (6)
20 Polite address for a woman (5)

PUZZLE 172

Across

1 Get off a horse (8)
5 Skin irritation (4)
8 Sound of an emergency vehicle (5)
9 Hinged surface on an aeroplane wing (7)
10 Small stones (7)
12 ___ Klass: TV presenter (7)
14 A dancer or singer (7)
16 Degraded (7)
18 Inspire with love (7)
19 Assertion (5)
20 Beach constituent (4)
21 Changing (8)

Down

1 Stage of twilight (4)
2 Plant of the dock family (6)
3 Decorations (9)
4 Subtle variation (6)
6 Large marine reptile (6)
7 Good-looking (8)
11 Yellow flower (9)
12 Lack of intensity (8)
13 Get hold of (6)
14 Worshipped (6)
15 Highly seasoned sausage (6)
17 Type of air pollution (4)

PUZZLE 173

Across

1 Arrived (4)
3 Roomy (8)
9 Reasonably to be believed (7)
10 Requirements (5)
11 In a greedy manner (12)
13 Deny of food (6)
15 Not awake (6)
17 Official praise (12)
20 Consumed (5)
21 Relating to Oxford (7)
22 Large game bird (8)
23 Units of electrical resistance (4)

Down

1 Cave in (8)
2 Hot fluid rock (5)
4 Insipid (6)
5 Spanish adventurer (12)
6 Position on top of (7)
7 Neither good nor bad (2-2)
8 Accomplishments (12)
12 Beginnings (8)
14 Disciple (7)
16 Urge to do something (6)
18 Nationality of Louis Walsh (5)
19 High-pitched noise (4)

PUZZLE 174

Across

8 Priority; emphasis (9)
9 High ball in tennis (3)
10 Looks slyly (5)
11 Those who catch prey (7)
12 Birds of the family Columbidae (7)
13 Mongrel dog (4)
17 Ancient boats (4)
18 Short trips on another's behalf (7)
22 Most difficult (7)
24 Blacksmith's workshop (5)
25 Father (3)
26 Doppelganger (9)

Down

1 Fabric with parallel ribs (5)
2 Close associate (8)
3 Speak very quietly (7)
4 Inside of (6)
5 Extreme pain (5)
6 Sheet of floating ice (4)
7 State of being overweight (7)
14 Form the base for (8)
15 Negative electrode (7)
16 Midpoint (7)
19 Share out food sparingly (6)
20 Repasts (5)
21 Gave up power (5)
23 Travel by horse (4)

PUZZLE 175

Across

1 Animate existence (4)
3 Relating to education and scholarship (8)
9 Element with atomic number 31 (7)
10 Saying (5)
11 Unit of weight (3)
12 Ben ___ : Scottish mountain (5)
13 Ellipses (5)
15 Tall narrow building (5)
17 Germaine ___ : Australian author (5)
18 Used a chair (3)
19 Settle for sleep (of birds) (5)
20 Slow mover (7)
21 Salad sauce (8)
22 Fervour (4)

Down

1 Given to thievery (5-8)
2 Criminal (5)
4 Photographic equipment (6)
5 One who takes part in a protest (12)
6 Reasons for action (7)
7 Dealing with different societies (5-8)
8 Type of cloud (12)
14 Absolutely incredible (7)
16 Fighting instrument (6)
18 Move sideways (5)

PUZZLE 176

Across

7 Instructions provided with a product (13)
8 Artful person (6)
9 Stringed instrument (6)
10 Ideas (8)
13 Bite or nibble at (4)
14 Eg haematite and magnetite (4)
16 Soak; drench (8)
19 Birthplace of St Francis (6)
20 Soothed (6)
22 Warily; cautiously (13)

Down

1 ___ stick: toy for bouncing on (4)
2 Generic term for a martial art (4,2)
3 Scarcity (6)
4 Averts something bad (6)
5 Powerful (6)
6 Most influential or important (8)
11 Great difficulty (8)
12 Popular beverage (3)
15 Sew (6)
16 Ragtime dance (6)
17 Spring flowers (6)
18 Artefacts (6)
21 Sell (anag) (4)

PUZZLE 177

Across

1 Images (anag) (6)
5 Large sticks (6)
8 Place with temporary accommodation (4)
9 Fanaticism (8)
10 Bolivian city (2,3)
11 Supplanted (7)
14 Refined (13)
16 Type of polish (7)
18 Propose; utter (5)
20 Aromatic plant used in cooking (8)
22 In the not too distant future (4)
23 Overrun in large numbers (6)
24 Utilise wrongly (6)

Down

2 Mexican dip (9)
3 Bring an accusation against (7)
4 Labyrinth (4)
5 Spacecraft (8)
6 Love affair (5)
7 Distant (3)
12 Efforts (9)
13 Daydreamer (8)
15 Swears (7)
17 Strain (5)
19 Soothing remedy (4)
21 Grandmother (3)

PUZZLE 178

Across

1 Of the stomach (7)
6 Quick sleep (3)
8 Japanese poem (5)
9 Aperture or hole (7)
10 Stringed instruments (5)
11 In these times (8)
13 Exhaled audibly (6)
15 Deprived of; lacking (6)
18 Until now (8)
19 Type of bus (5)
21 Accuse of a wrong (7)
22 Savoury jelly (5)
23 Thing that fails to work properly (3)
24 Withstands (7)

Down

2 Relating to knowledge based on deduction (1,6)
3 Eg Rudolph (8)
4 ___ Baker: English TV presenter and singer (6)
5 Small stream (4)
6 Bring up; rear (7)
7 Anapest (anag) (7)
12 Tied up (8)
13 Prosper; do well (7)
14 Knight of King Arthur (7)
16 Tiredness (7)
17 In a lively manner (6)
20 Rose fruits (4)

PUZZLE 179

Across

1 Liability (4)
3 Person who supports a cause (8)
9 Mix a deck of cards (7)
10 ___ Rhymes: rapper (5)
11 What a painter creates (3)
12 Regulations (5)
13 ___ Federer: tennis star (5)
15 Underside of a projecting roof (5)
17 Woodwind instruments (5)
18 Strong alkaline solution (3)
19 Astonish (5)
20 Piece of jewellery (7)
21 And so on (2,6)
22 Guinea pig (4)

Down

1 Unemotional (13)
2 Make less sharp (5)
4 Changing the colour of hair (6)
5 Awkward (12)
6 Fifth Greek letter (7)
7 Party lanterns (anag) (13)
8 Bubbling (12)
14 Mundane (7)
16 ___ Lynd: character in Casino Royale (6)
18 Camel-like animal (5)

PUZZLE 180

Across

1 Chips (6,5)
9 Recently (5)
10 Come together (3)
11 Angry dispute (3-2)
12 Tempts (5)
13 Extend beyond a surface (8)
16 Green vegetable (8)
18 Destined (5)
21 Number after seven (5)
22 Young bear (3)
23 Empty spaces (5)
24 Official agreements (11)

Down

2 Gathering of old friends (7)
3 Convent (7)
4 Offered goods for sale (6)
5 Regal (5)
6 ___ Allan Poe: American writer (5)
7 Correct to the last detail (4-7)
8 Mean (5-6)
14 Area of land (7)
15 Opposite of shortest (7)
17 ___ Tanner: tennis player (6)
19 Piece of furniture (5)
20 Clod of turf (5)

PUZZLE 181

Across

1 Fast musical composition (7)
6 In what way (3)
8 Breed of dog (5)
9 Look after an infant (7)
10 Flatten on impact (5)
11 Sharply discordant (8)
13 False (6)
15 Mythical sea monster (6)
18 Makes more elaborate (8)
19 Possessor (5)
21 Unintelligent (7)
22 Pertaining to the moon (5)
23 Observe (3)
24 Small shark (7)

Down

2 Charlie ___ : early comic actor (7)
3 Busiest time on the roads (4,4)
4 Navigational instrument (6)
5 Pots (4)
6 Small mound (7)
7 Set down on paper (7)
12 Meeting where instructions are given (8)
13 Confirms a decision (7)
14 Shine like a star (7)
16 Grows larger (7)
17 Recompense for hardship (6)
20 Tolled (4)

PUZZLE 182

Across

1 Chamber leading to a larger space (8)
5 Large wading bird (4)
8 Act of stealing (5)
9 Type of snake (informal) (7)
10 Young tree (7)
12 Belgian language (7)
14 Declare (anag) (7)
16 Compress (7)
18 Slope (7)
19 Creamy-white colour (5)
20 Emit light (4)
21 Plant of the primrose family (8)

Down

1 Social insects (4)
2 Multiply by three (6)
3 Fight back (9)
4 Surge forwards (6)
6 Sea in northern Europe (6)
7 Showed indifference (8)
11 Existing as a possibility (9)
12 Blinking like a light (8)
13 Papal representative (6)
14 Plant with edible stalks (6)
15 Make changes to improve something (6)
17 Blue-green colour (4)

PUZZLE 183

Across

1 Come together (8)
5 Heavy stick used as a weapon (4)
9 ___ shorts: item of clothing (7)
10 Titled (5)
11 Intrusive and interfering (10)
14 Bird of prey (6)
15 Sharp pain (6)
17 Suppression of objectionable material (10)
20 Relay device (5)
21 A curse; wicked look (4,3)
22 Peer (4)
23 Having no current (of a body of water) (8)

Down

1 Young lions (4)
2 Roman emperor (4)
3 A perfumed liquid (3,2,7)
4 Protects (6)
6 Satirises (8)
7 Pestered constantly (8)
8 Insuring (12)
12 Vessel for molten metal (8)
13 Unmarried woman (8)
16 State confidently (6)
18 Catherine ___ Jones: Welsh actress (4)
19 Warm up (4)

PUZZLE 184

Across

1 Traitorous (11)
9 Criminal deception (5)
10 Collection of paper (3)
11 Doglike mammal (5)
12 Relating to the kidneys (5)
13 Impudent (8)
16 Imposing (8)
18 Personal attendant (5)
21 Nobleman (5)
22 Young goat (3)
23 Shout of appreciation (5)
24 Component parts (11)

Down

2 Let out (7)
3 In a friendly manner (7)
4 Involving direct confrontation (4-2)
5 Detection technology (5)
6 Unfasten (5)
7 Pyotr ___ : Russian composer (11)
8 Youth (11)
14 Wordy (7)
15 Promising actress (7)
17 On a ship or train (6)
19 Burdened (5)
20 Underground enlarged stem (5)

PUZZLE 185

Across

1 Absurd representation of something (8)
5 Drive away (4)
9 Lively; cheerful (7)
10 Surprise result (5)
11 Decorative design style (3,7)
14 Smallest quantities (6)
15 Narrow sea inlets (6)
17 Expression of surprise (8,2)
20 Smell (5)
21 Copy; mimic (7)
22 Subsequently (4)
23 Dish of rice with fish and eggs (8)

Down

1 Thoughtfulness (4)
2 Corrosive substance (4)
3 Based on untested ideas (12)
4 Royal chair (6)
6 Inn (8)
7 Sudden release of emotion (8)
8 Pushing into a line of people (5-7)
12 Person who leaves a country (8)
13 Face-to-face conversation (3-2-3)
16 Seek ambitiously (6)
18 Place where a wild animal lives (4)
19 Venerable ___ : English monk (4)

PUZZLE 186

Across

1 Curved shapes (4)
3 Interfered with (8)
9 Goal; intention (7)
10 ___ Camera: band (5)
11 Body of water (5)
12 Support or strengthen (7)
13 Shipyard worker (6)
15 Country in central Africa (6)
17 State of disorder (7)
18 Christina ___ : actress (5)
20 Country in southern Asia (5)
21 Character in Hamlet (7)
22 Narrowly avoided accident (4,4)
23 A single time (4)

Down

1 Act of taking for one's own use (13)
2 Swerve; bend (5)
4 Strongly opposed (6)
5 Laudatory (12)
6 Learn new skills (7)
7 Remove dangerous substances from (13)
8 Circle amount (anag) (12)
14 A parent's mother (7)
16 Church councils (6)
19 Large intestine (5)

PUZZLE 187

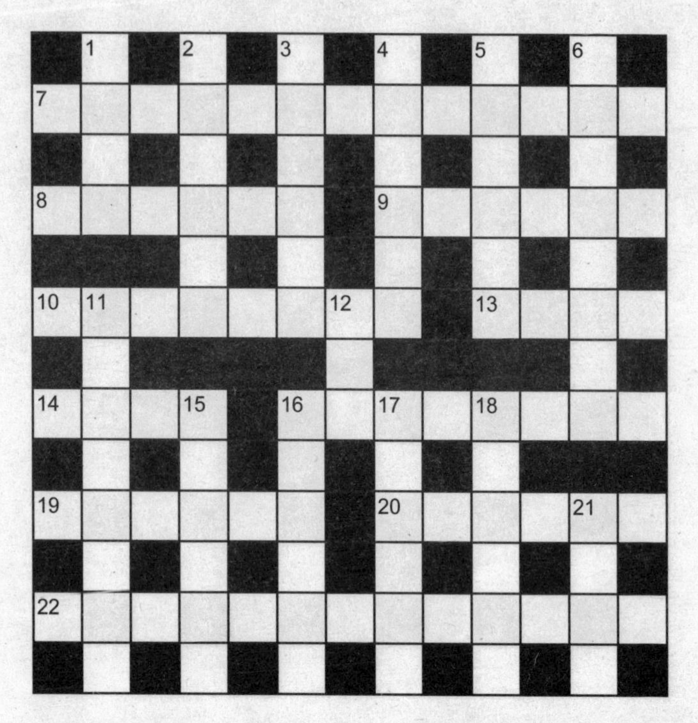

Across

7 Capable of being understood (13)
8 Unwind (6)
9 Workplace (6)
10 Base of a statue (8)
13 Greek god of love (4)
14 Familiar name for a potato (4)
16 Revere (8)
19 Costs (6)
20 One overly concerned with minor details (6)
22 Violation of a law (13)

Down

1 On top of (4)
2 Songbird (6)
3 Wooden house (6)
4 Unfurl (6)
5 Nonsense (6)
6 Complete loss of electrical power (8)
11 Roman leaders (8)
12 Playing card (3)
15 Pour from one container to another (6)
16 Countenance (6)
17 Young person (6)
18 Swollen edible root (6)
21 Midday (4)

PUZZLE 188

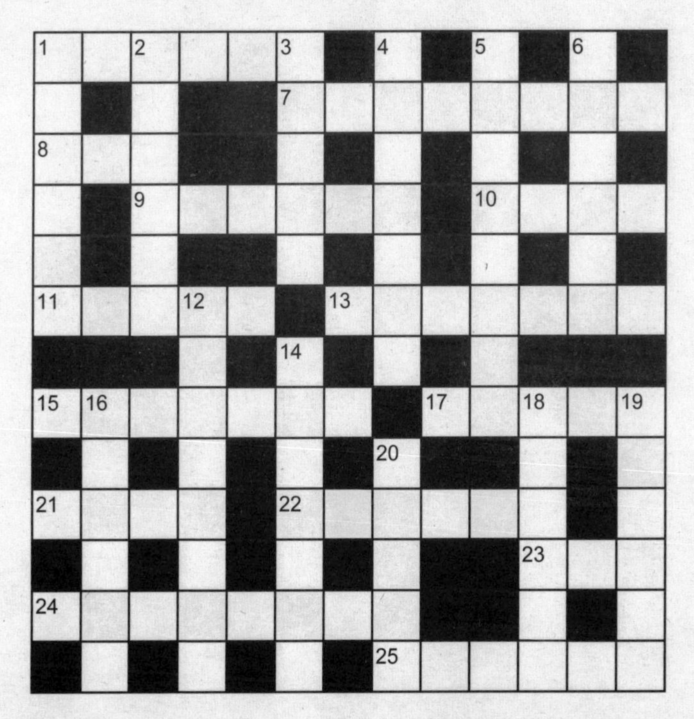

Across

1 Effect; force (6)
7 Street cleaners (8)
8 Blade for rowing a boat (3)
9 Charlize ___ : South African actress (6)
10 Bypass (4)
11 Respected person in a field (5)
13 Fugitive (7)
15 Version of a book (7)
17 ___ Lewis: British singer (5)
21 Pitcher (4)
22 Halogen (6)
23 Wander aimlessly (3)
24 Apparel (8)
25 Gained deservedly (6)

Down

1 Removed creases from clothes (6)
2 To some extent (6)
3 Rulers with total authority (5)
4 Dampness (7)
5 Religious deserter (8)
6 Reach a destination (6)
12 The whole of something (8)
14 Taxonomic group including humans (7)
16 Move slowly (6)
18 US state (6)
19 Lived by (6)
20 Saying (5)

PUZZLE 189

Across

1 Skilful (4)
3 Resolute; obstinate (8)
9 Feminine (7)
10 Solemn promises (5)
11 Atmospheric layer (12)
14 School of Mahayana Buddhism (3)
16 Higher in place (5)
17 Method; road (3)
18 Impossible to achieve (12)
21 Underground railway (5)
22 Salt lake in the Jordan valley (4,3)
23 Removing from office (8)
24 Proofreader's mark (4)

Down

1 Make smaller in number (8)
2 Thigh bone (5)
4 Plaything (3)
5 Male relation by marriage (7-2-3)
6 Got too big for something (7)
7 Food (informal) (4)
8 Directions (12)
12 Dark brown colour (5)
13 Always in a similar role (of an actor) (8)
15 Without interruption (3-4)
19 Surround and harass; beets (anag) (5)
20 Among (4)
22 Secret retreat (3)

PUZZLE 190

Across

8 Secure against legal responsibility (9)
9 Russian space station (3)
10 Applaud (5)
11 Comes into view (7)
12 Flatter (7)
13 Roman poet (4)
17 Weapons (4)
18 In a nimble manner (7)
22 Boastful behaviour (7)
24 Ire (5)
25 Small numbered cube (3)
26 A new creation (9)

Down

1 Chop meat into very small pieces (5)
2 Item of additional book matter (8)
3 Green gemstone (7)
4 Process food (6)
5 Uses a keyboard (5)
6 Self-satisfied (4)
7 Military expedition (7)
14 Explosively unstable (8)
15 Brazilian dance (7)
16 Exhaling air (7)
19 Rut (6)
20 ___ Major: constellation (5)
21 Makes less dense (5)
23 Greek god of war (4)

PUZZLE 191

Across

1 Taxis (4)
3 Recurring at intervals (8)
9 ___ bells: orchestral instrument (7)
10 Large fruit with pulpy flesh (5)
11 Young male (3)
12 Later (5)
13 Chris ___: British TV presenter (5)
15 Radio receiver (5)
17 Dried kernel of the coconut (5)
18 Opposite of high (3)
19 Short musical composition (5)
20 European country (7)
21 Small loudspeakers (8)
22 Keep away from (4)

Down

1 Lord of the Rings actress (4,9)
2 ___ Davro: comedian (5)
4 Moon of the planet Jupiter (6)
5 Limitless (12)
6 Widened (7)
7 Female politician in the US (13)
8 First part of the Bible (3,9)
14 Adopt or support a cause (7)
16 Quantity (6)
18 ___ Halfpenny: Welsh rugby player (5)

PUZZLE 192

Across

1 Stick of coloured wax (6)
4 Sayings (6)
9 Keepsake; reminder (7)
10 Spouts (7)
11 Small plant-sucking insect (5)
12 Eg arms and legs (5)
14 Bring about (5)
15 Roost (5)
17 Started (5)
18 West Indian musical style (7)
20 Harmful (7)
21 Eastern temple (6)
22 Companion (6)

Down

1 Musical instrument (6)
2 Comfy seat (8)
3 Possessed (5)
5 Very light rain (7)
6 Ancient France (4)
7 Detects; feels (6)
8 Decisions reached by reasoning (11)
13 Small flesh-eating mammal (8)
14 Cut pieces off something hard (7)
15 Gather or collect (4,2)
16 In mint condition (6)
17 Eg Amir Khan (5)
19 Breathing organ (4)

PUZZLE 193

Across

1 Oscillates (8)
5 Short hollow thud (4)
8 Hackneyed (5)
9 Spouse (7)
10 Stablemen (7)
12 A person in general (7)
14 Betrays (slang) (7)
16 Interstellar gas clouds (7)
18 Form a mental picture (7)
19 Revel (anag) (5)
20 Turn or slide violently (of a vehicle) (4)
21 Core mass of a country (8)

Down

1 Block a decision (4)
2 Old ___ : court building in London (6)
3 Based on casual observations (of an account) (9)
4 Give a job to (6)
6 Horizontal supporting beam (6)
7 Sunshades (8)
11 Athletic contest (9)
12 Administrative government units (8)
13 On fire (6)
14 Taxonomic groupings (6)
15 ___ Plath: author of The Bell Jar (6)
17 Push; poke (4)

PUZZLE 194

Across

1 Close-fitting necklace (6)
5 Hostility (6)
8 Puns (anag) (4)
9 Teaching (8)
10 Ways or tracks (5)
11 Try (7)
14 Understanding (13)
16 Assign (7)
18 Walks awkwardly (5)
20 Person with a degree (8)
22 Entice (4)
23 Complied with a command (6)
24 Favourable aspect of something (6)

Down

2 Seven-sided shapes (9)
3 Affinity (7)
4 Mud grooves (4)
5 Qualified for by right (8)
6 ___ Simpson: cartoon character (5)
7 Large beer cask (3)
12 Thrived (9)
13 Musical instrument (8)
15 Protects from harm (7)
17 Reddish (5)
19 List of food options (4)
21 Mock (3)

PUZZLE 195

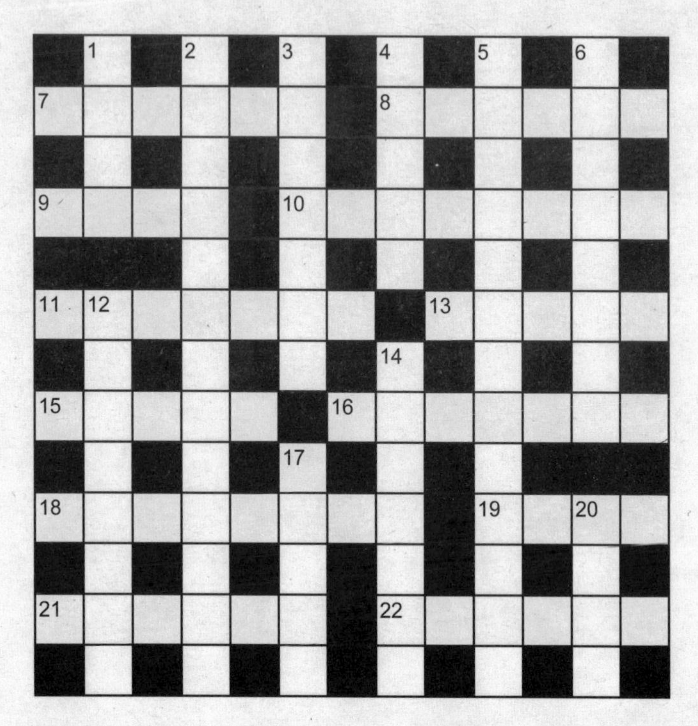

Across

- **7** Part of a gas cooker (6)
- **8** Victor (6)
- **9** Small pond (4)
- **10** Having a sweet nature (8)
- **11** Softly; not loudly (7)
- **13** Supply sparingly; sandpiper (5)
- **15** Pleasantly warm (of weather) (5)
- **16** Faster (7)
- **18** Wealthy and influential people (8)
- **19** Military force (4)
- **21** Visible warning device (6)
- **22** Pleasantly smooth; free from discord (6)

Down

- **1** Sixth month of the year (4)
- **2** Vagueness (13)
- **3** Sharp snapping sound (7)
- **4** Clean with a brush (5)
- **5** Indefensible (13)
- **6** Open resistance (8)
- **12** Without warning (8)
- **14** Couple (7)
- **17** Amazes (5)
- **20** Earth's satellite (4)

PUZZLE 196

Across

1 Deterred (11)
9 Very masculine (5)
10 Sharp projection (3)
11 Sing like a bird (5)
12 Entrance hallway (5)
13 A detail to be explained (5,3)
16 Neck injury (8)
18 Exchange of tennis strokes (5)
21 Tiny piece of food (5)
22 Bath vessel (3)
23 Gold measure (5)
24 Eg without a beard (5-6)

Down

2 Sharp tooth (7)
3 Complicated (7)
4 Sea ___ : marine animal (6)
5 Remote in manner (5)
6 Savour (5)
7 Eccentricity (11)
8 Fear of open spaces (11)
14 Precast (anag) (7)
15 Minute cavity in organic tissue (7)
17 Excessive self-confidence (6)
19 Name applied to something (5)
20 Woody-stemmed plant (5)

PUZZLE 197

Across

1 Soft drinks (US) (5)
4 Stop temporarily (7)
8 Increase in size (7)
9 ___ Witherspoon: actress (5)
10 Hollow in a cliff (4)
11 Omission from speech of superfluous words (8)
14 Very enthusiastic and eager (6)
15 Winged child (6)
18 Relinquish a throne (8)
19 Country in W Africa (4)
21 Ballroom dance (5)
23 Pestering constantly (7)
24 Fails to act decisively (7)
25 Heroic tales (5)

Down

1 Herbert ___: English philosopher (7)
2 Brought to a destination (9)
3 Indian dress (4)
4 Odours (6)
5 Not curly (of hair) (8)
6 First woman (3)
7 Eating plans (5)
12 Transmitting in a continuous flow (of data) (9)
13 Short account of an incident (8)
16 Structures that span rivers (7)
17 Large pebbles (6)
18 Performed on stage (5)
20 Chickens lay these (4)
22 Item for catching fish (3)

PUZZLE 198

Across

1 Spread throughout (8)
5 Respiratory organ of fish (4)
8 Standpoint (5)
9 Candid (7)
10 Smacking (7)
12 Chief officer (7)
14 Cut of meat (7)
16 Grotesque monster (7)
18 Sly (7)
19 Dry red wine (5)
20 One of the seven deadly sins (4)
21 Meddlesome person (8)

Down

1 Edible fruit (4)
2 System of doing things (6)
3 Act of becoming apparent (9)
4 Educated (6)
6 Symbolic (6)
7 Person engaged in a lawsuit (8)
11 Art of stuffing animals (9)
12 Calm and free from strife (8)
13 Cloud type (6)
14 Flat-bottomed rowing boat (6)
15 Japanese dress (6)
17 Fleet of ships (4)

PUZZLE 199

Across

7 Zoologist who studies birds (13)
8 Crazy (informal) (6)
9 Prayer (6)
10 Trachea (8)
13 What you hear with (4)
14 Narrow point of land projecting into water (4)
16 Aggressor (8)
19 Border (6)
20 Large bodies of water (6)
22 Forever honest (13)

Down

1 Official language of Pakistan (4)
2 Cut slightly (6)
3 ___ Goldberg: US actress (6)
4 Recess (6)
5 Set fire to (6)
6 Ozzy ___: Black Sabbath vocalist (8)
11 Cheeky (8)
12 Cooking utensil (3)
15 Three-legged support for a camera (6)
16 Omen (6)
17 Group of touring entertainers (6)
18 Recognition (6)
21 Invalid; void (4)

PUZZLE 200

Across

1 Wharf (4)
3 Region of a shadow (8)
9 Friendly (7)
10 Alters (5)
11 Male sheep (3)
12 Card game (5)
13 Faithful (5)
15 Shabby and worn (5)
17 Ironic metaphor (5)
18 Weeding tool (3)
19 Scoundrel (5)
20 Risky enterprise (7)
21 On the shore of a sea (8)
22 Insects that make honey (4)

Down

1 Four-sided figure (13)
2 Self-evident truth (5)
4 Force; vigour (6)
5 Joblessness (12)
6 Quickly (7)
7 Aggressive self-assurance (13)
8 Lowest possible temperature (8,4)
14 Mental process or idea (7)
16 Irrelevant pieces of information (6)
18 Dwelling (5)

PUZZLE 201

Across

1 Tiny arachnid (4)
3 Beneficial (8)
9 Stylishly (7)
10 Bottomless pit (5)
11 Heavy long-handled tool (12)
13 Small sword (6)
15 Of practical benefit (6)
17 Favouring private ownership (12)
20 Prize (5)
21 Distance travelled (7)
22 Working dough (8)
23 Rats (anag) (4)

Down

1 The priesthood (8)
2 Name of a book (5)
4 Sense of musical time (6)
5 Not allowable (12)
6 Blank page in a book (7)
7 Final (4)
8 Very determined (6-6)
12 Signal that danger is over (3-5)
14 Appease (7)
16 Male pub worker (6)
18 Shallow food containers (5)
19 Long and limp (of hair) (4)

PUZZLE 202

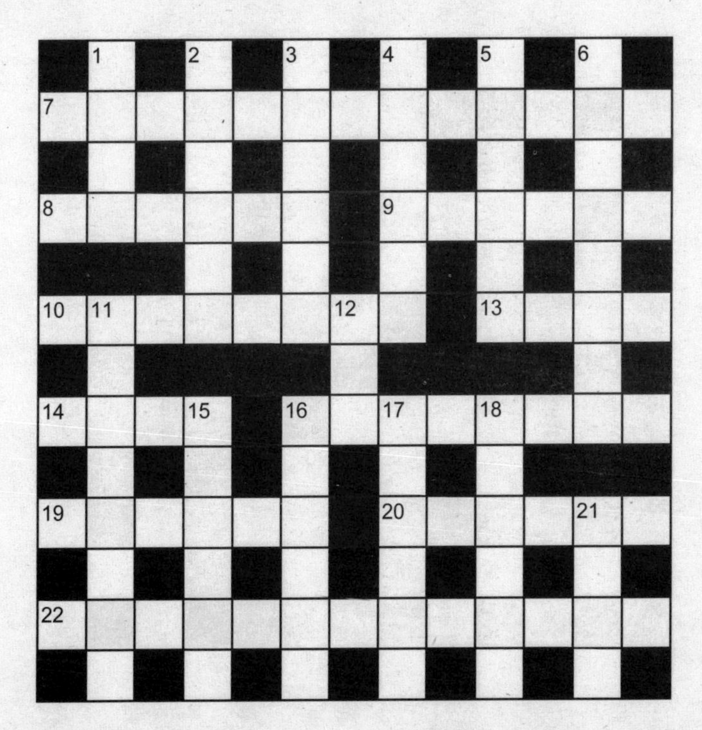

Across

7 British actress who became an MP (6,7)
8 In truth; really (6)
9 Equine sounds (6)
10 Extreme reproach (8)
13 Antelopes (4)
14 Decorated a cake (4)
16 Financial statements (8)
19 Assurance; composure (6)
20 Entices to do something (6)
22 Resonance (13)

Down

1 Scheme (4)
2 Make something new (6)
3 Type of bicycle (6)
4 Tree whose wood is used in cabinetmaking (6)
5 Snow sport (6)
6 Kennel (8)
11 Busy (8)
12 Tack (3)
15 Flocks of animals (6)
16 Drink (6)
17 The electorate (6)
18 Prisoner (6)
21 Ancient city (4)

PUZZLE 203

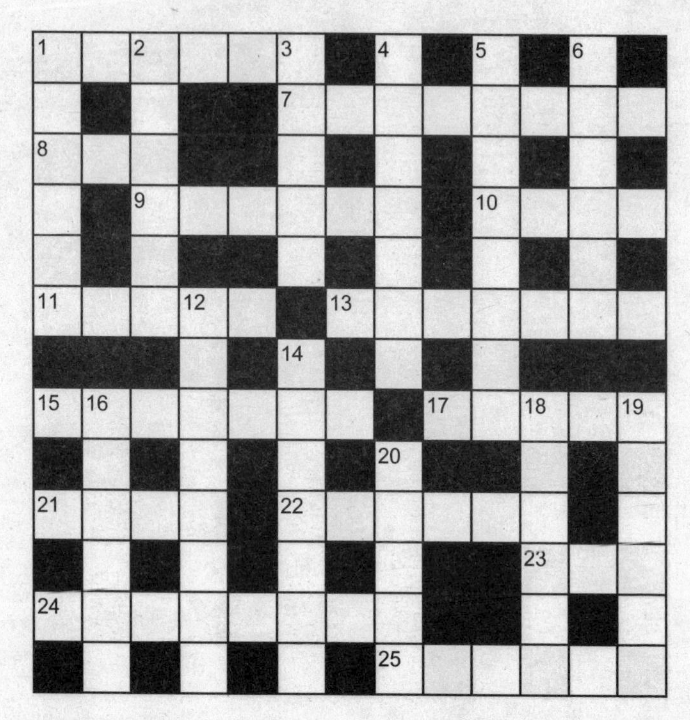

Across

1 Particular designs or versions (6)
7 Crucial (8)
8 State of matter (3)
9 Free of an obstruction (6)
10 Flat and smooth (4)
11 Workers (5)
13 Width (7)
15 Breaks into pieces (7)
17 Broom made of twigs (5)
21 Metric unit of mass (4)
22 Refrigerator compartment (6)
23 Foot extremity (3)
24 Summon to return (4,4)
25 Wrongdoer (6)

Down

1 Accosted; robbed (6)
2 Neglect (6)
3 Skin on top of the head (5)
4 Digits (7)
5 Set free (8)
6 Most recent (6)
12 Look similar to (8)
14 Type of conference (7)
16 Indefinitely large number (6)
18 Church official (6)
19 Extraterrestrial rock (6)
20 Work tables (5)

PUZZLE 204

Across

1 Warm up (6)
4 Manic (6)
9 Hermit (7)
10 Streets (7)
11 White waterbird (5)
12 Take place (5)
14 Loathe (5)
15 Great sorrow (5)
17 Stares with the mouth wide open (5)
18 Edible fish (7)
20 Withstood (7)
21 Towels (anag) (6)
22 Insect larvae (6)

Down

1 Pantry (6)
2 Type of pasta (8)
3 Show triumphant joy (5)
5 Tallest species of penguin (7)
6 You (archaic) (4)
7 Follow-up drink (6)
8 Unnecessarily forceful (5-6)
13 Rubbish (8)
14 Has enough money to pay for (7)
15 Thing that is totally true (6)
16 Incidental remarks (6)
17 Devout (5)
19 Once more (4)

PUZZLE 205

Across

1 Eg physics and biology (8)
5 Radio code word for 'P' (4)
8 Send someone to a medical specialist (5)
9 Not strict (7)
10 Clever but false argument (7)
12 Consume by fire (7)
14 Large retail stores (7)
16 Angered (7)
18 Greatest in height (7)
19 Perfume smell (5)
20 Too; in addition (4)
21 Fans (8)

Down

1 Put in order (4)
2 Impart knowledge (6)
3 Anxiously (9)
4 Enrol in the armed services (6)
6 ___ Mauresmo: French former tennis star (6)
7 Self-operating machines (8)
11 Pork and beef sausage (9)
12 Light afternoon meal (5,3)
13 Male relatives (6)
14 Amended (6)
15 Take away (6)
17 Distinct historical periods (4)

PUZZLE 206

Across

7 Period of the Paleozoic era (13)
8 Safe (6)
9 Call on (6)
10 Abruptly (8)
13 Robert De ___ : Taxi Driver actor (4)
14 Turn over (4)
16 Arithmetic operation (8)
19 Long pin (6)
20 One who wantonly destroys property (6)
22 Teasingly (13)

Down

1 Appear less full (of the moon) (4)
2 Utterly senseless (6)
3 Confine as a prisoner (6)
4 Representation of a person (6)
5 Cowardly (6)
6 Cowboy (8)
11 Improbable (8)
12 Boy (3)
15 Abilities (6)
16 Overseas (6)
17 Entirely lacking (6)
18 Organ in the mouth of a mammal (6)
21 Feels unwell (4)

PUZZLE 207

Across

1 Ask for; try to obtain (7)
6 Auction offer (3)
8 Less common (5)
9 Equality of political rights (7)
10 Gains possession of (5)
11 Estimating (8)
13 Trance (anag) (6)
15 Vocalist (6)
18 Immediately after this (8)
19 Sailing ship (5)
21 Pungent gas (7)
22 Phrase that is not taken literally (5)
23 Male child (3)
24 Corridor (7)

Down

2 Vague and uncertain (7)
3 Top of the goal structure in football (8)
4 Attempting (6)
5 A Crown document (4)
6 Slowing down (7)
7 Written record (7)
12 Difficult choices (8)
13 Serviettes (7)
14 Skipper (7)
16 Wearing away (7)
17 Renovate or restore (6)
20 Bristle (4)

PUZZLE 208

Across

1 Defer (8)
5 Tells an untruth (4)
9 Perennial plant with fleshy roots (7)
10 Trees (anag); organic compound (5)
11 Outspoken (10)
14 Broken fragments of glass (6)
15 Summing together (6)
17 Give off bubbles (10)
20 Condescend (5)
21 One event in a sequence (7)
22 Ruminant mammal (4)
23 Strong glove (8)

Down

1 Hogs (4)
2 Eg perform karaoke (4)
3 Surpassing in influence (12)
4 Periods of darkness (6)
6 An engraved design (8)
7 Plan of action (8)
8 Duplication (12)
12 Climbed (8)
13 Compound found in coffee (8)
16 ___ Williams: tennis star (6)
18 Girl's toy (4)
19 Cried (4)

PUZZLE 209

Across

1 Assent or agree to (6)
4 Scared (6)
9 Share information (7)
10 Gun (7)
11 Not illuminated (5)
12 Unbuttoned (5)
14 Sharply inclined (5)
15 Overcooked (5)
17 Rub out (5)
18 Pasta pockets (7)
20 Very eager to get something (7)
21 Country in Africa with capital Kampala (6)
22 Bodyguard (6)

Down

1 Burning passion (6)
2 Courtly gentleman (8)
3 Glazed earthenware (5)
5 Sudden outburst of something (5-2)
6 ___ Kournikova: former tennis star (4)
7 Condemned to a grim fate (6)
8 Respectful (11)
13 Leonardo ___ : actor (8)
14 Bent forwards and downwards (7)
15 Writing desk (6)
16 Group of seven (6)
17 The spirit of a people (5)
19 Entry document (4)

PUZZLE 210

Across

1 Large island of Indonesia (7)
6 Single in number (3)
8 Stylishness and originality (5)
9 The Pope (7)
10 Principle laid down by an authority (5)
11 Very large (8)
13 Heavy iron blocks (6)
15 Eerie; sinister (6)
18 Formidable (8)
19 George ___ : Middlemarch writer (5)
21 Exile; fugitive (7)
22 Start of (5)
23 Aggressive dog (3)
24 Unaccompanied musician (7)

Down

2 Idealistic (7)
3 Three-sided figure (8)
4 Matter (6)
5 Extol (4)
6 Perennial herb (7)
7 To the same degree (7)
12 Cooking measure (8)
13 Cherubic (7)
14 Guest (7)
16 Shelters for dogs (7)
17 Feels upset and annoyed (6)
20 Throw a coin in the air (4)

PUZZLE 211

Across

1 Apex (4)
3 Put forward an idea (8)
9 Number of attendees (7)
10 Mature person (5)
11 Modestly (12)
14 Water barrier (3)
16 Pen made from a bird's feather (5)
17 Japanese monetary unit (3)
18 Coming from outside (12)
21 Impair (5)
22 Held and used a tool (7)
23 Enclosed area in a farm (8)
24 Network of lines (4)

Down

1 Amazes (8)
2 ___ Sharapova: tennis player (5)
4 Trough (3)
5 Ordinary dress (5,7)
6 Stormy (7)
7 Facts and statistics collectively (4)
8 As a result (12)
12 Damp (5)
13 Unequal; biased (3-5)
15 Dirtier (7)
19 More mature (5)
20 Tabs (anag) (4)
22 State of armed conflict (3)

PUZZLE 212

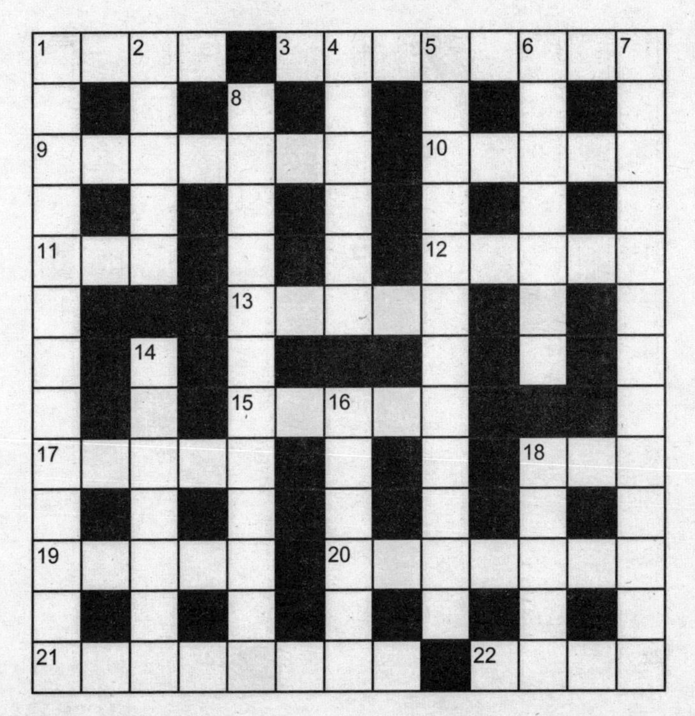

Across

1 Domestic cattle (4)
3 Large retail store (8)
9 Waterlogged areas of land (7)
10 Domesticates (5)
11 Suitable (3)
12 Between eighth and tenth (5)
13 Happening (5)
15 Upright (5)
17 Barack ___ : 44th US President (5)
18 Doctor ___ : TV show (3)
19 Good at (5)
20 Former student (7)
21 Speed up (8)
22 Extremely (4)

Down

1 Sympathetic and merciful (13)
2 Opposite of best (5)
4 Brawn; strength (6)
5 Intended to attract notice (12)
6 Vast (7)
7 Naughtily (13)
8 Showing complete commitment (12)
14 Shock physically (5-2)
16 Straying from the right course (6)
18 Flinch away in pain (5)

PUZZLE 213

Across

1 Boiled pudding (4)
3 Hair-cleansing preparations (8)
9 Wrongdoers (7)
10 Undo a knot (5)
11 Small antelope (5)
12 Vanquished; surpassed (7)
13 Not allowing light to pass through (6)
15 Entry pass (6)
17 Withstands (7)
18 Remove paint from a wall (5)
20 Spree (5)
21 Constantly present (7)
22 Boating (8)
23 Scream (4)

Down

1 Disgracefully (13)
2 What a mycologist studies (5)
4 Bushy plant of the mint family (6)
5 Hillside (12)
6 One's mental attitude (7)
7 Lacking originality (13)
8 Having a tendency to become liquid (12)
14 Chemical element with atomic number 33 (7)
16 Towards the rear (6)
19 Lover of Juliet (5)

PUZZLE 214

Across

1 Expression of gratitude (5,3)
5 Capital of the Ukraine (4)
8 Animal life of a region (5)
9 Part exchange for something new (5-2)
10 Method of presenting a play (7)
12 Dishonourable (7)
14 Newness (7)
16 Side of a coin bearing the head (7)
18 Speak excitedly of (7)
19 Temporary police force (5)
20 Conservative Party member (4)
21 Not ripe (of fruit) (8)

Down

1 Soya bean curd (4)
2 Keen insight (6)
3 Australian marsupial (5,4)
4 Dull (6)
6 Spain and Portugal (6)
7 Having a sour taste (8)
11 Non-canonical religious texts (9)
12 Not guilty (8)
13 Graphical representation of a person (6)
14 Restore honour (6)
15 Capital of the Bahamas (6)
17 Fundraising party (4)

PUZZLE 215

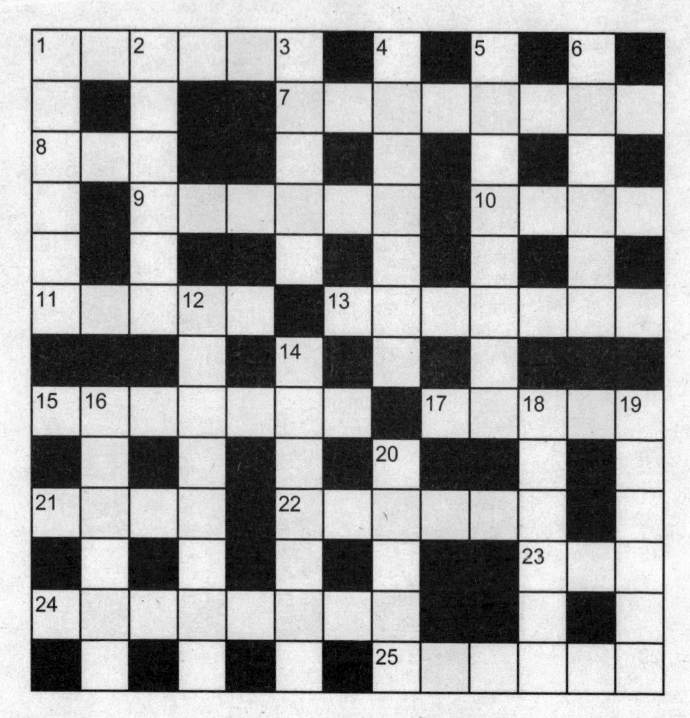

Across

1 Place where something is set (6)
7 Resolute (8)
8 Gratuity (3)
9 Show-off (6)
10 Optical device (4)
11 Relating to country life (5)
13 ___ Carlisle: US singer (7)
15 African wild pig (7)
17 Minute pore (5)
21 Bound (4)
22 Eccentricity (6)
23 Word expressing negation (3)
24 Glowing with heat (5-3)
25 Disturbance (6)

Down

1 Alphabetical character (6)
2 Metallic element (6)
3 Borders (5)
4 Flee (7)
5 Composer of a sacred song (8)
6 Flattened out (6)
12 Remedy to a poison (8)
14 Bath sponges (7)
16 Get off (6)
18 Lead batsman for a team (6)
19 Absence of passion (6)
20 View (5)

PUZZLE 216

Across

1 Intellectual (8)
5 Group of three (4)
9 Crazy about someone (7)
10 Be the same as (5)
11 Questioning after a mission (10)
14 Musician playing a double-reed instrument (6)
15 ___ Kay: TV presenter (6)
17 Item published at regular intervals (10)
20 Cloak (5)
21 Disturb (7)
22 Situation involving danger (4)
23 Constant movement backwards and forwards (2,3,3)

Down

1 Silence (4)
2 Smile broadly (4)
3 Type of sweet (12)
4 Possessors (6)
6 Social gatherings for old friends (8)
7 Accommodating (8)
8 Act of slowing down (12)
12 Machine used to surf the internet (8)
13 Gin rooms (anag) (8)
16 Fierce woman (6)
18 Stick with a hook (4)
19 Repeat an action (4)

PUZZLE 217

Across

1 Saturated (6)
7 Took into account (8)
8 Group of whales (3)
9 Containerful (6)
10 Crush or grind food with the teeth (4)
11 Emits a breath of relief (5)
13 Into parts (7)
15 Mistake in printing or writing (7)
17 Extra component (3-2)
21 Princess ___ : Star Wars character (4)
22 Nigella ___ : English food writer (6)
23 Expected at a certain time (3)
24 Increase rapidly (8)
25 Tropical bird (6)

Down

1 Contributes information (6)
2 Bloodsucking insect (6)
3 Rough version of a document (5)
4 Eternal (7)
5 Spider (8)
6 Go back on (6)
12 Nuisance; unpleasant problem (8)
14 Sturdy thickset canine (7)
16 Expressing regret (6)
18 Flakes of skin in an animal's fur (6)
19 Freshest (6)
20 Waterlogged ground (5)

PUZZLE 218

Across

1 ___ Novello: Welsh composer and actor (4)
3 Source of annoyance (8)
9 Diagrams or pictures (7)
10 Big (5)
11 Observed (5)
12 Greek goddess of retribution (7)
13 Very reliable (6)
15 Deer horn (6)
17 Spend lavishly (7)
18 Cards used for fortune-telling (5)
20 Civilian dress (5)
21 Sign of the zodiac (7)
22 Person who hears (8)
23 Computer memory unit (4)

Down

1 Extremely small (13)
2 Should (5)
4 Rinses (anag) (6)
5 Clarification (12)
6 Container releasing a fine spray (7)
7 Hidden store of valuables (8,5)
8 Decide in advance (12)
14 Raises (7)
16 Tenant (6)
19 Make good on a debt (5)

PUZZLE 219

Across

1 Dejected (8)
5 SI unit of electromotive force (4)
9 Where you watch films (7)
10 Speak; total (5)
11 Precise; scrupulous (10)
14 Serving no functional purpose (6)
15 Hold fast (6)
17 Ahead of the times (10)
20 Be alive; be real (5)
21 Massaging (7)
22 Garden outbuilding (4)
23 Comes into flower (8)

Down

1 Court enclosure (4)
2 Departed (4)
3 Corresponding; proportionate (12)
4 Small finch (6)
6 Antique; obsolete (8)
7 Beat out grain (8)
8 Dark towering cloud (12)
12 Uncovered (of a building) (8)
13 Verbal attack (8)
16 Relating to stars (6)
18 Luxurious car (abbrev) (4)
19 Grows older (4)

PUZZLE 220

Across

1 Supernatural (6)
4 Predatory marine fish (pl) (6)
9 Capital of Ontario (7)
10 Contradicted; neutralised (7)
11 Female human (5)
12 Spacious (5)
14 Crazy (5)
15 Brief appearance in a film by someone famous (5)
17 Indian lute (5)
18 Temporary stay (7)
20 Has an impact on (7)
21 Belief in a god (6)
22 Putting lawns in golf (6)

Down

1 Capital of Canada (6)
2 Metallic element (8)
3 Cloth woven from flax (5)
5 Country in central Europe (7)
6 Repose (4)
7 Of inferior quality (6)
8 Not absolute (11)
13 Something in the way (8)
14 Small rounded lumps (7)
15 Small box (6)
16 Iridaceous plants (6)
17 More secure (5)
19 ___ Law: actor (4)

PUZZLE 221

Across

1 ___ out: extinguished a cigarette (7)
6 Animal fodder (3)
8 Showery (5)
9 Eg kings and queens (7)
10 Person who always puts in a lot of effort (5)
11 Womanly (8)
13 Artist such as Picasso or Braque (6)
15 Lengthen (6)
18 Equality of measure (8)
19 Period of time in history (5)
21 ___ case: item for carrying documents (7)
22 Supply with; furnish (5)
23 Primary colour (3)
24 Old (7)

Down

2 Henry David ___ : US author and poet (7)
3 Audacity (8)
4 Eg using a towel (6)
5 Droop; lose energy (4)
6 Cleanliness (7)
7 Longed for (7)
12 Freed from doing (8)
13 Someone who provides food (7)
14 Dearly cherished (7)
16 Small Arctic whale (7)
17 Get away from (6)
20 Pull something heavy (4)

PUZZLE 222

Across

1 Towering (5)
4 Disperse (7)
8 Atomic particle (7)
9 Musical sounds (5)
10 Consumes (4)
11 Large aeroplane (5,3)
14 Pivot; turn around a point (6)
15 Stop talking (4,2)
18 Devilry (8)
19 High fidelity (abbrev) (2-2)
21 Relating to a city (5)
23 Remove an obstruction (7)
24 Aural pain (7)
25 Stiff with age (5)

Down

1 Surgical knives (7)
2 Ornamental water features (9)
3 Three feet (4)
4 Wicked (6)
5 German motorway (8)
6 Chemical element (3)
7 Steer (anag) (5)
12 Throws overboard (9)
13 Person who repairs cars (8)
16 Irritable (7)
17 Reprimand (6)
18 Electronic device one clicks (5)
20 Seal of the Archbishop of York (4)
22 Prevent (3)

PUZZLE 223

Across

1 Reason for not doing something (6)
4 Fruits with pips (6)
9 Spiral cavity of the inner ear (7)
10 Expressed audibly (7)
11 Group of eight (5)
12 Awake from slumber (5)
14 Labour organisation (5)
15 Ceases (5)
17 Silk dress fabric (5)
18 Type of lettuce (7)
20 Curved structure forming a passage (7)
21 Walks (6)
22 Whipped cream dessert (6)

Down

1 Cowers (anag) (6)
2 Alcoholic drink with several ingredients (8)
3 Divide; separate (5)
5 Decorative design (7)
6 Look slyly (4)
7 Snow vehicle with runners (6)
8 Nitrous oxide (8,3)
13 Things we are not familiar with (8)
14 Showed a person to their seat (7)
15 Altitude (6)
16 Biochemical catalyst (6)
17 Tortilla topped with cheese (5)
19 Fencing sword (4)

PUZZLE 224

Across

1 Intrusive (8)
5 Unit of transmission speed (4)
9 Not legally recognised; void (7)
10 British noblemen (5)
11 Completely (10)
14 Enjoy greatly; piquant sauce (6)
15 Dung beetle (6)
17 Activity of writing articles (10)
20 Fish and ___ : classic dish (5)
21 Become faster (7)
22 Type of starch (4)
23 Definitions (8)

Down

1 ___ Duncan Smith: politician (4)
2 ___ Forever: Spice Girls hit (4)
3 Altruism (12)
4 Records on tape (6)
6 Breed of dairy cattle (8)
7 Explain using words (8)
8 Consequence of an event (12)
12 Protrudes (8)
13 Making less clear (8)
16 Ornamental tablet fixed to a wall (6)
18 Of similar character (4)
19 Noes (anag) (4)

PUZZLE 225

Across

1 Collarbone (8)
5 Type of light (4)
8 Head monk of an abbey (5)
9 Horse's fodder container (7)
10 Type of alcohol (7)
12 Changed gradually over time (7)
14 Road or roofing material (7)
16 Act of reading carefully (7)
18 Japanese flower arranging (7)
19 Alphabetical list in a book (5)
20 Nest (anag) (4)
21 Grotesquely carved figure (8)

Down

1 Natter (4)
2 Ratio of reflected to incident light (6)
3 Breaks in activities (9)
4 Touched down (6)
6 Having colourless skin (6)
7 Boxer (8)
11 Event (9)
12 Eg resident of Cairo (8)
13 Fervent (6)
14 Mammal related to the llama (6)
15 Eagerly (6)
17 Driving shaft (4)

PUZZLE 226

Across

1 Solemn promise (4)
3 Done away with (8)
9 Obesity (7)
10 Leader or ruler (5)
11 In a self-satisfied manner (12)
13 Restart a computer (6)
15 Purify then condense (6)
17 Very skilful act (12)
20 Vascular tissue in plants (5)
21 Plain-woven cotton cloth (7)
22 Travelling too quickly (8)
23 A parent's mother (4)

Down

1 People holding positions of authority (8)
2 Motet (anag) (5)
4 Divide into two parts (6)
5 Not staying the same throughout (12)
6 Set of three things (7)
7 Tip the hat (4)
8 Flared (of trousers) (4-8)
12 Co-opted council member (8)
14 Written language for blind people (7)
16 Fire-breathing monster (6)
18 Opposite one of two (5)
19 Hatchets (4)

PUZZLE 227

	1		2		3		4		5		6	

Across

7 Miscellaneous equipment (13)
8 George ___ : composer (6)
9 Scribble or draw aimlessly (6)
10 Period during which you live (8)
13 Messy substance (4)
14 Protruding part of the lower jaw (4)
16 Improves in flavour (8)
19 Attribute to (6)
20 Trite remark (6)
22 Ineptly (13)

Down

1 Mother (4)
2 Seat on the back of a horse (6)
3 Hot pepper (6)
4 Feeling of resentment (6)
5 Groans (anag) (6)
6 Aggressive use of force (8)
11 Cruel (8)
12 Adult males (3)
15 Nerve cell (6)
16 Absolve (6)
17 Repeat from memory (6)
18 Customer (6)
21 Position of leadership (4)

PUZZLE 228

Across

- **1** Cast doubt upon (6)
- **4** Erase a mark from a surface (6)
- **9** Vent for molten lava (7)
- **10** Exhausted (4,3)
- **11** Things to be done (5)
- **12** Device that clears a car windscreen (5)
- **14** Groups together (5)
- **15** Foot-operated lever (5)
- **17** Leases (5)
- **18** Better for the environment (7)
- **20** Share; portion (7)
- **21** Vehement speech (6)
- **22** Glowing remains of a fire (6)

Down

- **1** Ask a person to come (6)
- **2** Buffed (8)
- **3** Snatches (5)
- **5** Narrow trenches (7)
- **6** Ship used by Jason and followers (4)
- **7** The boss at a newspaper (6)
- **8** Sensible and practical (4,2,5)
- **13** Lofty peak (8)
- **14** Fell quickly (7)
- **15** Young hog (6)
- **16** Judge (6)
- **17** Furnish with new weapons (5)
- **19** Mire (anag) (4)

PUZZLE 229

Across

1 Organism that exploits another (8)
5 Vehicle with four-wheel drive (4)
9 Type of ship (7)
10 Crisp; pleasantly cold (5)
11 Ludicrous version of something (10)
14 ___ Buffay: character in Friends (6)
15 Wolfgang ___ : Austrian composer (6)
17 Act of making known (10)
20 Female servants (5)
21 Country in West Africa (7)
22 Gear wheels (4)
23 Fervently (8)

Down

1 Opposite of pull (4)
2 Unpleasant smell (4)
3 Sleepwalking (12)
4 Oppressively hot (6)
6 Marriage ceremony (8)
7 Remittances (8)
8 Adverse (12)
12 Large outbreak of a disease (8)
13 Enhancing; encouraging (8)
16 Stableman (6)
18 Scamp (4)
19 Wife of a knight (4)

PUZZLE 230

Across

1 Gets away (7)
6 Your (poetic) (3)
8 State indirectly (5)
9 Type of humour (7)
10 Lindsay ___ : actress (5)
11 Disturb (8)
13 You may have these while asleep (6)
15 Reigns (anag) (6)
18 Opposite of westward (8)
19 More ashen in appearance (5)
21 Savings for the future (4,3)
22 Faint southern constellation (5)
23 Opposite of no (3)
24 Go before (7)

Down

2 Data input device (7)
3 School break (8)
4 Easily (6)
5 Quartz-like gem (4)
6 Tropical cyclone (7)
7 Not as old (7)
12 Mild aversion (8)
13 Cook in hot fat (4-3)
14 Symbolic objects (7)
16 Livid (7)
17 Doze (6)
20 Status (4)

PUZZLE 231

Across

1 Item of sweet food (8)
5 Nobleman (4)
9 Irrigated (7)
10 Strangely (5)
11 Security for a loan (10)
14 Continue (6)
15 Frequents a place (6)
17 Companionship (10)
20 Espresso coffee and steamed milk (5)
21 Wild (of an animal) (7)
22 Jedi Master in Star Wars films (4)
23 Marriages (8)

Down

1 Cuts the grass (4)
2 Rodents (4)
3 Lacking tolerance or flexibility (6-6)
4 Excessively (6)
6 Abiding; lasting (8)
7 Monarchist (8)
8 Showed not to be true (12)
12 Skilfully; cleverly (8)
13 Aided (8)
16 Guarantee (6)
18 Superhero film based on comic characters (1-3)
19 Lyric poems (4)

PUZZLE 232

Across

1 Naughty; roguish (11)
9 Buffalo (5)
10 Particle that is electrically charged (3)
11 Main artery (5)
12 District council head (5)
13 Vehicle that is beyond repair (5-3)
16 Hymn or chant (8)
18 Obtain information from various sources (5)
21 Unexpected plot element (5)
22 Definite article (3)
23 Jump over (5)
24 Designed for usefulness (11)

Down

2 Firmly establish (7)
3 Variety show (7)
4 Stifle (anag) (6)
5 Snake toxin (5)
6 Oneness (5)
7 Eg Shakespeare and Bernard Shaw (11)
8 Increasing gradually by degrees (11)
14 Stammer (7)
15 Spiny anteater (7)
17 Clear from a charge (6)
19 Apply pressure (5)
20 A central point (5)

PUZZLE 233

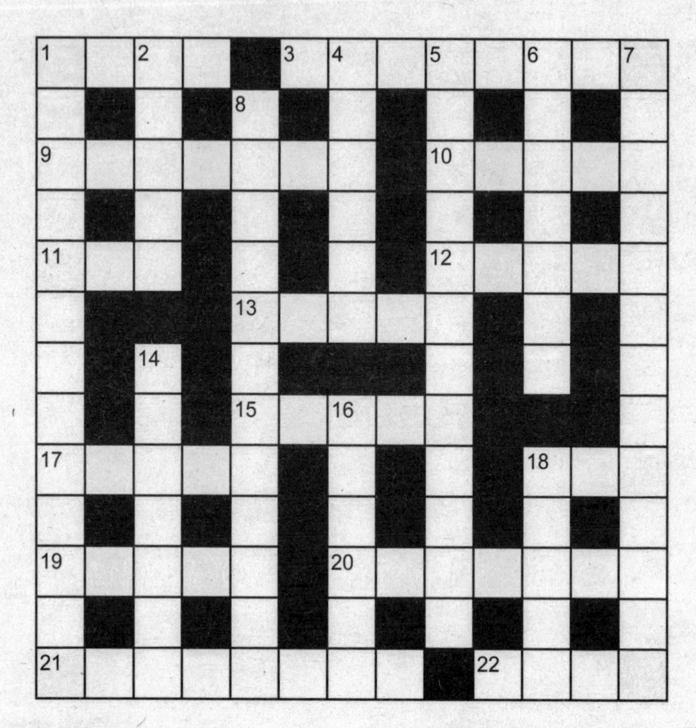

Across

1 Engrossed (4)
3 Fugitives (8)
9 Elevate (7)
10 Chimes (5)
11 24-hour period (3)
12 Denise van ___ : English actress (5)
13 Triangular river mouth (5)
15 Deciduous coniferous tree (5)
17 Latin American dance (5)
18 By way of (3)
19 Leaves out (5)
20 Duty-bound (7)
21 Memento (8)
22 Soon; shortly (4)

Down

1 Without stopping; continuous (5,3,5)
2 Social gathering (5)
4 Israeli monetary unit (6)
5 Easy to converse with (12)
6 Demanded (7)
7 Thelma & Louise actress (5,8)
8 Binoculars (5,7)
14 First light (7)
16 Amend; change (6)
18 One who avoids animal products (5)

PUZZLE 234

Across

1 Drop (4)
3 Reading quickly (8)
9 Act of getting rid of something (7)
10 Sages (anag) (5)
11 Understandably (12)
13 Prove to be false (6)
15 Penetrate (6)
17 Not special (3-2-3-4)
20 Porcelain (5)
21 State emphatically (7)
22 Extravagant fuss (8)
23 Tidy (4)

Down

1 People who shape horseshoes (8)
2 Threshold (5)
4 SI unit of thermodynamic temperature (6)
5 Grandeur (12)
6 Separated; remote (7)
7 Lesion (4)
8 Developmental (12)
12 Recklessly determined (4-4)
14 Pertaining to a river (7)
16 Workroom of a painter (6)
18 Visual representation (5)
19 Protective crust (4)

PUZZLE 235

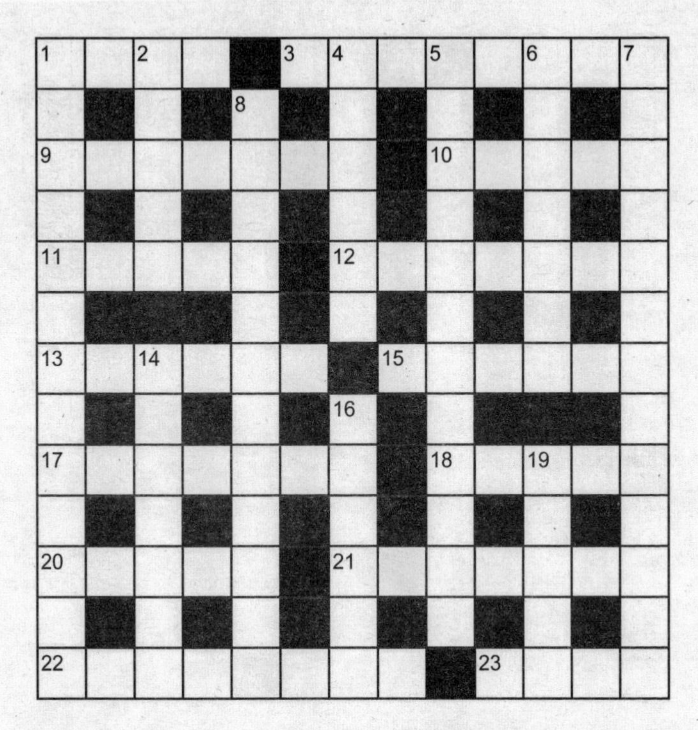

Across

1 Gangs (4)
3 Last (8)
9 Found out about (7)
10 Supply with food (5)
11 Pertaining to the Netherlands (5)
12 Deficiency of red blood cells (7)
13 Weak through age or illness (6)
15 Lie in a relaxed way; living room (6)
17 Asked to come along (7)
18 ___ Arabia: country in the Middle East (5)
20 Palpitate (5)
21 Combining together (7)
22 Blushed (8)
23 Unattractive (4)

Down

1 Manage badly (13)
2 Wild animal (5)
4 Eg from New Delhi (6)
5 Absolute authority in any sphere (12)
6 Piece of furniture (7)
7 Menacingly (13)
8 Unkind; unsympathetic (12)
14 Highly excited (7)
16 Request earnestly (6)
19 Exploiting (5)

PUZZLE 236

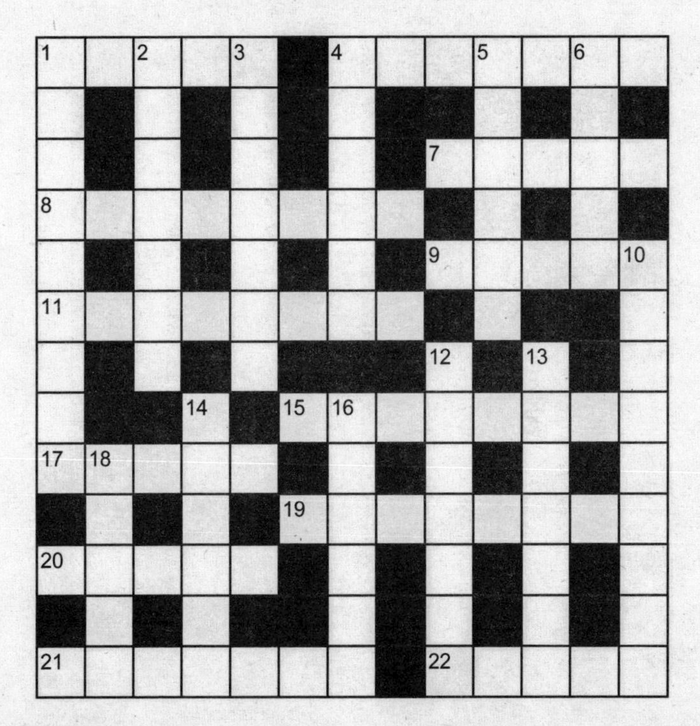

Across

1 Draw or bring out (5)
4 Traditional ways of doing things (7)
7 Assess; rank (5)
8 Device recording distance travelled (8)
9 Rocks back and forth (5)
11 Thing serving as an appropriate model (8)
15 Shelter for pigeons (8)
17 Restraining straps (5)
19 Dull (8)
20 Bedfordshire town (5)
21 Boats (7)
22 Group of singers (5)

Down

1 Something that is revealing (3-6)
2 Impassive (7)
3 Extract (7)
4 Where one goes to see a film (6)
5 Confused or disconcerted (6)
6 Dirty (5)
10 Inducement (9)
12 Extremely cruel (7)
13 Country in NW Africa (7)
14 Pungent edible bulbs (6)
16 Egg-shaped solids (6)
18 Display freely (5)

PUZZLE 237

Across

1 Swamping (8)
5 Walk awkwardly (4)
9 Porch (7)
10 Mother-of-pearl (5)
11 Rigid (10)
14 Simple; unrefined (6)
15 Fitness; condition (6)
17 Direct opposite of something (10)
20 Refrain from (5)
21 Comfort (7)
22 Clay (anag) (4)
23 Discouraged from doing (8)

Down

1 One more than four (4)
2 Blades for rowing a boat (4)
3 Condemnation (12)
4 Tidily (6)
6 Sit on eggs (of a bird) (8)
7 Goes before (8)
8 Lack of practical knowledge (12)
12 Terrible (8)
13 Recondite (8)
16 Free from danger (6)
18 Having no money (4)
19 Heavy metal (4)

PUZZLE 238

Across

1 Opposite of highs (4)
3 Protective garments (8)
9 Having three sections (7)
10 Christmas show (abbrev) (5)
11 Protective cover (3)
12 Discharge (5)
13 Vegetables (5)
15 Country in NE Africa (5)
17 Public disturbances (5)
18 Edible mushroom (3)
19 Continuing in existence (5)
20 More amusing (7)
21 Broke down food (8)
22 Curve in a road (4)

Down

1 The ___ / ___ : Fairy tale by Hans Christian Andersen (6,7)
2 Planet (5)
4 Journey by sea (6)
5 Symbolising (12)
6 Portable lamp (7)
7 Easily angered (5-8)
8 Failure to act with prudence (12)
14 Getting bigger (7)
16 Coarse woollen cloth (6)
18 South American country (5)

PUZZLE 239

Across

1 Companionable (6)
4 Tips and instruction (6)
9 Pierre ___ : French mathematician (7)
10 Inquisitive (7)
11 Particle that holds quarks together (5)
12 Very pale (5)
14 Test or examine (5)
15 Small woody plant (5)
17 Edible seaweed (5)
18 Garden flower (7)
20 Moderates; mitigates (7)
21 Gathering up leaves in the garden (6)
22 Very difficult or complex (6)

Down

1 Untamed; barbarous (6)
2 Round (8)
3 Negatively charged ion (5)
5 Opening to a room (7)
6 Knowledge (abbrev) (4)
7 Thomas ___ : US inventor (6)
8 Coordinate (11)
13 Weighing the most (8)
14 Give up (7)
15 Military engineer (6)
16 Dry and brittle (of food) (6)
17 Yellow citrus fruit (5)
19 Type of wood (4)

PUZZLE 240

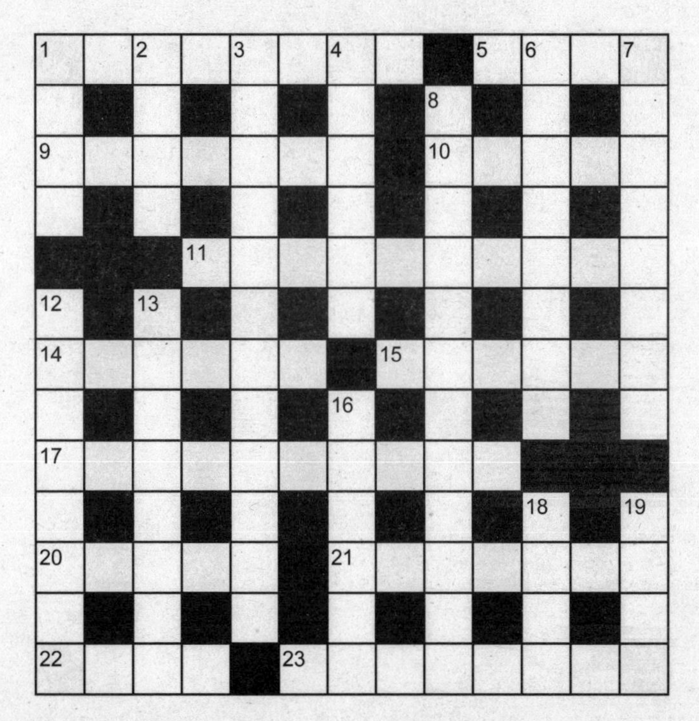

Across

1 Waste disposal site (8)
5 Days before major events (4)
9 Currents of air (7)
10 Henrik ___ : Norwegian author (5)
11 Covert (10)
14 Steep in liquid (6)
15 Bring forth (6)
17 Specified conditions (10)
20 Select class (5)
21 Mound made by insects (7)
22 As expected (4)
23 Protected; toughened (8)

Down

1 Doing little (4)
2 Short sleeps (4)
3 UFO (6,6)
4 Pay attention to what is said (6)
6 Volcano near Naples (8)
7 Watchmen (8)
8 Unplugged (12)
12 Squander money (8)
13 Public and formal (8)
16 Ottawa is the capital here (6)
18 Manner or appearance (4)
19 Clothed (4)

PUZZLE 241

Across

1 Insensitivity (11)
9 Relating to a city (5)
10 Metric unit of measurement (historical) (3)
11 Reluctant (5)
12 Bundle of wheat (5)
13 In an unequal manner (8)
16 Native of the United States (8)
18 Small open pies (5)
21 Elevated step (5)
22 Opposite of old (3)
23 Changes direction suddenly (5)
24 Diaphanous (11)

Down

2 Wears away (7)
3 Chinese fruits (7)
4 Uncover (6)
5 Giraffes have long ones (5)
6 Five lines on which music is written (5)
7 Shrewd (11)
8 Egotistical (4-7)
14 Piece of furniture (7)
15 Eight-sided shape (7)
17 Cosmetics (4-2)
19 Oarsman (5)
20 Number of deadly sins (5)

PUZZLE 242

Across

1 Splendid display (4)
3 Wanderer (8)
9 Saunter (anag) (7)
10 Frozen fruit juice on a stick (5)
11 Amazement (12)
13 Long essay (6)
15 Excessively ornate (of literature) (6)
17 Thick-skinned herbivorous animal (12)
20 Balance (5)
21 Canopies (7)
22 Someone paddling a light boat (8)
23 Mischievous fairies (4)

Down

1 Pieces of jewellery (8)
2 Short choral composition (5)
4 Support; help (6)
5 Crucial (3,9)
6 ___ Bloom: English actor (7)
7 24 hour periods (4)
8 Principal face of a building (12)
12 Is composed of (8)
14 Omission of a sound when speaking (7)
16 Flower arrangements (6)
18 Musical note (5)
19 Long poem (4)

PUZZLE 243

Across

1 Type of music (4,3,4)
9 Domesticated (5)
10 Bitumen (3)
11 Pertaining to sound (5)
12 Open disrespect (5)
13 Floating masses of frozen water (8)
16 Large wine bottle (8)
18 Bird claw (5)
21 Recorded on video (5)
22 Solemn promise (3)
23 Happen again (5)
24 Pretentious display (11)

Down

2 Citrus fruits (7)
3 Room used for preparing food (7)
4 Labelling (6)
5 Travels on a bicycle (5)
6 Random number game (5)
7 Done without thinking (11)
8 Award for third place (6,5)
14 Ballroom dance (7)
15 Underwater projectile (7)
17 Evoke (6)
19 Areas of mown grass (5)
20 The Norwegian language (5)

PUZZLE 244

Across

1 Where bees are kept (4)
3 Alloy of copper and tin (8)
9 Readable (7)
10 Shy; fearful (5)
11 Easy-going (4-8)
14 ___ Ivanovic: tennis star (3)
16 Worthiness (5)
17 Wonder (3)
18 Valetudinarianism (12)
21 Fertile spots in deserts (5)
22 Uma ___ : US actress (7)
23 Lessening; diminishing (8)
24 Rich savoury paste (4)

Down

1 Flat image that looks 3D (8)
2 ___ Mortensen: actor (5)
4 Midge ___ : Ultravox musician (3)
5 First language (6,6)
6 Painting medium (7)
7 Outdoor swimming pool (4)
8 In a sparing manner (12)
12 Undergo gradual transformation (5)
13 Someone in custody (8)
15 At the ocean floor (7)
19 Cuban folk dance (5)
20 Particles around a comet (4)
22 Number of toes (3)

PUZZLE 245

Across

1 Work hard (5)
4 Most feeble (7)
7 Hebrew prophet (5)
8 Device controlling flow of fuel to an engine (8)
9 Perceives audibly (5)
11 Person who goes to bed late (5,3)
15 Plot outline for a play (8)
17 Besmirch (5)
19 Shimmered (8)
20 Went down on one knee (5)
21 Person who shoes horses (7)
22 Coarse rock used for polishing (5)

Down

1 Sticky (9)
2 Mediocre (7)
3 Having a valid will (7)
4 Flounder about (6)
5 Danish monetary unit (pl) (6)
6 Give a solemn oath (5)
10 Of lesser importance (9)
12 Avenger (anag) (7)
13 Eg a bishop (7)
14 Pastiness (6)
16 Person who imprisons another (6)
18 Obsession (5)

PUZZLE 246

Across

1 Adult male singing voice (4)
3 Affecting only the appearance (8)
9 Plausible; defensible (7)
10 Venomous snake (5)
11 Boldness; courage (5)
12 Give up or surrender something (3,4)
13 Security (6)
15 Remains preserved in rock (6)
17 Create a positive feeling in a person (7)
18 Strong ringing sound (5)
20 Reduce to small particles (5)
21 Cynic (7)
22 Compliant; submissive (8)
23 By word of mouth (4)

Down

1 Amazingly (13)
2 Singing voice (5)
4 Frankly (6)
5 Afraid to speak frankly (5-7)
6 Tiresome (7)
7 Arranged in temporal order (13)
8 Lost in thought (6-6)
14 Jovially celebratory (7)
16 Diminish (6)
19 Change (5)

PUZZLE 247

Across

1 Britney ___ : singer (6)
4 Leave a place (6)
9 Illuminate (5,2)
10 Prompts (7)
11 Seat (5)
12 First Greek letter (5)
14 Gamble (5)
15 Type of confection (5)
17 Adhesive (5)
18 Rotate (7)
20 Alcoholic drinks (7)
21 Economy; providence (6)
22 Superior (6)

Down

1 Join together (6)
2 Etched into a surface (8)
3 Armature of a generator (5)
5 Branch of linguistics (7)
6 Energy and enthusiasm (4)
7 Afternoon snooze in Spain (6)
8 Capital of Illinois (11)
13 Stop gradually (5,3)
14 Wealthy (4-3)
15 Animal used to catch rabbits (6)
16 Moral guardian (6)
17 Wound the pride of (5)
19 Change direction suddenly (4)

PUZZLE 248

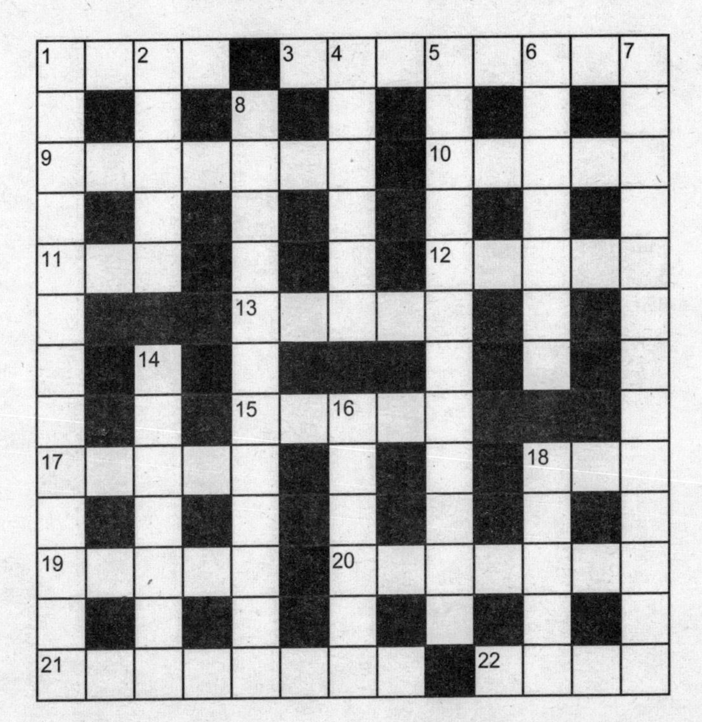

Across

1 After the beginning of (4)
3 Laziness (8)
9 Small plum-like fruits (7)
10 Standing frame used by an artist (5)
11 Use a chair (3)
12 Historic nobleman (5)
13 External (5)
15 Cry of excitement (5)
17 Wash one's body in water (5)
18 Sum charged (3)
19 Uproarious party or fight (5)
20 Disentangle (7)
21 Very large animal (8)
22 Type of high-energy radiation (1-3)

Down

1 Incapable of being expressed in words (13)
2 Entice to do something (5)
4 Tyrant (6)
5 Coat with a metal (12)
6 Great happiness (7)
7 Obviously (4-9)
8 A grouping of states (12)
14 Contaminate (7)
16 Dispute the truth of (6)
18 ___ Tuck: friend of Robin Hood (5)

PUZZLE 249

Across

1 12th month (8)
5 Circular storage medium (4)
8 Language of the Romans (5)
9 Alan ___ : former England footballer (7)
10 Small explosive bomb (7)
12 Flat-bottomed boat (7)
14 Suits; turns into (7)
16 Person in overall charge (7)
18 Softens with age (7)
19 Praise enthusiastically (5)
20 Facial feature (4)
21 Divert one's attention (8)

Down

1 ___ Steyn: South African bowler (4)
2 Soft white fibre (6)
3 Speech by one actor (9)
4 Banner or flag (6)
6 An advance; progress (6)
7 Removes errors (8)
11 Law that is passed (9)
12 Male journalists (8)
13 Falls out unintentionally (6)
14 Art of growing dwarfed trees (6)
15 Vedic hymn (6)
17 Piece of wood; last (anag) (4)

PUZZLE 250

Across

7 Desiring worldly possessions (13)
8 Electric generator (6)
9 Throes (anag) (6)
10 Abounding (8)
13 Unit of power (4)
14 Merriment (4)
16 Angel of the highest order (8)
19 Pull back from (6)
20 Limited in scope (6)
22 25th anniversary of marriage (6,7)

Down

1 Far from difficult (4)
2 Keep hold of (6)
3 ___ Ryder: actress (6)
4 Very nearly (6)
5 Shun (6)
6 Opera texts (8)
11 Official statement (8)
12 Born (3)
15 Change gradually (6)
16 Payment for regular work (6)
17 Cause to become (6)
18 Spoof (6)
21 Possesses (4)

PUZZLE 251

Across

1 Bring together (5)
4 Fix (7)
7 Expressed clearly (5)
8 Registered for something (8)
9 Haggard (5)
11 Madly (8)
15 Sit with legs wide apart (8)
17 Propel forwards (5)
19 Roman building (8)
20 ___ Dumbledore: Harry Potter character (5)
21 Repository (7)
22 Ravine (5)

Down

1 Not yet determined (9)
2 Have a positive impact (7)
3 Screaming (7)
4 Vend again (6)
5 Bird with a long coloured beak (6)
6 Pretend (5)
10 Schedule (9)
12 Moving along the ground (of aircraft) (7)
13 Suitor (7)
14 Admit openly (6)
16 Half-conscious state (6)
18 Measuring stick (5)

PUZZLE 252

Across

7 Deep pit (6)
8 Violent gust of wind (6)
9 Unit of heredity (4)
10 Cornerstone (8)
11 Celebrations (7)
13 ___ Elliott: US singer (5)
15 Item of cutlery (5)
16 Clothes for washing (7)
18 Space ___ : arcade game (8)
19 Having pains (4)
21 Named (6)
22 A true belief (6)

Down

1 At liberty (4)
2 Deliberately (13)
3 Punched (7)
4 Up and about (5)
5 Survey (13)
6 Skin care product (8)
12 Supplemental part of a book (8)
14 Plant with starchy tuberous roots (7)
17 Fixes (5)
20 Small shelters (4)

PUZZLE 253

Across

1 Soft pear-shaped fruits (4)
3 Believes tentatively (8)
9 Allocations (7)
10 Lubricated (5)
11 Made in bulk (4-8)
13 Appeared to be (6)
15 US state (6)
17 Stretched out completely (12)
20 Exit (5)
21 Land with fruit trees (7)
22 Wood preserver (8)
23 Dairy product (4)

Down

1 First in importance (8)
2 Entrance barriers (5)
4 Eventual outcome (6)
5 Bump (12)
6 Volcanic crater (7)
7 Soft drink (US) (4)
8 Entirety (12)
12 Frankly (8)
14 Make amends (7)
16 Clever or skilful (6)
18 Animal restraint (5)
19 ___ Stewart: ex-England cricketer (4)

PUZZLE 254

Across

7 Where you were born (6,7)
8 Long mountain chain (6)
9 Standards of perfection (6)
10 Disperses (8)
13 Solitary (4)
14 Single entity (4)
16 Create an account deficit (8)
19 Held in great esteem (6)
20 Insurgents (6)
22 Not proper (13)

Down

1 Large desert in Asia (4)
2 Desire for water (6)
3 Fatty matter (6)
4 Themes (6)
5 Imaginary (6)
6 Formerly Ceylon (3,5)
11 Includes (8)
12 Increase the running speed of an engine (3)
15 Outdoes (6)
16 Commands (6)
17 Continent (6)
18 Old plodding horse (6)
21 Stringed instrument (4)

PUZZLE 255

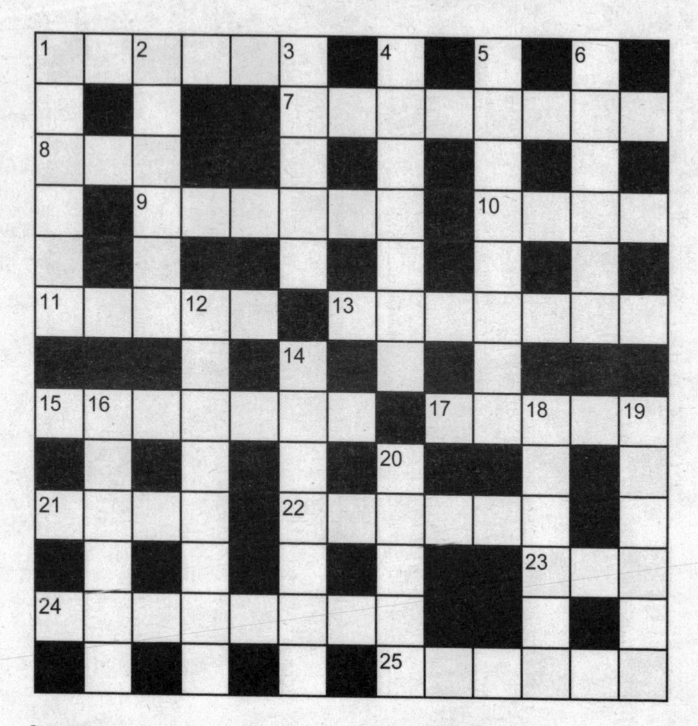

Across

1 Paths (6)
7 Awful (8)
8 Add together (3)
9 Reach (6)
10 Tiny bird (4)
11 Spoken for (5)
13 Demureness (7)
15 People who are in a club (7)
17 Apart from (5)
21 Effervesce (4)
22 Majestic (6)
23 Widely cultivated cereal grass (3)
24 Spoilsports (8)
25 Having a human crew (6)

Down

1 Place that is frequented for holidays (6)
2 Uncover (6)
3 Wander off track (5)
4 Wooden bar across a window (7)
5 Sightings (8)
6 Extraterrestrials (6)
12 Steal or misappropriate money (8)
14 Process of wearing away (7)
16 Cure-all (6)
18 Innate (6)
19 Overjoyed (6)
20 Sudden constriction (5)

PUZZLE 256

Across

1 Engrave; carve (4)
3 Delicate ornamental work (8)
9 Female ruler (7)
10 Group of witches (5)
11 Unseasonably warm period (6,6)
13 Easily remembered (6)
15 US state of islands (6)
17 Shrewdness (12)
20 Funny person (5)
21 Army rank (7)
22 Uneasy (8)
23 ___ and cons: pluses and minuses (4)

Down

1 Telescope lens (8)
2 Managed (5)
4 Demand forcefully to have something (6)
5 Without equal (12)
6 Mediterranean resort area (7)
7 Sea eagle (4)
8 Highly abstract (12)
12 Two-wheeled vehicles (8)
14 Vacuum flask (7)
16 12th sign of the zodiac (6)
18 Opposite of outer (5)
19 Skin mark from a wound (4)

PUZZLE 257

Across

1 Father of a parent (7)
6 Seabird (3)
8 Fantastic (5)
9 Calls for (7)
10 Device for sharpening razors (5)
11 Country of East Asia (8)
13 Chamber of the heart (6)
15 Positively charged atomic particle (6)
18 Pays homage to (8)
19 Encounters (5)
21 Looked up to (7)
22 Make law (5)
23 Possesses (3)
24 Strangeness (7)

Down

2 Harmonious relationship (7)
3 Conversation (8)
4 Attack someone (6)
5 Primates (4)
6 Part of a chair (7)
7 Inert gaseous element (7)
12 Took for granted (8)
13 Horizontal angle of a compass bearing (7)
14 Retreats (7)
16 Fish-eating birds of prey (7)
17 Edible tuber (6)
20 Examine quickly (4)

PUZZLE 258

Across

1 Symbol or representation (6)
4 Eluded (6)
9 The ___ in the Rye: novel (7)
10 Sour in taste (7)
11 Style of Greek architecture (5)
12 Film directed by Ridley Scott (5)
14 Court official (5)
15 Evil spirit (5)
17 At that place; not here (5)
18 Hide (5-2)
20 Conjuring up feelings (7)
21 Give satisfaction (6)
22 Taken illegally (6)

Down

1 Old Portuguese currency (6)
2 Where one has a shower (8)
3 Set of moral principles (5)
5 Impure acetic acid (7)
6 Spread clumsily on a surface (4)
7 Ordained minister of an order below a priest (6)
8 Plant-eating insect (11)
13 Relating to an empire (8)
14 Remove clothes (7)
15 Abscond (6)
16 Ronald ___ : former US President (6)
17 Game fish (5)
19 Make a choice through a ballot (4)

PUZZLE 259

Across

1 Person who practises self-discipline (7)
6 Level golf score (3)
8 Got up (5)
9 V-shaped mark (7)
10 Satisfied a desire (5)
11 Supplied with (8)
13 Dreary (6)
15 Spherical objects (6)
18 Aromatic spice (8)
19 Takes part in a game (5)
21 Great ___ : island (7)
22 Rice dish (5)
23 Small winged insect (3)
24 Piece; part (7)

Down

2 Playful musical compositions (7)
3 End of a railway route (8)
4 Small boats (6)
5 Extremities of the feet (4)
6 Agitate (7)
7 People who attack at speed (7)
12 Very intense (of pain) (8)
13 Decline gradually (4-3)
14 Fragmentary (7)
16 Eg hate or joy (7)
17 Grey rain cloud (6)
20 Ales (anag) (4)

PUZZLE 260

1		2			3	4		5		6		7
				8								
9								10				
11						12						
13		14					15					
						16						
17								18		19		
20						21						
22									23			

Across

1 Cries (4)
3 Dispute (8)
9 Additional and supplementary part (7)
10 Kingdom (5)
11 Adolescence (5)
12 Understand (7)
13 Flowing back (6)
15 Ukrainian port (6)
17 Young goose (7)
18 Door hanger (5)
20 Small branch (5)
21 Remnant (7)
22 Recently married person (5-3)
23 Small freshwater duck (4)

Down

1 Black Eyed Peas star (5,8)
2 Small and elegant (5)
4 Semiaquatic fish-eating mammals (6)
5 Preservative chemical (12)
6 Slanted characters (7)
7 Unpredictable (13)
8 Bewitchingly (12)
14 Cover or partly cover (7)
16 Pay no attention to (6)
19 Female relation (5)

PUZZLE 261

Across

1 Cleans (5)
4 Altered (7)
7 Danielle ___ : US romantic novelist (5)
8 Critical explanation (8)
9 Horse carts (5)
11 Worm (8)
15 Clothing that covers the legs (8)
17 Wrong (anag) (5)
19 Soonest (8)
20 Heavy iron tool (5)
21 Upward slopes (7)
22 ___ Mirren: English actress (5)

Down

1 Degrading (9)
2 Flowing bodies of water (7)
3 Next after sixth (7)
4 Emulated (6)
5 Person authorised to draw up contracts (6)
6 Military opponent (5)
10 Feeling (9)
12 Prepare and issue for sale (7)
13 More than two (7)
14 For a short time (6)
16 Domains (6)
18 Positions in a hierarchy (5)

PUZZLE 262

Across

1 Beginning (6)
5 Insanity (6)
8 Burkina ___: African country (4)
9 Mathematically aware (8)
10 Helmet part for protecting the face (5)
11 Rousing songs (7)
14 Shape or arrangement (13)
16 Able to read minds (7)
18 Dividing boundaries (5)
20 Catch a conversation between others (8)
22 Wizard (4)
23 Those expelled from a country (6)
24 Assumes as a fact (6)

Down

2 Of one mind (9)
3 Exhibitionist (4-3)
4 Army vehicle (4)
5 One who inspires others (8)
6 ___ Jones: American singer-songwriter (5)
7 Bed for a baby (3)
12 Form of illumination at night (9)
13 Hideousness (8)
15 Emotional shocks (7)
17 Christmas song (5)
19 Enclose in paper (4)
21 Annoy (3)

PUZZLE 263

Across

1 Virtuoso solo passage (7)
6 Circulating life force (3)
8 Tropical fruit (5)
9 Retention of data (7)
10 Capital of Egypt (5)
11 Adolescent (8)
13 Alter or move slightly (6)
15 Puzzle (6)
18 Eastern (8)
19 Ahead of time (5)
21 Before or by now (7)
22 ___ DeGeneres: US comedienne (5)
23 Month of the year (3)
24 Look something over (7)

Down

2 Amaze (7)
3 Tidiness (8)
4 Ancient (3-3)
5 Bathroom mineral powder (4)
6 Reindeer (7)
7 Type of bill (7)
12 Practise for a later performance (8)
13 Belief that there is no God (7)
14 Travel somewhere (7)
16 Thing causing outrage (7)
17 Refined in manner (6)
20 Part of an egg (4)

PUZZLE 264

Across

1 Steals from (4)
3 Opposite of departures (8)
9 Vocation (7)
10 Stringed instrument (5)
11 Animal foot (3)
12 Correct (5)
13 Keen (5)
15 Opposite of old (5)
17 Long and imposing poems (5)
18 Criticise strongly (3)
19 Do extremely well at (5)
20 Release (7)
21 Flowering plant (5,3)
22 Fail totally (4)

Down

1 Open-mindedness (13)
2 Local authority rule (2-3)
4 Experiencing violent anger (6)
5 Incurably bad (12)
6 Quick musical tempo (7)
7 Fairness in following the rules (13)
8 As quickly as possible (7-5)
14 Light bun or roll (7)
16 Uncertain (6)
18 Jewel from an oyster shell (5)

PUZZLE 265

Across

1 ___ in: eat heartily (4)
3 Pennant (8)
9 Good luck charms (7)
10 Sacred song (5)
11 River cove; bay (5)
12 Opposite of later (7)
13 Force that causes rotation (6)
15 HMS ___ : boat Darwin sailed on (6)
17 The growth of crystals (7)
18 Garbage or drivel (5)
20 Snow leopard (5)
21 Flowering shrubs (7)
22 Sanctions (8)
23 Disgust with an excess of sweetness (4)

Down

1 Sausages baked in batter (4-2-3-4)
2 Excessively mean (5)
4 Flipped a coin (6)
5 Derived from past events (12)
6 Significance (7)
7 Pitilessly (13)
8 The proprietor of an eating establishment (12)
14 Ruled (7)
16 Revolve quickly (6)
19 Perfect (5)

PUZZLE 266

Across

1 Association created for mutual benefit (8)
5 One of two equal parts (4)
8 Any finger or toe (5)
9 Edible mollusc (7)
10 Entrap (7)
12 Made less narrow (7)
14 Easily moulded (7)
16 Ostentatious (7)
18 Revival (7)
19 Dreadful (5)
20 Not seen very often (4)
21 Formal curse by a pope (8)

Down

1 Assistant (4)
2 Fell behind (6)
3 This follows morning (9)
4 Covered with an outer layer (6)
6 Waterproof jacket (6)
7 Frenzied (8)
11 Unwavering (9)
12 Traveller (8)
13 Arched shape of a road (6)
14 Snake (6)
15 Cold dessert (6)
17 Leaf (anag) (4)

PUZZLE 267

Across

1 Person who goes underwater (5)
4 Juicy soft fruit (7)
7 Fire (5)
8 US name for the aubergine (8)
9 Dines (anag) (5)
11 Went along to an event (8)
15 Form of carbon (8)
17 Insect larva (5)
19 Blissful (8)
20 Capable of flowing (5)
21 Serving no purpose (7)
22 Mistaken (5)

Down

1 Polygon having 12 sides (9)
2 Colloquial speech (7)
3 Lean back (7)
4 Broad road (6)
5 Away from the coast (6)
6 Seeped (5)
10 Giving a job to (9)
12 Trailer (7)
13 Cyclone (7)
14 Difficult (6)
16 Dog-like mammals (6)
18 Egg centres (5)

PUZZLE 268

Across

1 Mark written under the letter c (7)
6 Extremity (3)
8 Rugby formation (5)
9 Small bunch of flowers (7)
10 Musical instrument (5)
11 Glassy (8)
13 Increase in intensity (4,2)
15 Tidies one's appearance (6)
18 Wanders at random (8)
19 Feign (3,2)
21 Fabled monster (7)
22 Flour dough used in cooking (5)
23 Exclamation of surprise (3)
24 Show (7)

Down

2 Selfish person (7)
3 Woody (8)
4 Shelter (6)
5 Hold tightly (4)
6 Ban on trade with a country (7)
7 Makes misshapen (7)
12 Wave or flourish a weapon (8)
13 Shoulder blade (7)
14 Statement of commemoration (7)
16 Type of vermouth (7)
17 Style of popular music (6)
20 Overly curious (4)

PUZZLE 269

Across

- **1** Assert without proof (6)
- **4** Wild dog (6)
- **9** Island in the West Indies (7)
- **10** Thinning out a tree by removing branches (7)
- **11** Marie ___ : winner of two Nobel prizes (5)
- **12** Sharp blade (5)
- **14** Lose consciousness (5)
- **15** Comedian (5)
- **17** Solids with six equal square faces (5)
- **18** Bathing tub with bubbles (7)
- **20** Tenth month of the year (7)
- **21** Deleted (6)
- **22** Fast (6)

Down

- **1** Showing utter resignation (6)
- **2** Humorous verse (8)
- **3** Move effortlessly through air (5)
- **5** Flight hub (7)
- **6** Flightless bird (4)
- **7** Bigger (6)
- **8** Curse (11)
- **13** Formerly Southern Rhodesia (8)
- **14** Fry until crisp (7)
- **15** Puerile; superficial (6)
- **16** Fish hawk (6)
- **17** Destroy (3,2)
- **19** Sparkling wine (4)

PUZZLE 270

Across

1 Reinstatement (11)
9 From the capital of Italy (5)
10 Violate a law of God (3)
11 Pointed part of a fork (5)
12 Dance club (5)
13 Manner; mental state (8)
16 Usain Bolt is one (8)
18 Municipalities (5)
21 Locomotive (5)
22 Tree of the genus Quercus (3)
23 Draw off liquid from (5)
24 Small room that leads to a main one (11)

Down

2 Bodyguards (7)
3 Goals (7)
4 Very crowded (of a place) (6)
5 Shaped up (5)
6 Fertile area in a desert (5)
7 Reason given for doing something (11)
8 Unwillingness to accept the views of others (11)
14 Country in SE Asia (7)
15 Odd (7)
17 Deliver a sermon (6)
19 Rouse from sleep (5)
20 Grasslike marsh plant (5)

PUZZLE 271

Across

1 Curved shape (4)
3 Moment of great revelation (8)
9 Type of treatment for a disorder (7)
10 Type of black tea (5)
11 Unseen observer (3,2,3,4)
13 ___ fruit: eg orange or lemon (6)
15 Greek goddess (6)
17 Charmingly (12)
20 Our planet (5)
21 Italian fast racing car (7)
22 Shameless (8)
23 Second-hand (4)

Down

1 Cunning; contrivance (8)
2 Requiring much mastication (5)
4 The spirit or soul (6)
5 Do something high risk (4,4,4)
6 Forgive (7)
7 Sweet potatoes (US) (4)
8 Poorly fed (12)
12 Spotted beetle (8)
14 A general proposition (7)
16 Smells (6)
18 Dales (anag) (5)
19 Abominable snowman (4)

PUZZLE 272

Across

1 Soccer (8)
5 Endure; large animal (4)
9 Lattice (7)
10 Exposes to danger (5)
11 Lack of courtesy (10)
14 More difficult (6)
15 Screen of metal bars (6)
17 UFOs (10)
20 Having three dimensions (5)
21 Incidental result of a larger project (4-3)
22 In ___ : instead (4)
23 Harshness of tone (8)

Down

1 Greek cheese (4)
2 Comply (4)
3 Hostile aggressiveness (12)
4 Surface coating (6)
6 Opposite of westerly (8)
7 Flower-shaped competition awards (8)
8 Dictatorial (12)
12 Pertaining to the body (8)
13 Introduction (8)
16 Deep fissures (6)
18 ___ Berra: baseball player (4)
19 Doubtful (4)

PUZZLE 273

Across

1 Fluffy and soft (5)
4 Seriousness (7)
7 Burn with hot liquid (5)
8 Person who maintains machines (8)
9 Anxiety (5)
11 Very capable (8)
15 Morally compel (8)
17 Clamorous (5)
19 Intended to appeal to ordinary people (8)
20 Seabirds (5)
21 Official pardon (7)
22 Appears (5)

Down

1 Discovery (9)
2 Squirm (7)
3 Expressing boredom with the mouth (7)
4 Where one finds Athens (6)
5 Empty (6)
6 Cash registers (5)
10 Menaces (9)
12 Periods of 60 seconds (7)
13 Emit energy (7)
14 Large property with land (6)
16 Umbrella (informal) (6)
18 Loose fibre used in caulking wooden ships (5)

PUZZLE 274

Across

1 Someone who writes the words for a song (8)
5 Bond movie (2,2)
9 Varnish (7)
10 Hermann ___ : author of Steppenwolf (5)
11 Wayfarers (10)
14 Hatred (anag) (6)
15 Fine-drawn (6)
17 Punctuation mark (10)
20 African country (5)
21 Quality of lacking transparency (7)
22 Fathers (4)
23 Support (8)

Down

1 Gentle accent (4)
2 Suggestive (4)
3 Military judicial body (5,7)
4 Run fast (6)
6 Evoke memories (8)
7 Supervisor (8)
8 Street (12)
12 Took military action against (8)
13 Second-hand (8)
16 Silkworm covering (6)
18 Speech defect (4)
19 Church song (4)

PUZZLE 275

Across

1 Tennis shots (4)
3 Taught (8)
9 Sport using swords (7)
10 Calls out loudly (5)
11 Style of blues (6-6)
14 Nay (anag) (3)
16 Meat juices (5)
17 Mouth (informal) (3)
18 Capable of being moved (12)
21 Bird droppings used as fertiliser (5)
22 Troughs that carry rainwater (7)
23 Prayer service (8)
24 Football boot grip (4)

Down

1 Sea rescue vessel (8)
2 Small drum (5)
4 Man's best friend (3)
5 Major type of food nutrient (12)
6 Mocking (7)
7 Quantity of medication (4)
8 Insincere (12)
12 Fixed platform by water (5)
13 Completely preoccupied with (8)
15 Golfing measure of distance (7)
19 Sheep sound (5)
20 Fit of shivering (4)
22 Snare or trap (3)

PUZZLE 276

Across

1 Acquires a new skill (6)
4 Rebukes angrily (6)
9 Country house (7)
10 Sedentary (7)
11 Thermosetting resin (5)
12 Expulsion (5)
14 Proposal (5)
15 Old French currency (5)
17 Samantha ___ : Irish singer (5)
18 Move something; agitate (7)
20 Vocabulary list (7)
21 Push forcefully (6)
22 Witches cast these (6)

Down

1 Composite fungus and alga (6)
2 Large snake (8)
3 Destitute (5)
5 Talk informally (7)
6 Mischievous god in Norse mythology (4)
7 Solitary; not married (6)
8 Defensible (11)
13 Harmful (8)
14 Conceals something from view (7)
15 Move restlessly (6)
16 Very holy people (6)
17 Confusion (3-2)
19 Scorch (4)

PUZZLE 277

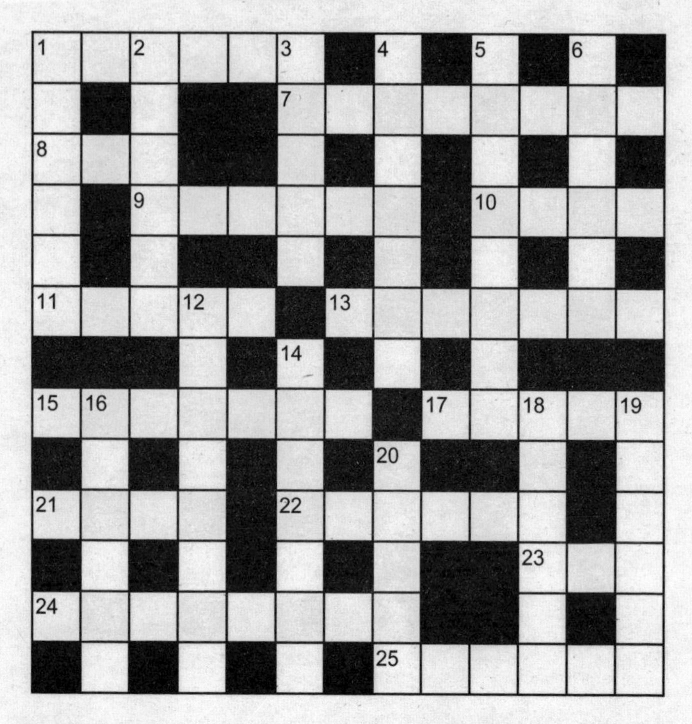

Across

1 Becomes subject to (6)
7 Square scarf worn over the head (8)
8 Strange (3)
9 Put briefly into liquid (6)
10 Woes; problems (4)
11 Moved slowly (5)
13 Requests forcefully (7)
15 Accelerate (5,2)
17 Change (5)
21 Letters and parcels generally (4)
22 Mustang; wild horse (6)
23 Great distress (3)
24 Person walking aimlessly (8)
25 Gramophone needle (6)

Down

1 Humorously sarcastic (6)
2 Hug (6)
3 Leaps over a rope (5)
4 Vessel that cleans rivers (7)
5 Country in SE Asia (8)
6 Hidden from view (6)
12 Make impossible (8)
14 Fourth book of the Bible (7)
16 Flat; two-dimensional (6)
18 Assertion (6)
19 Stopwatches (6)
20 Hinged barriers between rooms (5)

PUZZLE 278

Across

1 Wipes up (4)
3 Makes remote; cuts off (8)
9 Place out of sight (7)
10 Have an irritating effect (5)
11 Dissatisfaction (5)
12 Equalled (7)
13 Long and very narrow (6)
15 African antelope (6)
17 Modern; up to date (7)
18 Bird sound; chirp (5)
20 Mythical unpleasant giants (5)
21 Absence of sound (7)
22 Magnificent (8)
23 Female chickens (4)

Down

1 Of mixed character (13)
2 Brown nut (5)
4 Passionate (6)
5 Lawfully (12)
6 Windpipe (7)
7 Loyalty in the face of trouble (13)
8 Food shop (12)
14 Impartial (7)
16 Breakfast food (6)
19 ___ Els: golfing star (5)

PUZZLE 279

Across

1 Run-down and in poor condition (6)
4 Bring into the country (6)
9 River in South America (7)
10 Model of the body (7)
11 Huge mythical creature (5)
12 Hazy (5)
14 Ice cream is often served in these (5)
15 Aromatic herb of the mint family (5)
17 The papal court (5)
18 Japanese dish of raw fish (7)
20 Make ineffective (7)
21 Scented ointment (6)
22 Book of the Bible (6)

Down

1 Hard to digest (of food) (6)
2 Gives life to (8)
3 Puff up (5)
5 Large wine bottles (7)
6 The sound a pig makes (4)
7 Up-to-date and fashionable (6)
8 Mixing together (11)
13 Echinoderm with a distinctive shape (8)
14 Decimal (anag) (7)
15 Spiritual supervisor (6)
16 Solicitor (6)
17 Prison compartments (5)
19 Appear (4)

PUZZLE 280

Across

1 Style of popular dance music (4)
3 Type of leather (8)
9 Failure to be present (7)
10 Harsh and serious in manner (5)
11 Minimum purchase cost at auction (7,5)
14 Don (anag) (3)
16 Establish as the truth (5)
17 Small legume (3)
18 Jail term without end (4,8)
21 Strong thick rope (5)
22 Anybody (7)
23 Raise one's ___ : show surprise (8)
24 Smack with the hand (4)

Down

1 Having a pleasing scent (8)
2 Birds lay their eggs in these (5)
4 Organ of sight (3)
5 Revival of something (12)
6 Patella (7)
7 Not any of (4)
8 Someone who sets up their own business (12)
12 Decay (5)
13 Refer to famous people one knows (4-4)
15 Fall slowly (of a liquid) (7)
19 Maritime (5)
20 Spots (4)
22 Exclamation of amazement (3)

PUZZLE 281

Across

1 Large family (4)
3 Renovated (8)
9 Stands about idly (7)
10 Annoyed (5)
11 Filled with a humming sound (5)
12 Building (7)
13 Argue against (6)
15 Regain (6)
17 With reference to (7)
18 Theme for a discussion (5)
20 Island in the Mediterranean Sea (5)
21 Flesher (anag) (7)
22 Speculative (8)
23 Celebrity hero (4)

Down

1 Cooperation; alliance (13)
2 Word of farewell (5)
4 Christian festival (6)
5 Practice of designing buildings (12)
6 Precondition (7)
7 Rude and discourteous (13)
8 Female singing voice (5-7)
14 Persevere with (7)
16 Respiratory condition (6)
19 Ask for earnestly (5)

PUZZLE 282

Across

8 Fresh precipitation (9)
9 Possess (3)
10 Legendary stories (5)
11 Blanked (7)
12 Alphabetical lists (in books) (7)
13 Opposite of thick (4)
17 Beers (4)
18 Wealthiest (7)
22 Tidy (5,2)
24 Isolated (5)
25 Atmospheric murk; obscure (3)
26 Conjecturing (9)

Down

1 Hat edges (5)
2 Space between two objects (8)
3 Tornado (7)
4 Hit hard (6)
5 Eccentric person (5)
6 Grey-haired with age (4)
7 Painkilling drug (7)
14 Belonging to the past (8)
15 Embellish (7)
16 Sayings (7)
19 Be imminent (6)
20 Scowl (5)
21 Woollen fabric (5)
23 ___ bread: French toast (4)

PUZZLE 283

Across

1 Embodies (11)
9 Tears (anag) (5)
10 Loud noise (3)
11 Small lakes (5)
12 Stitched (5)
13 Wrongdoings (8)
16 Wine container (8)
18 Garden tools (5)
21 Avoid (danger) (5)
22 Golf peg (3)
23 Narrow valleys (5)
24 Basically (11)

Down

2 Absorb all the attention of (7)
3 Broke into pieces (7)
4 Snared (6)
5 Areas of agricultural land (5)
6 Bequeath an income to (5)
7 Immoderate (11)
8 Unintentional (11)
14 ___ Hudgens: US actress and singer (7)
15 Fruit pastry (7)
17 Of the greatest age (6)
19 Flat-bottomed vessels (5)
20 Smooth transition (5)

PUZZLE 284

Across

1 Mix socially (6)
7 Made subject to (8)
8 23rd Greek letter (3)
9 Unthinkingly eager (4-2)
10 Thwart (4)
11 Stylish (5)
13 Angular units (7)
15 Extremely bad (7)
17 Tree (5)
21 Conceal (4)
22 Scarcity (6)
23 Floor covering (3)
24 Diminished in size (8)
25 US state (6)

Down

1 Occur (6)
2 Plant disease (6)
3 Game of chance (5)
4 Performer of gymnastic feats (7)
5 Unauthorised writing on walls (8)
6 Not malignant (6)
12 Refined (8)
14 Powdered spice (7)
16 Radiating light; clever (6)
18 Poems; sounds alike (6)
19 Interruption or gap (6)
20 Imbibed (5)

PUZZLE 285

Across

1 Minute organisms in the sea (8)
5 Goad on (4)
8 Sticky sap (5)
9 Encroach (7)
10 Steeps in liquid (7)
12 Bows (7)
14 Largest (7)
16 Soft woven fabric (7)
18 Musical composition (7)
19 Robbery (5)
20 Piece of office furniture (4)
21 Personal magnetism (8)

Down

1 Piece of open land (4)
2 Soak up (6)
3 Female relative (9)
4 Egyptian god (6)
6 Subject to a penalty (6)
7 Type of resistor (8)
11 Assemble (9)
12 Blushing with embarrassment (3-5)
13 Steam rooms (6)
14 Remove colour from (6)
15 Morals (6)
17 Volcano in Sicily (4)

PUZZLE 286

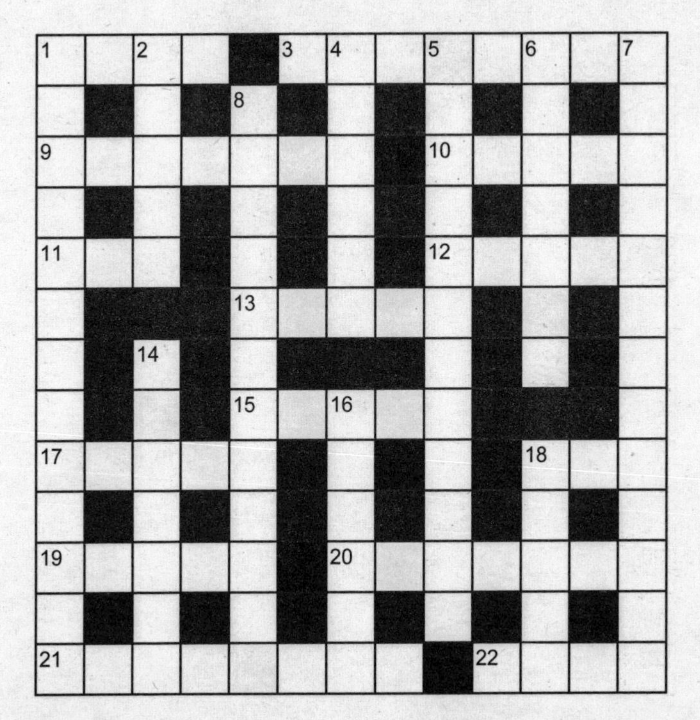

Across

1 Cramped (of a room) (4)
3 In the open air (8)
9 Walks for pleasure (7)
10 Opposite of below (5)
11 Not in (3)
12 Wise men (5)
13 Wash in water to remove soap or dirt (5)
15 Stares at amorously (5)
17 Genuinely (5)
18 Hair colourant (3)
19 Colour of milk chocolate (5)
20 Tax imposed on ships (7)
21 Weaken (8)
22 Intertwined segment of rope (4)

Down

1 Chart of chemical elements (8,5)
2 Well cared for (5)
4 Period of instruction (6)
5 Re-evaluation (12)
6 Aquatic invertebrates (7)
7 Exaggeration (13)
8 Ability to see the future (12)
14 Stem the flow of (4,3)
16 Edible pulse (6)
18 Looking tired (5)

PUZZLE 287

Across

1 Primitive plant (4)
3 A division between people (8)
9 Pleased (7)
10 Become ready to eat (of fruit) (5)
11 Pass a rope through (5)
12 Civil action brought to court (7)
13 Adjusts (6)
15 Interfere (6)
17 English county (7)
18 Grade (anag) (5)
20 Country in SE Asia (5)
21 Member of the band Blue (3,4)
22 Type of coffee (8)
23 Type of footwear (4)

Down

1 Capable of being found out (13)
2 Type of chisel (5)
4 Treat indulgently (6)
5 Sweet red fruits (12)
6 Seize and take legal custody of (7)
7 Failure to be present at (13)
8 Loving (12)
14 Deliver by parachute (3-4)
16 Abilities; talents (6)
19 Sculptured symbol (5)

PUZZLE 288

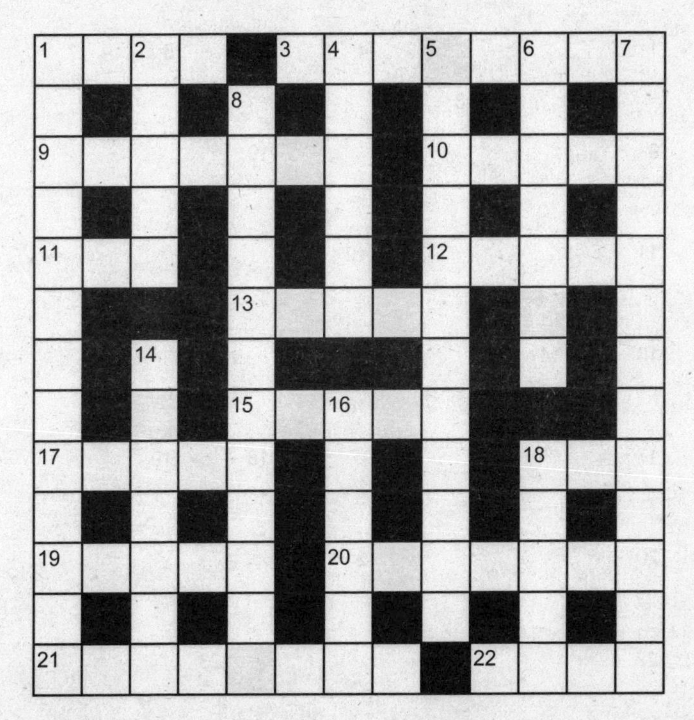

Across

1 Near (4)
3 Atmospheric gas (8)
9 Person proposed for office (7)
10 Go about stealthily (5)
11 Tap (anag) (3)
12 US R&B singer (5)
13 Smells strongly (5)
15 Mountain range in South America (5)
17 Vertical part of a step (5)
18 Small truck (3)
19 Shallow recess (5)
20 Form of an element (7)
21 Expulsion (8)
22 Heroic tale (4)

Down

1 Failure to be present (13)
2 The entire scale (5)
4 Time of widespread glaciation (3,3)
5 Act of reclamation (12)
6 Grumbles (7)
7 Former President of South Africa (6,7)
8 Clothing such as a vest (12)
14 Small bone in the ear (7)
16 Gaming tile (6)
18 Musical instrument (5)

PUZZLE 289

1		2			3	4		5		6		7
				8								
9								10				
11						12						
13		14					15					
						16						
17								18		19		
20						21						
22									23			

Across

1 Spur on (4)
3 Cramped (8)
9 Basements (7)
10 School tests (5)
11 Of the nose (5)
12 Motorcycle attachment (7)
13 Deep blue colour (6)
15 Church services (6)
17 Install; establish (7)
18 Japanese food (5)
20 Indentation; nick (5)
21 Controlling a vehicle (7)
22 Resembling a hare (8)
23 Large group or collection (4)

Down

1 Absolute (13)
2 Covers with gold (5)
4 Be preoccupied with something (6)
5 A type of error in speech (8,4)
6 Subtleties (7)
7 Upsettingly (13)
8 Someone skilled in penmanship (12)
14 Type of computer (7)
16 Deprive of force; stifle (6)
19 Glisten (5)

PUZZLE 290

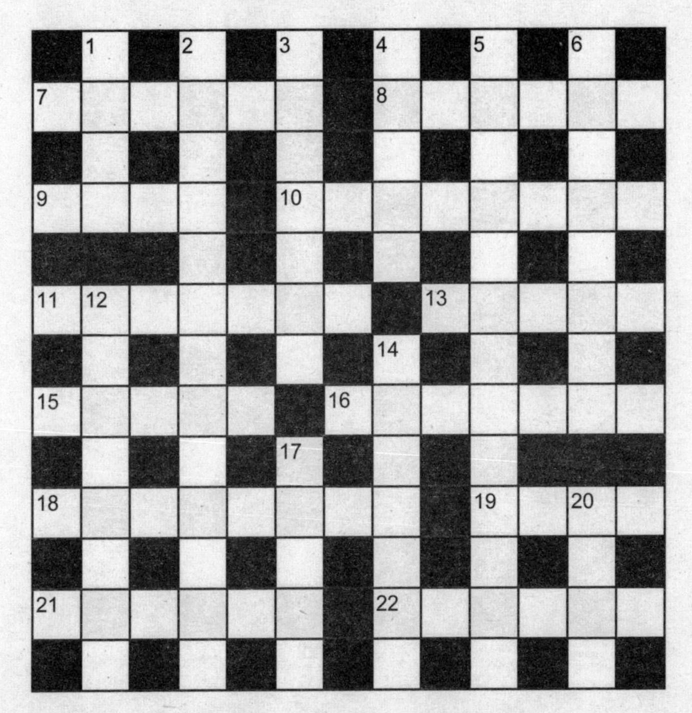

Across

7 Physical strength and good health (6)
8 Fissures (6)
9 Chemical salt (4)
10 Film starring Juliette Binoche (8)
11 Put in the ground (7)
13 Rounded mass (5)
15 Liquid served with food; relish (5)
16 Weaves; clothing (7)
18 Fleet of ships (8)
19 Surrounding glow (4)
21 Flash intermittently (6)
22 Calculate; think that (6)

Down

1 Bird beak (4)
2 Activity of conveying information (13)
3 Chirping insect (7)
4 Go swiftly (5)
5 Enforcement policy with no leeway (4,9)
6 Achieved (8)
12 Pamphlets (8)
14 Playhouse (7)
17 Works one's trade steadily (5)
20 Public disturbance (4)

PUZZLE 291

Across

1 Fully (6)
4 Body of running water (6)
9 Bring and hand over (7)
10 Capital of Georgia in the US (7)
11 Arrives (5)
12 Quartzlike gems (5)
14 Attach (5)
15 Bring into a line (5)
17 Pants (5)
18 Martial art (2-5)
20 Series of boat races (7)
21 Small hole (6)
22 Bumps into (6)

Down

1 Lower (6)
2 Squid dish (8)
3 Resides (5)
5 Chest for implements (7)
6 Near (anag) (4)
7 Military decorations (6)
8 Change in appearance (11)
13 Uncertain if God exists (8)
14 Whenever (7)
15 Renounce an oath (6)
16 Academy Awards (6)
17 Start (5)
19 Plant fibre (4)

PUZZLE 292

Across

1 Callous (11)
9 Gardeners sow these (5)
10 Chris ___ : English singer (3)
11 Not heavy (5)
12 ___ Sarandon: US actress (5)
13 Husband of one's daughter (3-2-3)
16 Cocktail (8)
18 ___ gas: eg neon or argon (5)
21 Common edible fruit (5)
22 Wily (3)
23 Asian pepper plant (5)
24 One who held a job previously (11)

Down

2 Prodding with the elbow (7)
3 London district (4,3)
4 ___ McCartney: fashion designer (6)
5 Tries out (5)
6 Infective agent (5)
7 Type of magician (11)
8 Superb (11)
14 Gusty winds (7)
15 River of SE Africa (7)
17 Very cold (of weather) (6)
19 Purchaser (5)
20 Receded (5)

PUZZLE 293

Across

1 Strain (4)
3 Deserving blame (8)
9 Specify by name (7)
10 Country in the Himalayas (5)
11 Connection or association (12)
14 Steal (3)
16 Rafael ___ : Spanish tennis star (5)
17 Make imperfect (3)
18 Reverse of vaporisation (12)
21 Conjuring trick (5)
22 Left out (7)
23 Blue toys (anag) (8)
24 Occupations (4)

Down

1 Straw hat (8)
2 Ultimate (5)
4 Type of vase (3)
5 US state (12)
6 Sacrament (7)
7 ___ Macpherson: Australian supermodel (4)
8 Easy targets (7,5)
12 ___ days: long ago (5)
13 Explosive shells (8)
15 Took along (7)
19 Prologue (abbrev) (5)
20 Eg bullets (abbrev) (4)
22 Eg Hedwig in Harry Potter (3)

PUZZLE 294

Across

1 Outer part of a bird's wing (6)
4 Diminished (6)
9 Cigarette constituent (7)
10 Untanned leather (7)
11 Pertaining to the sun (5)
12 Angered; irritated (5)
14 Eccentric (5)
15 Sweet substance (5)
17 Eg mallards (5)
18 Become more rigid (7)
20 Musical wind instrument (7)
21 Live in (6)
22 Signal (anag) (6)

Down

1 Potassium compound (6)
2 Eating by taking small bites (8)
3 Academy award (5)
5 Establishment for making beer (7)
6 ___ Amos: US singer-songwriter (4)
7 Be contingent upon (6)
8 Flower (6-2-3)
13 Eating a midday meal (8)
14 Moved slowly with the current (7)
15 Female sibling (6)
16 Pieces of writing (6)
17 Speak in a slow manner (5)
19 Electrically charged particles (4)

PUZZLE 295

Across

1 Send off to a destination (8)
5 Pack carefully and neatly (4)
9 Walk unsteadily (7)
10 Lazes; does nothing (5)
11 Aversion to (10)
14 Sloping (of a typeface) (6)
15 Jail (6)
17 Talkative person (10)
20 Muscular strength (5)
21 An oral communication (7)
22 Seek (anag) (4)
23 Infancy (8)

Down

1 Fine powder (4)
2 Speak indistinctly (4)
3 Shortening (12)
4 Religious leader (6)
6 Loftiness (8)
7 Cowboy films (8)
8 Triumphantly (12)
12 Capable of being conquered (8)
13 Hard shell of a crustacean (8)
16 Black Sea peninsula (6)
18 Ring around the head of a holy person (4)
19 Long grass (4)

PUZZLE 296

Across

1 Performance by one actor (4)
3 Strong inclination (8)
9 Last longer than (7)
10 Ashley ___ : actress (5)
11 Ancestors (12)
13 Subtle detail (6)
15 Popular soup flavour (6)
17 Changes to a situation (12)
20 Bonds of union (5)
21 Plant-eating aquatic mammal (7)
22 Moving at speed (8)
23 Money given to the poor (4)

Down

1 Process of buying things (8)
2 Metric unit of capacity (5)
4 One who has a salary (6)
5 Question in great detail (5-7)
6 European country (7)
7 ___ Turner: US singer (4)
8 Incessantly (12)
12 Groups of similar things (8)
14 Verifier (7)
16 Archer (6)
18 Pertaining to birth (5)
19 Legendary story (4)

PUZZLE 297

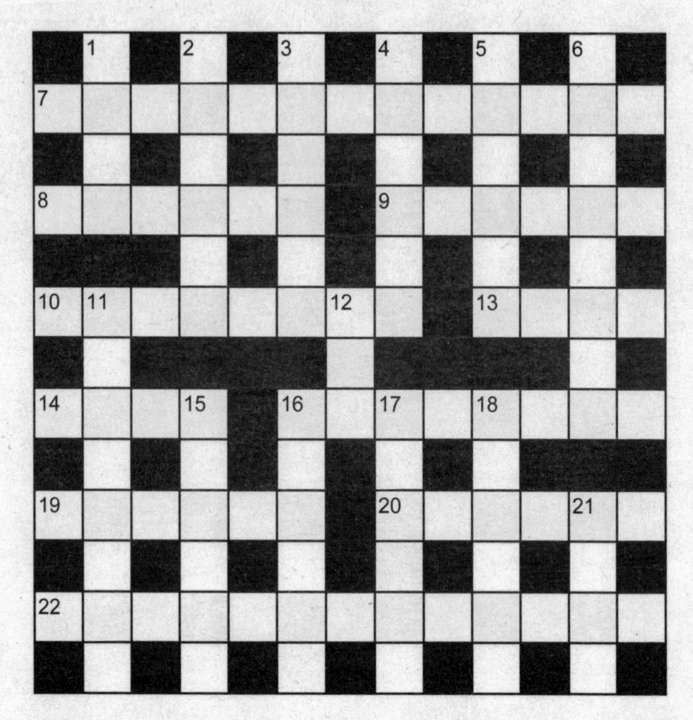

Across

7 Untiring (13)
8 Respire with difficulty (6)
9 Glowing with light (6)
10 Financially ruined (8)
13 Reflection of sound (4)
14 Type of earring (4)
16 Opposite of eastward (8)
19 Stick to a surface (6)
20 Poser; enigma (6)
22 Originality (13)

Down

1 Imperial unit (4)
2 Decorate (6)
3 Rich cake (6)
4 ___-doux: love letter (6)
5 Socially awkward (6)
6 Conclusive argument (8)
11 Evading (8)
12 Type of statistical chart (3)
15 Written in verse (6)
16 Beetle that damages grain (6)
17 Cover or conceal (6)
18 Broadly (6)
21 Slot (anag) (4)

PUZZLE 298

1		2		3	■	4		5		6		7
	■		■		■		■		■		■	
8							■	9				
	■		■		■		■		■	■	■	
10				■	11					12		
	■		■	13	■		■		■		■	■
14						■	15					16
■	■		■		■	17	■		■		■	
18								■	19			
	■	■	■		■		■	20	■		■	
21		22			■	23						
	■		■		■		■		■		■	
24							■	25				

Across

1 Wishes for (5)
4 Frenzied (7)
8 Assistant (7)
9 Gold block (5)
10 Small narrow opening (4)
11 Progresses (8)
14 Gives in (6)
15 Part of the eye (6)
18 Discard (8)
19 Midge (4)
21 Male relation (5)
23 Sets out on a journey (7)
24 Diplomatic building (7)
25 Republic in the Middle East (5)

Down

1 Gossip (7)
2 Conspicuous (9)
3 Island of the Inner Hebrides (4)
4 Where crops are grown (6)
5 One who stirs up trouble (8)
6 Label (3)
7 Gives as a reference (5)
12 Riddle (9)
13 Anxiousness (8)
16 Skilled worker (7)
17 Exclusively (6)
18 Unit of energy (5)
20 Skilfully; adeptly (4)
22 Taxi (3)

PUZZLE 299

Across

1 Make physically stronger (11)
9 Respond to (5)
10 Space or interval (3)
11 Tight; taut (5)
12 Employer (5)
13 Immature (8)
16 Scatter upon impact (8)
18 Parts of the cerebrum (5)
21 Strong lightweight wood (5)
22 Pen point (3)
23 Foolishly credulous (5)
24 Coming close to (11)

Down

2 Alfresco (4-3)
3 Long speeches (7)
4 Rents out (6)
5 Trench (5)
6 Big cat (5)
7 Type of weather system (11)
8 Fitting (11)
14 Tragedy by Shakespeare (7)
15 Eg a resident of Rome (7)
17 Surface film; coating (6)
19 Type of jazz (5)
20 Acoustic detection system (5)

PUZZLE 300

Across

1 Derives the benefits (5)
4 Easy shots or catches (in sport) (7)
8 Pig's foot (7)
9 Insurgent or revolutionary (5)
10 Ark builder (4)
11 Country in NE Africa (8)
14 Dwells in (6)
15 Flowers arranged in a ring (6)
18 Not usual (8)
19 So be it (4)
21 Many times (5)
23 Challenges the truth of (7)
24 Royal attendant (7)
25 Heavy noble gas (5)

Down

1 Round building (7)
2 Lack of ethics or principles (9)
3 Badger's home (4)
4 Squirt (6)
5 Third in order (8)
6 Decline (3)
7 Latin American dance; sauce (5)
12 Northern grouse (9)
13 Novice (8)
16 Involving active participation (5-2)
17 Gingerly (6)
18 Worship (5)
20 The highest point (4)
22 19th Greek letter (3)

SOLUTIONS

1

C	O	D	E		D	O	C	K	Y	A	R	D
O		E		A		R		A		L		I
M	E	L	A	N	I	N		L	I	F	T	S
P		H		N		A		E		A		A
A	M	I	G	O		T	W	I	R	L	E	D
N				U		E		D		F		V
I	S	L	A	N	D		S	O	N	A	T	A
O		O		C		L		S				N
N	O	W	H	E	R	E		C	L	I	N	T
A		L		M		A		O		C		A
B	R	I	D	E		N	I	P	P	I	N	G
L		F		N		T		E		N		E
E	L	E	C	T	R	O	N		A	G	E	D

2

	P	R	E	M	O	N	I	T	I	O	N	
F		O		O		E		R		P		B
R		O		P	U	R	G	E		E	T	A
A	E	S	O	P		V		A		R		T
G		T		I		E		T	O	A	S	T
M	E	E	K	N	E	S	S					L
E		R		G				G		V		E
N					S	H	R	U	G	O	F	F
T	I	M	E	S		O		A		L		I
A		I		E		N		R	O	U	T	E
R	U	G		W	I	E	L	D		B		L
Y		H		E		S		E		L		D
	S	T	A	R	S	T	U	D	D	E	D	

3

E	M	B	E	D		F	I	N	A	L	L	Y
G		A		O		E		E		E		O
O	C	C	L	U	D	E		U	R	G	E	D
T		K		R		L		R				E
I	D	L	E		A	E	R	O	F	O	I	L
S		I		M		R		T		P		
M	A	G	P	I	E		L	I	K	E	L	Y
		H		D		C		C		R		I
E	N	T	A	N	G	L	E		T	A	M	E
M				I		A		D		T		L
A	X	I	N	G		S	T	U	D	I	E	D
I		N		H		S		P		N		E
L	E	N	G	T	H	Y		E	G	G	E	D

4

	C		D		A		F		U		P	
B	E	M	O	A	N		A	R	N	O	L	D
	L		U		C		L		I		A	
G	L	I	B		H	E	L	P	M	A	T	E
			L		O		S		A		Y	
O	B	S	E	R	V	E		A	G	A	P	E
	R		C		Y		C		I		U	
T	I	G	H	T		H	A	R	N	E	S	S
	S		E		M		R		A			
S	T	A	C	C	A	T	O		T	I	N	Y
	L		K		R		U		I		I	
B	E	R	E	T	S		S	A	V	I	N	G
	S		D		H		E		E		E	

5

D	A	N	C	E	R		S	T	A	N	Z	A
	R		O		A		Y		B		O	
G	R	O	W		G	A	R	R	I	S	O	N
	O		S		E		I		D			
S	W	I	L	L		I	N	T	E	N	S	E
	R		I		S		G				P	
C	O	M	P	L	E	M	E	N	T	A	R	Y
	O				R		S		W		I	
S	T	E	E	P	E	N		B	E	I	N	G
			X		N		L		L		K	
U	N	T	I	M	E	L	Y		F	O	L	K
	I		T		L		R		T		E	
F	L	A	S	H	Y		E	X	H	O	R	T

6

N	O	M	A	D		E	N	L	I	S	T	S
O		O		A		X		I		A		T
T	I	T	A	N	I	C		S	T	Y	L	E
I		H		E		E		T				E
O	W	E	D		E	S	T	E	E	M	E	D
N		A		R		S		N		I		
S	E	T	T	E	R		J	E	T	S	A	M
		E		P		S		D		B		I
M	A	N	F	U	L	L	Y		B	E	A	N
I				B		I		O		H		E
T	R	O	L	L		C	E	N	T	A	U	R
R		A		I		E		U		V		A
E	F	F	E	C	T	S		S	P	E	L	L

7

P	L	A	N	S		C	A	T	F	I	S	H
R		V		P		L			U		I	
O		I		I		A		A	S	K	E	W
O	R	D	I	N	A	R	Y		I		G	
F		I		N		E		L	O	W	E	R
R	E	T	R	E	A	T	S		N			E
E		Y		R				P		A		A
A			S		A	C	C	O	R	D	E	D
D	E	I	T	Y		O		A		V		I
	N		R		L	U	N	C	H	E	O	N
A	V	O	I	D		N		H		R		E
	O		D			T		E		T		S
S	Y	N	E	R	G	Y		R	O	S	E	S

8

O	V	E	R	T	U	R	E		I	C	O	N
U		M		R		E				L		O
Z	E	B	R	A		M	A	R	R	I	E	S
O		A		D		A				N		E
		R		E		R	O	B	B	I	N	G
T	O	K	A	M	A	K		O		C		A
R				A				A				Y
U		F		R		O	P	T	I	O	N	S
F	R	A	N	K	E	D		H		C		
F		C				D		O		T		E
L	I	T	T	E	R	S		U	N	A	R	M
E		O				O		S		N		U
S	U	R	F		I	N	T	E	G	E	R	S

9

H	A	S	H		C	R	E	D	I	T	O	R
O		C		T		E		I		H		E
N	U	R	S	I	N	G		S	T	E	A	M
O		E		T		I		A		M		O
R	O	W		T		O		G	R	A	N	T
B				L	I	N	E	R		S		E
L		H		E				E		K		C
A		A		T	H	O	S	E				O
C	O	M	M	A		U		A		R	O	N
K		B		T		T		B		E		T
M	O	U	N	T		P	A	L	A	V	E	R
A		R		L		U		E		U		O
N	E	G	L	E	C	T	S		D	E	L	L

10

R	U	N	N	E	R	U	P		R	H	Y	S
I		I		X		N		S		O		T
C	O	P	Y	C	A	T		T	I	B	I	A
H		S		H		I		R		B		R
			H	A	R	D	B	O	I	L	E	D
A		S		N		Y		N		I		U
S	M	U	D	G	E		A	G	E	N	T	S
S		N		E		I		W		G		T
E	A	S	T	A	N	G	L	I	A			
S		H		B		U		L		O		A
S	H	A	W	L		A	L	L	E	G	E	D
E		D		E		N		E		L		A
S	U	E	T		D	A	Y	D	R	E	A	M

11

I	V	A	N		R	O	M	A	N	T	I	C
N		P		C		U		U		O		L
C	A	R	T	O	O	N		T	E	M	P	I
O		I		U		C		H		B		V
N	O	L	I	N		E	Y	E	S	O	R	E
V				T		S		N		L		A
E	X	U	D	E	S		S	T	R	A	I	N
N		N		R		C		I				D
I	N	D	E	P	T	H		C	U	R	S	E
E		Y		O		A		A		A		R
N	T	I	N	I		N	O	T	I	C	E	S
C		N		N		C		E		E		O
E	I	G	H	T	E	E	N		B	R	A	N

12

L	I	G	H	T	I	N	G		E	C	R	U
U		R		E		E				O		N
L	O	O	M	S		E	P	I	C	U	R	E
U		U		T		D				G		N
		C		A		E	N	G	L	A	N	D
A	S	H	A	M	E	D		E		R		I
M				E				N				N
B		U		N		J	E	E	R	I	N	G
R	I	S	O	T	T	O		R		S		
O		A				S		A		R		T
S	U	B	V	E	R	T		L	E	A	C	H
I		L				L		L		E		U
A	X	E	D		R	E	C	Y	C	L	E	S

13

S	C	A	L	E	D		C	R	A	B	B	Y
	L		U		O		O		L		I	
L	O	A	M		G	A	M	B	L	I	N	G
	S		B		E		M		E			
D	E	L	A	Y		B	U	R	Y	I	N	G
	K		G		A		N				O	
U	N	C	O	M	P	L	A	I	N	I	N	G
	I				P		L		E		P	
S	T	I	L	T	O	N		P	E	E	R	S
			O		I		Z		D		O	
P	R	O	V	I	N	C	E		L	O	F	T
	A		E		T		B		E		I	
T	W	I	S	T	S		U	P	D	A	T	E

14

D	A	C	T	Y	L		A		L		B	
E		L			A	P	P	E	A	R	E	D
B	O	A			P		P		U		H	
U		M	I	S	S	A	L		R	U	E	D
N		M			E		I		E		S	
K	A	Y	A	K		D	E	F	A	C	T	O
			P		H		D		T			
A	D	A	P	T	E	D		D	E	P	O	T
	E		A		A		D			E		H
A	J	A	R		L	O	A	N	E	R		I
	E		E		T		I			I	A	N
A	C	A	N	T	H	U	S			S		G
	T		T		Y		Y	A	C	H	T	S

15

	M	A	N	U	F	A	C	T	U	R	E	
D		S		N		K		U		I		A
I		K		I	V	I	E	S		F	I	N
S	T	A	F	F		M		K		L		O
O		N		I		B		S	K	E	I	N
B	A	C	H	E	L	O	R					Y
E		E		D				W		U		M
D					M	A	C	H	I	S	M	O
I	T	E	M	S		P		I		U		U
E		N		A		P		P	U	R	R	S
N	I	T		B	L	E	E	P		P		L
T		R		R		A		E		E		Y
	T	Y	P	E	W	R	I	T	E	R	S	

16

C	O	S	Y		S	P	R	A	Y	I	N	G
H		W		H		E		M		N		O
O	R	I	G	I	N	S		B	E	R	Y	L
R		N		N		E		I		O		D
E	R	G		D		T		D	R	A	P	E
O				Q	U	A	K	E		D		N
G		B		U				X		S		J
R		E		A	B	O	U	T				U
A	L	D	E	R		R		R		B	O	B
P		B		T		A		O		O		I
H	A	U	T	E		C	O	U	N	S	E	L
E		G		R		L		S		O		E
R	E	S	I	S	T	E	D		I	N	C	E

17

	I	R	R	E	V	O	C	A	B	L	E	
F		E		N		B		R		A		U
A		D		T	I	L	D	E		R	U	N
C	O	W	E	R		O		N		G		N
T		I		E		N		A	N	O	D	E
F	A	N	D	A	N	G	O					C
I		G		T				S		C		E
N					A	M	B	U	S	H	E	S
D	O	D	G	Y		O		S		O		S
I		O		I		S		P	A	R	K	A
N	I	P		E	L	A	T	E		I		R
G		E		L		I		C		Z		Y
	S	Y	N	D	I	C	A	T	I	O	N	

18

C	A	K	E		N	E	B	R	A	S	K	A
A		A		D		M		E		C		N
P	A	R	V	E	N	U		C	H	A	R	T
A		A		L				O		L		E
C	O	N	V	I	N	C	I	N	G	L	Y	
I				B		L		S		O		P
T	I	C		E	R	U	P	T		P	R	O
Y		A		R		N		I				L
	S	T	R	A	I	G	H	T	A	W	A	Y
C		C		T				U		A		G
O	C	H	R	E		F	A	T	E	F	U	L
D		U		L		E		E		E		O
A	P	P	L	Y	I	N	G		F	R	E	T

19

B	A	R	I	T	O	N	E		O	C	H	E
R		O		O		O				A		S
A	U	D	I	T		R	E	M	O	V	E	S
S		E		T		M				E		A
		N		E		A	R	I	D	I	T	Y
L	I	T	E	R	A	L		N		N		I
I				I				T				S
G		E		N		I	N	E	X	A	C	T
H	E	X	A	G	O	N		R		G		
T		C				S		A		A		P
E	L	E	V	A	T	E		L	O	S	E	R
S		E				C		I		S		A
T	I	D	Y		S	T	E	A	D	I	L	Y

20

P	E	E	L	S		D	I	S	A	R	M	S
L		N		U		E			V		A	
A		S		C		F		B	E	A	N	S
C	O	U	S	C	O	U	S		R		O	
E		I		E		S		S	T	A	R	R
M	I	N	I	S	T	E	R		S			E
E		G		S				D		R		I
N			A		O	B	S	I	D	I	A	N
T	E	A	M	S		U		S		T		S
	M		O		O	B	S	T	R	U	C	T
S	P	I	E	D		B		O		A		A
	T		B			L		R		L		T
S	Y	N	A	P	S	E		T	A	S	T	E

21

S	U	P	P	O	R	T	S		S	N	U	B
O		R		T		U		P		U		R
F	E	A	T	H	E	R		R	E	T	R	O
A		M		E		P		E		R		A
			B	R	A	I	N	C	H	I	L	D
P		V		W		N		O		E		W
O	C	E	L	O	T		A	G	E	N	D	A
T		R		R		T		N		T		Y
B	A	T	T	L	E	S	H	I	P			
E		E		D		H		T		P		F
L	I	B	E	L		I	N	I	T	I	A	L
L		R		Y		R		O		C		E
Y	E	A	R		S	T	A	N	D	A	R	D

22

R	I	L	L	S		B	O	O	S	T	E	D
E		A		T		A			U		L	
C		S		Y		N		D	R	O	V	E
E	T	H	O	L	O	G	Y		V		I	
I		I		I		L		G	E	E	S	E
V	A	N	I	S	H	E	S		Y			S
I		G		H				S		B		T
N			F		Z	U	C	C	H	I	N	I
G	R	E	A	T		S		H		Z		M
	O		I		P	A	N	O	R	A	M	A
O	V	E	R	S		G		O		R		T
	E		L			E		L		R		O
P	R	A	Y	E	R	S		S	H	E	E	R

23

M	I	N	G		M	A	L	A	Y	S	I	A
I		O		C		N		S		A		P
S	W	O	L	L	E	N		T	R	U	M	P
M		K		O		U		R		S		R
A	S	S	E	T		A	V	O	C	A	D	O
N				H		L		N		G		P
A	M	U	L	E	T		C	A	R	E	E	R
G		P		S		B		U				I
E	A	R	T	H	L	Y		T	H	E	T	A
M		I		O		L		I		N		T
E	L	G	A	R		I	N	C	E	N	S	E
N		H		S		N		S		I		L
T	O	T	T	E	R	E	D		E	S	P	Y

24

L	A	M	I	N	A		P		I		F	
E		A			S	L	A	N	D	E	R	S
A	F	T			K		R		O		I	
P		U	P	R	E	A	R		L	O	G	S
E		R			D		O		A		H	
D	E	E	M	S		S	T	A	T	U	T	E
			A		B		S		R			
P	A	P	Y	R	U	S		T	Y	S	O	N
	C		O		R		T			E		I
T	H	O	R		S	P	H	E	R	E		B
	I		E		A		U			S	O	B
A	N	G	S	T	R	O	M				A	L
	G		S		Y		B	R	O	W	S	E

25

U	N	D	O		J	A	P	A	N	E	S	E
N		E		C		G		R		N		N
S	A	B	B	A	T	H		R	E	G	A	L
Y		A		T		A		A		L		I
M	E	R	G	E		S	E	N	D	I	N	G
P				R		T		G		S		H
A	C	C	E	P	T		R	E	D	H	O	T
T		O		I		F		M				E
H	A	G	G	L	E	R		E	L	T	O	N
E		N		L		I		N		R		M
T	I	A	R	A		N	E	T	L	I	K	E
I		T		R		G		S		B		N
C	H	E	S	S	M	E	N		B	E	L	T

26

A	N	E	M	O	N	E		D		I	R	K
	A			P		V	E	I	N	S		A
U	M	B	R	A	G	E		P		S		R
	I			Q		N		S	A	U	N	A
U	B	I	Q	U	I	T	Y			I		O
	I			E		S		P		N		K
C	A	T	T	L	E		B	R	O	G	U	E
O		R		Y		P		O			N	
N		I			W	I	L	D	F	I	R	E
C	A	R	E	T		L		I			O	
I		E		I		L	I	G	H	T	L	Y
S		M	E	D	I	A		A			L	
E	K	E		E		R	E	L	A	P	S	E

27

D	O	M	E		M	A	S	S	E	U	R	S
O		O		H		N		U		R		I
U	N	C	L	O	A	K		B	A	G	E	L
B		H		M		L		S		E		V
L	O	A		E		E		C	A	N	O	E
E				L	A	T	E	R		C		R
C		A		E				I		Y		J
R		M		S	H	E	E	P				U
O	P	E	N	S		C		T		P	U	B
S		R		N		L		I		R		I
S	L	I	C	E		A	X	O	L	O	T	L
E		C		S		I		N		X		E
R	E	A	B	S	O	R	B		H	Y	P	E

28

	F	A	M	I	L	I	A	R	I	T	Y	
E		N		L		M		O		E		S
X		A		L	A	P	E	L		R	U	M
P	I	T	O	N		A		L		S		I
E		O		E		R		S	P	E	N	T
C	A	M	P	S	I	T	E					H
T		Y		S				D		A		E
A					O	F	F	E	N	D	E	R
T	A	C	O	S		O		C		J		E
I		A		O		R		A	M	U	S	E
O	F	F		F	A	M	E	D		D		N
N		E		I		A		E		G		S
	E	S	T	A	B	L	I	S	H	E	D	

29

C	A	S	E	Y		F	I	S	T	F	U	L
A		T		U		A		O		O		I
S	P	R	E	A	D	S		R	O	B	I	N
T		O		N		T		C				E
O	N	L	Y		D	E	S	E	R	V	E	D
F		L		S		N		R		O		
F	E	I	N	T	S		W	E	A	L	T	H
		N		I		S		R		U		E
R	E	G	U	L	A	T	E		I	N	C	A
E				E		A		E		T		R
E	X	A	C	T		L	A	Z	I	E	S	T
D		L		T		K		R		E		E
S	U	I	T	O	R	S		A	P	R	O	N

30

C	L	O	I	S	T	E	R		S	P	I	N
O		V		L		X		E		L		O
P	R	E	T	E	X	T		L	E	A	R	N
Y		N		E		O		E		C		S
			A	P	P	R	E	C	I	A	T	E
T		E		W		T		T		R		N
R	A	S	C	A	L		G	R	A	D	E	S
I		C		L		T		I		S		E
C	R	A	N	K	S	H	A	F	T			
Y		L		I		R		Y		L		S
C	H	A	I	N		I	R	I	D	I	U	M
L		T		G		L		N		M		U
E	V	E	R		F	L	A	G	R	A	N	T

31

C	L	A	P		S	I	D	E	S	T	E	P
O		L		C		D		C		W		R
N	A	I	R	O	B	I		C	H	I	N	O
S		B		N		O		E		S		G
T	H	I	E	F		M	O	N	I	T	O	R
R				E		S		T		E		E
U	N	P	A	C	K		P	R	I	D	E	S
C		A		T		E		I				S
T	U	R	N	I	P	S		C	A	P	R	I
I		A		O		T		I		L		V
O	R	G	A	N		E	X	T	R	E	M	E
N		O		E		E		Y		A		L
S	Y	N	D	R	O	M	E		S	T	A	Y

32

P	U	M	A		T	U	S	S	O	C	K	S
R		O		B		P		U		L		T
O	U	T	C	R	O	P		P	I	E	C	E
D		I		O		I		E		A		W
U	N	F	L	A	T	T	E	R	I	N	G	
C				D		Y		N		E		B
E	X	P	E	C	T		H	A	I	R	D	O
S		E		A		T		T				D
	C	O	N	S	T	I	T	U	E	N	C	Y
C		N		T		S		R		U		W
H	A	I	T	I		S	O	A	N	D	S	O
E		E		N		U		L		G		R
R	E	S	I	G	N	E	D		J	E	R	K

33

	S		A		M		C		E		B	
P	A	E	D	I	A	T	R	I	C	I	A	N
	G		V		K		I		H		C	
D	E	L	E	T	E		S	T	O	R	K	S
			R		D		P		E		S	
E	M	O	T	I	O	N	S		D	R	I	P
	U					A					D	
F	L	I	T		O	B	S	E	S	S	E	S
	B		H		U		P		A			
R	E	G	R	E	T		E	X	T	R	A	S
	R		O		L		E		U		V	
T	R	I	A	L	A	N	D	E	R	R	O	R
	Y		T		W		S		N		N	

34

	P		D		S		S		E		L	
S	L	E	E	V	E		P	U	M	M	E	L
	E		T		A		O		B		V	
F	A	R	E		G	A	R	N	E	R	E	D
			R		U		E		L		R	
B	R	A	M	B	L	E		C	L	E	A	R
	E		I		L		L		I		G	
S	C	A	N	S		B	O	L	S	T	E	R
	L		A		A		Z		H			
S	U	I	T	A	B	L	E		M	A	T	E
	S		I		A		N		E		A	
H	E	R	O	I	C		G	E	N	T	L	E
	S		N		K		E		T		K	

35

S	A	C	K		M	O	C	C	A	S	I	N
O		A		N		I		O		I		E
L	I	N	G	U	A	L		U	L	T	R	A
E		D		R				N		D		P
C	R	O	S	S	S	E	C	T	I	O	N	
I				E		A		R		W		I
S	H	E		R	A	S	P	Y		N	U	T
M		X		Y		E		W				E
	S	H	A	R	P	S	H	O	O	T	E	R
O		O		H				M		E		A
P	E	R	K	Y		W	H	A	T	N	O	T
U		T		M		E		N		T		E
S	U	S	P	E	N	D	S		U	S	E	S

36

A	F	A	R		M	E	D	I	O	C	R	E
B		T		S		I		N		H		A
R	O	T	T	I	N	G		C	O	I	N	S
A		I		G		H		O		A		T
S	E	C	O	N	D	T	O	N	O	N	E	
I				I		Y		V		T		P
V	I	L	I	F	Y		M	E	R	I	N	O
E		O		I		M		N				N
	C	O	N	C	L	U	S	I	V	E	L	Y
C		P		A		S		E		N		T
O	R	I	O	N		C	A	N	A	S	T	A
M		N		C		A		T		U		I
B	A	G	U	E	T	T	E		F	E	E	L

37

	B		U		A		H		S		S	
M	A	S	S	A	C	H	U	S	E	T	T	S
	K		U		C		S		N		E	
Q	U	A	R	T	O		H	A	S	T	E	N
			E		S		U		O		R	
O	V	E	R	S	T	E	P		R	E	A	R
	I					A					G	
A	L	P	S		S	U	B	O	R	D	E	R
	L		T		A		E		A			
C	A	V	E	A	T		H	A	V	I	N	G
	G		W		I		A		A		A	
M	E	T	E	O	R	O	L	O	G	I	S	T
	S		D		E		F		E		H	

38

	P	L	A	N	T	A	T	I	O	N	S	
R		I		O		D		D		A		M
E		M		U	S	U	R	Y		D	R	E
S	L	I	N	G		L		L		I		A
I		T		H		T		L	A	R	K	S
G	R	E	A	T	E	S	T					U
N		D		S				S		B		R
A					T	H	E	O	R	I	S	E
T	O	D	D	Y		O		P		T		M
I		E		A		T		R	E	U	S	E
O	R	B		H	Y	D	R	A		M		N
N		U		O		O		N		E		T
	S	T	R	O	N	G	P	O	I	N	T	

39

H	O	S	T		G	O	L	D	F	I	S	H
Y		L		C		V		E		C		A
P	L	U	M	A	G	E		C	R	E	E	L
E		R		N		R		O		P		F
R	I	P		T		D		N	E	I	G	H
C				A	L	O	N	G		C		E
R		A		N				E		K		A
I		V		K	U	D	O	S				R
T	W	I	C	E		A		T		K	I	T
I		G		R		H		A		N		E
C	O	N	G	O		L	I	N	S	E	E	D
A		O		U		I		T		E		L
L	I	N	E	S	M	A	N		P	L	O	Y

40

	O		A		B		A		P		S	
C	H	A	C	H	A		S	E	A	D	O	G
	I		C		S		L		N		U	
P	O	L	O		H	Y	A	C	I	N	T	H
			M		F		N		C		H	
P	O	M	P	O	U	S		A	S	H	E	S
	U		A		L		C		T		R	
S	T	O	N	E		S	O	A	R	I	N	G
	C		I		S		R		I			
C	O	M	M	U	T	E	R		C	O	R	N
	M		E		A		U		K		E	
F	E	N	N	E	L		P	R	E	L	I	M
	S		T		L		T		N		N	

41

M	A	I	L	S		P	I	T	F	A	L	L
A		N		K		I		O		L		A
S	E	T	T	E	E	S		I	D	E	A	S
T		H		W		T		L				E
I	C	E	S		C	O	N	S	U	M	E	R
F		D		M		N		O		A		
F	L	A	G	O	N		I	M	A	G	E	S
		R		N		H		E		N		C
M	A	K	E	O	V	E	R		W	E	I	R
A				C		R		S		S		A
I	M	P	E	L		O	P	E	N	I	N	G
Z		A		E		E		E		U		G
E	X	P	O	S	E	S		R	U	M	M	Y

42

	R	E	C	O	M	M	E	N	D	E	D	
S		N		R		O		O		D		S
E		J		D	I	N	A	R		G	O	T
C	R	O	W	E		T		T		E		R
O		Y		A		H		H	O	R	D	E
N	E	E	D	L	E	S	S					N
D		D		S				S		T		U
C					V	I	R	T	U	O	S	O
L	E	M	M	A		N		U		D		U
A		I		N		N		C	O	D	E	S
S	A	C		T	H	A	N	K		L		L
S		R		O		T		U		E		Y
	C	O	U	N	T	E	R	P	A	R	T	

43

A	N	T	I		G	A	T	H	E	R	E	D
N		O		S		G		E		O		I
A	U	T	O	C	U	E		N	O	T	E	S
C		A		H		N		C		A		G
H	E	L	L	O		C	H	E	A	T	E	R
R				O		Y		F		E		A
O	V	E	R	L	Y		N	O	R	D	I	C
N		S		M		E		R				E
I	N	S	T	A	L	L		W	H	I	F	F
S		E		S		E		A		N		U
T	E	N	E	T		V	I	R	T	U	A	L
I		C		E		E		D		R		L
C	H	E	E	R	I	N	G		D	E	N	Y

44

C	R	A	V	E		R	E	T	R	A	C	T
O		N		M		A			U		H	
N		O		B		G		P	L	A	I	D
C	A	M	E	R	O	O	N		I		L	
I		A		O		U		K	N	O	L	L
S	O	L	O	I	S	T	S		G			I
E		Y		L				C		T		G
L			I		A	L	T	H	O	U	G	H
Y	A	W	N	S		I		A		I		T
	N		T		O	V	E	R	S	T	A	Y
A	G	R	E	E		E		M		I		E
	R		N			L		E		O		A
M	Y	S	T	E	R	Y		D	I	N	E	R

45

S	E	C	T		F	A	N	C	I	F	U	L
O		H		S		L		O		U		A
U	N	U	S	U	A	L		N	E	R	V	Y
L		R		R		E		S		L		S
M	A	N	I	P	U	L	A	T	I	O	N	
A				R		E		I		N		D
T	R	A	G	I	C		S	T	I	G	M	A
E		L		S		N		U				Y
	A	G	R	I	C	U	L	T	U	R	A	L
I		E		N		C		I		A		I
D	E	B	U	G		L	O	O	K	I	N	G
E		R		L		E		N		S		H
A	N	A	L	Y	S	I	S		L	E	F	T

46

M	I	S	T	S		M	A	T	T	H	E	W
A		U		W		E			E		L	
L		F		I		T		P	E	E	V	E
I	N	F	A	N	T	R	Y		M		E	
G		I		D		I		D	E	I	S	M
N	E	C	K	L	A	C	E		D			A
A		E		E				R		B		G
N			T		F	O	R	E	W	A	R	N
T	H	A	W	S		P		T		R		E
	O		E		A	U	T	O	C	R	A	T
A	V	I	A	N		S		U		A		I
	E		K			E		C		C		S
P	R	I	S	O	N	S		H	O	K	U	M

47

K	I	L	O		C	O	C	K	A	T	O	O
I		A		C		U		I		R		A
N	E	I	T	H	E	R		L	E	A	K	S
G		R		E				L		C		T
D	I	S	H	E	A	R	T	E	N	E	D	
O				S		O		R		R		F
M	U	D		E	L	B	O	W		Y	O	U
S		O		B		O		H				N
	I	L	L	U	S	T	R	A	T	I	O	N
A		E		R				L		D		I
B	E	F	O	G		W	H	E	E	L	I	E
U		U		E		I		S		E		S
T	O	L	E	R	A	N	T		E	D	I	T

48

S	U	D	S		T	R	A	M	W	A	Y	S
Y		W		I		E		A		R		A
C	L	E	A	N	U	P		T	A	C	K	Y
A		L		D		L		T		H		S
M	U	L	T	I	L	A	T	E	R	A	L	
O				V		Y		R		I		R
R	U	B	R	I	C		P	O	N	C	H	O
E		A		D		C		F				L
	T	H	O	U	G	H	T	F	U	L	L	Y
A		R		A		O		A		O		P
S	N	A	I	L		P	I	C	C	O	L	O
I		I		L		I		T		S		L
A	N	N	O	Y	I	N	G		D	E	F	Y

49

	D	I	S	S	I	P	A	T	I	O	N	
N		C		U		O		H		R		O
O		I		B	I	L	G	E		C	O	P
T	A	N	K	S		I		R		A		I
H		E		I		T		M	A	S	O	N
I	N	S	I	S	T	E	D					I
N		S		T				B		T		O
G					C	H	I	L	D	R	E	N
N	E	A	R	S		E		O		I		A
E		V		E		R		S	I	G	H	T
S	U	E		V	I	E	W	S		G		E
S		R		E		I		O		E		D
	A	S	T	R	O	N	O	M	E	R	S	

50

A	I	M	S		P	U	S	S	Y	C	A	T
C		A		C		N		E		A		H
C	O	M	P	O	S	E		L	I	E	G	E
I		B		N		A		F		S		S
D	R	A	G	S		S	T	I	M	U	L	I
E				I		Y		N		R		X
N	I	C	E	S	T		S	T	R	A	I	T
T		A		T		A		E				H
P	U	P	P	E	T	S		R	I	F	T	S
R		A		N		S		E		O		E
O	R	B	I	T		I	N	S	U	L	I	N
N		L		L		G		T		I		S
E	V	E	R	Y	O	N	E		Z	O	N	E

51

S	C	O	U	R		R	E	L	A	T	E	D
T		D		E		H		R		B		
A		Y		U		I		S	T	O	O	D
R	E	S	O	N	A	N	T		E		N	
B		S		I		A		F	R	A	Y	S
O	V	E	R	F	I	L	L		Y			H
A		Y		Y				D		M		U
R			P		T	O	N	E	D	E	A	F
D	A	L	E	S		P		M		L		F
	L		E		M	E	M	O	R	I	A	L
C	O	Y	L	Y		R		T		S		I
	U		E			A		I		S		N
A	D	D	R	E	S	S		C	R	A	I	G

52

T	R	A	I	T		S	A	D	D	L	E	S
R		B		A		O		I		O		W
E	T	H	I	C	A	L		P	A	T	I	O
M		O		K		E		L				O
O	G	R	E		E	M	B	O	L	D	E	N
R		R		S		N		M		E		
S	T	E	P	P	E		D	A	N	C	E	D
		N		L		S		T		E		O
E	N	T	H	A	L	P	Y		O	P	E	N
A				S		L		J		T		K
R	E	A	C	H		E	M	O	T	I	V	E
N		T		E		E		S		O		Y
S	T	E	T	S	O	N		H	A	N	D	S

53

M	E	T	E		S	A	T	C	H	E	L	S
A		I		I		I		O		N		A
N	O	M	I	N	A	L		N	I	G	E	R
I		E		S				S		U		K
F	O	R	T	U	I	T	O	U	S	L	Y	
E				F		E		L		F		E
S	I	R		F	I	R	S	T		S	O	Y
T		E		E		R		A				E
	O	V	E	R	C	A	U	T	I	O	U	S
C		A		A				I		X		I
A	D	L	I	B		B	O	O	T	L	E	G
T		U		L		Y		N		I		H
O	P	E	N	E	Y	E	D		S	P	O	T

54

	O		I		G		B		S		C	
U	N	I	N	H	A	B	I	T	A	B	L	E
	T		S		R		S		T		I	
H	O	S	T	E	L		T	H	R	O	N	G
			E		I		R		A		G	
G	A	Z	P	A	C	H	O		P	A	I	N
	V						U				N	
M	I	N	I		R	E	D	E	S	I	G	N
	A		N		A		E		Q			
S	T	A	T	E	S		B	O	U	G	H	T
	R		A		P		R		E		O	
D	I	S	C	R	E	D	I	T	A	B	L	E
	X		T		D		S		L		Y	

55

	B		S		R		S		D		L	
G	R	I	E	V	E		P	R	E	F	I	X
	I		L		D		A		P		F	
H	O	O	F		H	O	R	S	E	M	E	N
			R		E		S		N		S	
M	U	S	I	C	A	L		A	D	O	P	T
	N		G		D		H		A		A	
W	I	G	H	T		G	I	B	B	O	N	S
	V		T		C		G		I			
T	E	L	E	P	A	T	H		L	A	T	E
	R		O		V		W		I		U	
A	S	T	U	T	E		A	T	T	E	S	T
	E		S		S		Y		Y		K	

56

T	E	A	M		C	H	A	P	L	A	I	N
H		L		H		I		O		D		O
R	E	A	D	E	R	S		L	A	D	L	E
E		R		A				E		E		S
N	A	M	E	D	R	O	P	P	I	N	G	
O				Q		S		O		D		F
D	I	G		U	N	I	T	S		A	X	E
Y		R		A		E		I				C
	H	O	R	R	O	R	S	T	R	U	C	K
I		W		T				I		M		L
S	E	N	S	E		G	O	O	D	B	Y	E
L		U		R		U		N		E		S
A	P	P	O	S	I	T	E		E	R	R	S

57

C	U	R	E		I	N	T	R	E	P	I	D
O		U		S		E		I		A		O
W	H	I	S	T	L	E		O	W	I	N	G
S		N		U		S		D		N		S
L	O	S	T	P	R	O	P	E	R	T	Y	
I				E		N		J		E		B
P	A	C	I	F	Y		L	A	U	R	E	L
S		U		A		A		N				U
	D	I	S	C	O	N	T	E	N	T	E	D
A		R		T		I		I		A		G
Q	U	A	S	I		M	I	R	A	C	L	E
U		S		O		A		O		I		O
A	B	S	E	N	T	L	Y		E	T	O	N

58

I	N	F	E	C	T		P	L	A	S	M	A
N		R		O		B		E		O		R
S	T	A	M	M	E	R		S		R		I
I		C		F		O	Y	S	T	E	R	S
D	I	T	T	Y		A		O				E
E		U				D		N	O	R	M	S
		R		N	I	C	K	S		E		
C	R	E	D	O		A				T		L
O				T		S		A	B	A	T	E
S	O	L	V	E	N	T		P		I		G
M		A		P		E	X	P	E	N	S	E
O		M		A		R		L		E		N
S	T	A	N	D	S		H	Y	B	R	I	D

59

G	A	S	P		S	P	U	R	I	O	U	S
L		Y		I		A		E		R		E
O	A	R	S	M	E	N		D	R	I	L	L
R		I		P		A		I		G		F
I	N	A	N	E		M	A	S	C	A	R	A
F				R		A		T		M		W
I	M	P	I	S	H		T	R	O	I	K	A
C		L		O		S		I				R
A	G	A	I	N	S	T		B	U	L	G	E
T		T		A		R		U		A		N
I	N	E	P	T		O	U	T	S	I	Z	E
O		A		O		L		E		R		S
N	E	U	T	R	A	L	S		A	D	D	S

60

R	A	Z	O	R	S		D		W		D	
O		E			P	O	W	D	E	R	E	D
W	E	B			E		I		L		P	
I		R	E	G	A	I	N		L	O	O	N
N		A			R		D		T		S	
G	U	S	T	S		A	L	L	O	W	E	D
			A		B		E		D			
C	O	U	R	S	E	D		S	O	B	E	R
	D		R		N		A			O		O
A	I	R	Y		E	N	S	U	E	D		O
	O		I		F		P			E	L	K
T	U	R	N	P	I	K	E			G		I
	S		G		T		N	E	G	A	T	E

61

	C		A		R		T		T		E	
G	O	O	D	N	A	T	U	R	E	D	L	Y
	O		D		G		R		N		O	
S	T	R	U	N	G		N	A	D	I	N	E
			C		E		E		O		G	
O	F	F	E	N	D	E	D		N	E	A	R
	R					W					T	
L	A	M	B		R	E	S	T	O	R	E	D
	G		L		U		A		C			
A	M	O	U	R	S		F	E	T	T	E	R
	E		F		H		E		A		L	
I	N	O	F	F	E	N	S	I	V	E	L	Y
	T		S		S		T		E		A	

62

O	R	C	A		E	P	I	S	O	D	E	S
R		Y		T		U		U		I		I
D	U	N	G	E	O	N		B	I	P	E	D
E		I		M				S		L		E
R	E	C	U	P	E	R	A	T	I	O	N	
I				E		I		A		M		C
N	A	G		R	A	D	O	N		A	D	O
G		E		A		G		T				M
	P	O	S	T	M	E	R	I	D	I	E	M
P		R		U				A		D		E
A	U	G	U	R		C	U	T	D	O	W	N
I		I		E		O		E		L		C
R	O	A	D	S	I	D	E		A	S	H	E

63

C	H	L	O	R	I	N	E		M	A	G	I
U		O		E		O				B		N
F	L	I	N	G		R	E	P	R	O	O	F
F		T		I		W				U		L
		E		S		A	L	B	A	N	I	A
F	I	R	S	T	L	Y		A		D		T
L				E				C				E
A		U		R		A	R	T	I	S	T	S
M	I	T	O	S	I	S		E		A		
E		O				S		R		F		S
N	E	P	T	U	N	E		I	M	A	G	O
C		I				N		U		R		N
O	V	A	L		S	T	A	M	P	I	N	G

64

A	G	A	R		S	H	E	E	P	I	S	H
R		M		E		A		A		N		E
C	H	I	F	F	O	N		V	I	G	I	L
H		T		F		G		E		R		T
I	C	Y		O		U		S	T	E	V	E
T				R	A	P	I	D		S		R
E		P		T				R		S		S
C		R		L	I	M	B	O				K
T	R	O	V	E		I		P		W	E	E
U		V		S		N		P		R		L
R	E	E	F	S		C	H	E	R	O	O	T
A		R		L		E		R		T		E
L	O	B	B	Y	I	S	T		B	E	E	R

65

H	O	O	K	S		G	O	D	H	E	A	D
A		R		T		H		I		L		E
L	E	I	S	U	R	E		A	D	M	I	T
L		G		N		T		P				E
W	H	I	M		S	T	R	A	N	G	E	R
A		N		B		O		S		L		
Y	E	A	R	L	Y		S	O	L	A	C	E
		T		U		E		N		M		F
P	R	E	T	E	N	D	S		L	O	A	F
I				C		I		F		R		O
P	I	T	C	H		C	L	A	M	O	U	R
E		O		I		T		I		U		T
S	C	R	I	P	T	S		R	E	S	T	S

66

H	I	K	E		P	R	O	D	U	C	E	R
A		E		Q		I		E		O		E
R	E	B	O	U	N	D		S	I	N	G	E
D		A		I				P		G		L
C	A	B	I	N	E	T	M	A	K	E	R	
O				T		H		I		A		S
P	E	N		E	R	R	O	R		L	E	A
Y		E		S		U		I				U
	P	A	R	S	I	M	O	N	I	O	U	S
A		T		E				G		N		A
P	A	E	A	N		S	E	L	L	I	N	G
S		S		C		E		Y		O		E
E	N	T	R	E	N	C	H		I	N	K	S

67

O	R	G	A	N	Z	A		C		A	R	C
	E			O		S	T	O	R	M		O
I	M	P	E	T	U	S		L		P		N
	O			I		U		A	C	H	E	S
O	V	E	R	C	O	M	E			O		I
	E			I		E		W		R		S
A	D	V	E	N	T		T	H	W	A	R	T
C		I		G		A		A			E	
E		B			E	M	I	T	T	I	N	G
T	H	R	E	E			I		E		E	
O		A		M		D	I	V	E	R	G	E
N		N	A	M	E	S		E			E	
E	A	T		Y		T	A	R	N	I	S	H

68

A	C	R	E		G	I	U	S	E	P	P	E
I		A		D		N		H		L		Y
R	E	D	E	E	M	S		A	G	A	T	E
S		I		M		E		R		C		D
P	H	O	T	O	G	R	A	P	H	E	R	
A				N		T		T		B		T
C	O	A	R	S	E		B	O	N	O	B	O
E		T		T		T		N				D
	S	H	O	R	T	S	I	G	H	T	E	D
Y		L		A		E		U		E		L
O	V	E	R	T		T	R	E	A	D	L	E
G		T		E		S		D		D		R
A	B	E	R	D	E	E	N		G	Y	M	S

69

E	L	S	E		P	L	A	T	O	O	N	S
N		W		O		A		O		U		A
C	H	I	E	F	L	Y		G	E	T	U	P
R		R		F				E		P		S
O	B	L	I	T	E	R	A	T	I	O	N	
A				H		A		H		S		N
C	O	W		E	A	G	L	E		T	O	O
H		I		R		E		R				N
	U	N	R	E	A	S	O	N	A	B	L	E
S		D		C				E		E		V
P	H	O	T	O		U	P	S	U	R	G	E
A		W		R		M		S		T		N
R	E	S	I	D	U	A	L		S	H	U	T

70

	C	O	M	P	U	N	C	T	I	O	N	
F		V		L		I		H		T		S
A		E		A	N	G	E	R		T	O	T
S	T	R	U	T		G		E		E		O
T		J		I		L		W	I	R	E	R
F	L	O	U	N	D	E	R					Y
O		Y		G				C		C		T
R					O	M	N	I	V	O	R	E
W	A	G	O	N		A		T		R		L
A		A		A		L		A	T	O	L	L
R	E	F		I	L	I	A	D		N		E
D		F		L		G		E		E		R
	P	E	R	S	O	N	A	L	I	T	Y	

71

C	O	S	T		A	C	A	D	E	M	I	A
U		N		C		A		E		A		U
C	R	A	S	H	E	D		M	I	N	E	D
U		R		R		D		O		U		I
M	U	L	T	I	L	I	N	G	U	A	L	
B				S		E		R		L		E
E	X	C	I	T	E		C	A	U	S	E	D
R		L		M		A		P				U
	N	O	N	A	L	C	O	H	O	L	I	C
S		S		S		C		I		A		A
T	H	E	M	E		E	N	C	R	U	S	T
O		S		V		N		S		G		O
P	A	T	I	E	N	T	S		C	H	A	R

72

B	L	U	R		C	U	L	D	E	S	A	C
E		S		A		N		I		L		O
A	Q	U	I	F	E	R		S	H	E	E	N
S		R		O		E		C		I		S
T	A	P	E	R		S	T	O	P	G	A	P
O				E		T		U		H		I
F	I	E	S	T	A		C	R	I	T	I	C
B		X		H		E		A				U
U	N	I	C	O	R	N		G	U	S	T	O
R		T		U		I		I		I		U
D	O	I	N	G		G	E	N	E	S	I	S
E		N		H		M		G		A		L
N	I	G	H	T	C	A	P		C	L	A	Y

73

	C		C		P		A		C		C	
C	O	L	L	A	R		V	I	O	L	A	S
	R		O		E		A		N		L	
F	E	E	S		M	A	I	N	T	A	I	N
			E		I		L		R		G	
S	T	U	D	I	E	S		B	O	N	U	S
	U		C		R		G		V		L	
B	R	A	I	N		A	R	S	E	N	A	L
	N		R		W		I		R			
I	C	E	C	R	E	A	M		S	W	A	B
	O		U		D		A		I		W	
S	A	Y	I	N	G		C	E	A	S	E	D
	T		T		E		E		L		S	

74

	R	E	S	T	R	I	C	T	I	O	N	
R		N		A		N		O		U		E
O		V		D	E	F	E	R		S	U	N
C	H	E	E	P		A		C		T		T
K		L		O		M		H	A	S	T	E
T	R	O	L	L	E	Y	S					R
H		P		E				S		O		T
E					C	R	I	T	E	R	I	A
B	E	L	O	W		E		A		A		I
O		A		A		F		F	U	T	O	N
A	N	T		S	T	U	F	F		I		E
T		H		T		S		E		O		R
	N	E	V	E	R	E	N	D	I	N	G	

75

R	E	P	E	A	T	S		R		C	U	P
	A			L		I	D	A	H	O		O
P	R	E	V	A	I	L		S		N		W
	N			R		I		H	A	T	E	D
C	E	R	A	M	I	C	S			A		E
	R			I		A		A		I		R
A	S	C	E	N	T		M	E	A	N	L	Y
I		L		G		S		S			A	
M		O			N	E	U	T	R	I	N	O
L	A	S	S	O		X		H			O	
E		E		D		T	R	E	M	O	L	O
S		U	N	D	U	E		T			I	
S	A	P		S		T	E	E	M	I	N	G

76

I	N	H	E	R	E		T	R	U	D	G	E
N		O		U		E		E		O		M
J	U	M	B	L	E	D		A		O		B
E		E		E		U	N	D	E	R	G	O
C	A	S	E	D		C		I				S
T		P				A		L	I	O	N	S
		U		P	U	T	T	Y		B		
P	A	N	D	A		I				S		I
U				T		O		P	R	E	E	N
T	O	R	S	I	O	N		I		R		U
S		O		E		A	L	L	O	V	E	R
C		T		N		L		O		E		E
H	E	A	L	T	H		S	T	A	S	I	S

77

R	E	T	S	I	N	A		B		D	O	E
	X			M		S	O	L	V	E		P
S	P	A	N	I	S	H		O		F		I
	L			T		O		C	L	I	N	G
P	O	D	I	A	T	R	Y			N		R
	R			T		E		D		E		A
H	E	N	D	O	N		W	I	S	D	O	M
E		O		R		E		S			A	
C		S			P	L	E	A	S	U	R	E
T	I	T	A	N		A		G			S	
A		R		E		P	E	R	F	U	M	E
R		I	R	O	N	S		E			A	
E	E	L		N		E	L	E	G	A	N	T

78

C	E	N	T	S		J	U	P	I	T	E	R
O		O		T		U		U		O		A
L	O	R	R	I	E	S		R	E	M	I	T
U		M		R		T		V				T
M	E	A	D		A	L	L	E	Y	W	A	Y
N		L		W		Y		Y		I		
S	P	I	N	A	L		C	O	O	L	E	R
		T		R		W		R		L		E
R	H	Y	T	H	M	I	C		M	I	D	I
I				O		D		G		N		S
G	I	V	E	R		E	N	R	A	G	E	S
I		I		S		S		I		L		U
D	E	E	P	E	S	T		T	H	Y	M	E

79

B	O	W	L		M	A	N	D	I	B	L	E
A		O		R		S		I		I		E
C	O	R	N	E	A	S		N	O	V	E	L
K		M		C		O		N		O		S
D	I	S	C	O	U	R	T	E	O	U	S	
A				L		T		R		A		E
T	A	T	T	L	E		E	J	E	C	T	S
E		H		E		I		A				S
	C	I	R	C	U	M	S	C	R	I	B	E
C		N		T		P		K		C		N
H	A	N	O	I		E	L	E	G	I	A	C
E		E		O		L		T		L		E
F	I	R	M	N	E	S	S		D	Y	E	S

80

	E		G		B		A		I		A	
E	X	T	R	A	O	R	D	I	N	A	R	Y
	P		O		O		M		V		G	
C	O	B	W	E	B		I	C	A	R	U	S
			T		O		R		D		M	
B	A	T	H	R	O	B	E		E	D	E	N
	E					O					N	
I	R	I	S		O	P	P	O	S	I	T	E
	A		T		P		R		P			
U	T	M	O	S	T		I	N	L	A	W	S
	I		R		I		O		I		A	
C	O	M	M	E	M	O	R	A	T	I	V	E
	N		Y		A		Y		S		E	

81

L	U	P	I	N	E		B		S		B	
O		R			V	O	L	A	T	I	L	E
W	O	O			E		A		A		A	
K		P	L	A	N	E	T		N	E	R	D
E		E			S		A		D		E	
Y	A	R	N	S		U	N	W	I	N	D	S
			O		S		T		N			
S	T	A	S	H	E	D		A	G	E	N	T
	H		T		N		P			N		I
B	O	O	R		A	L	L	O	U	T		T
	R		I		T		U			R	A	T
B	A	L	L	R	O	O	M			A		E
	X		S		R		B	U	M	P	E	R

82

	O	C	C	U	P	A	T	I	O	N	S	
O		A		N		C		N		I		I
U		P		L	O	C	A	L		N	U	N
T	I	T	R	E		E		A		E		E
O		I		A		S		W	A	S	P	S
F	E	V	E	R	I	S	H					T
B		E		N				G		L		I
O					B	O	T	U	L	I	S	M
U	N	D	E	R		R		E		Q		A
N		O		I		A		S	Q	U	I	B
D	I	D		T	O	N	G	S		E		L
S		G		E		G		E		U		E
	N	E	W	S	R	E	A	D	E	R	S	

83

C	L	U	E		D	A	N	D	R	U	F	F
R		N		H		R		I		N		A
Y	T	T	R	I	U	M		S	P	A	I	N
P		I		E		A		C		W		T
T	I	L	E	R		D	I	O	R	A	M	A
O				O		A		N		R		S
G	A	R	A	G	E		A	S	P	E	C	T
R		O		L		A		O				I
A	N	A	L	Y	S	T		L	O	G	I	C
P		S		P		O		A		R		A
H	A	T	C	H		N	E	T	B	A	L	L
E		E		I		A		E		N		L
R	I	D	I	C	U	L	E		I	D	L	Y

84

F	A	C	E		B	O	N	H	O	M	I	E
I		H		O		D		Y		I		A
E	Q	U	A	B	L	E		P	I	C	K	S
F		M		S				O		R		E
D	I	S	S	E	R	T	A	T	I	O	N	
O				R		O		H		B		T
M	R	S		V	I	N	C	E		E	R	A
S		H		A		I		T				K
	H	A	U	T	E	C	U	I	S	I	N	E
S		C		I				C		T		H
T	O	K	Y	O		C	H	A	R	A	D	E
E		L		N		A		L		L		E
P	L	E	A	S	I	N	G		D	Y	E	D

85

M	O	S	S		C	O	M	P	O	S	E	R
A		O		H		U		R		U		O
N	E	R	V	O	U	S		E	X	P	E	L
U		R		U		T		M		P		L
F	R	Y		S		E		E	L	O	P	E
A				E	N	D	E	D		S		R
C		S		O				I		E		C
T		H		F	A	C	E	T				O
U	S	U	A	L		H		A		B	A	A
R		D		O		E		T		R		S
E	I	D	E	R		E	V	E	R	E	T	T
R		E		D		S		D		V		E
S	T	R	E	S	S	E	D		J	E	E	R

86

S	P	E	N	D	I	N	G		E	D	A	M
W		V		I		O		I		R		A
A	L	I	A	S	E	S		N	O	U	N	S
T		L		S		H		T		M		S
			F	A	V	O	U	R	A	B	L	E
P		V		T		W		A		E		U
L	E	A	D	I	N		A	N	N	A	L	S
A		U		S		F		S		T		E
C	A	L	I	F	O	R	N	I	A			
A		T		I		E		G		F		D
B	E	I	G	E		S	T	E	R	I	L	E
L		N		D		C		N		E		A
E	R	G	O		M	O	U	T	H	F	U	L

87

	T		I		G		B		S		S	
C	O	N	S	T	E	L	L	A	T	I	O	N
	G		S		M		I		U		C	
L	A	Z	U	L	I		T	A	C	T	I	C
			E		N		H		C		A	
W	I	L	D	L	I	F	E		O	R	B	S
	M						I				L	
O	M	A	R		G	R	U	M	B	L	E	S
	I		E		R		N		E			
I	N	H	A	L	E		P	I	C	N	I	C
	E		R		E		A		O		N	
E	N	T	E	R	T	A	I	N	M	E	N	T
	T		D		S		D		E		S	

88

T	R	U	S	T		S	W	I	M	M	E	R
A		N		O		A		M		O		A
C	O	W	B	O	Y	S		P	I	P	I	T
T		O		K		H		E				E
F	U	R	Y		P	E	L	L	U	C	I	D
U		L		B		S		L		H		
L	E	D	G	E	R		R	E	W	I	N	D
		L		R		A		D		R		I
S	T	Y	L	I	S	T	S		B	O	N	O
A				B		T		T		P		C
L	I	T	H	E		A	D	I	P	O	S	E
V		I		R		C		E		D		S
O	B	E	L	I	S	K		R	H	Y	M	E

89

O	P	E	R	A	T	E	D		A	M	I	R
A		N		N		M				A		E
K	A	F	K	A		I	N	T	E	R	I	M
S		O		L		N				L		E
		L		G		E	M	P	T	I	E	D
M	I	D	T	E	R	M		O		N		I
A				S				R				E
S		V		I		L	A	T	C	H	E	S
T	R	E	A	C	L	E		F		E		
E		N				E		O		Y		M
R	A	I	N	B	O	W		L	O	D	G	E
E		C				A		I		A		S
D	E	E	P		S	Y	N	O	N	Y	M	S

90

C	A	S	K		T	I	N	C	T	U	R	E
H		A		I		V		O		N		U
A	P	L	E	N	T	Y		N	I	C	E	R
N		O		T				V		L		O
C	O	N	C	E	N	T	R	A	T	E	D	
E				R		U		L		A		H
R	H	O		M	I	D	G	E		R	I	O
Y		P		E		O		S				R
	M	I	S	D	I	R	E	C	T	I	O	N
S		N		I				E		N		B
E	V	I	T	A		C	O	N	V	E	N	E
M		O		T		A		T		R		A
I	N	N	U	E	N	D	O		I	T	E	M

91

	B		H		M		P		Z		U	
F	E	L	I	C	I	T	A	T	I	O	N	S
	T		C		L		S		P		I	
F	A	S	C	I	A		T	Y	P	I	F	Y
			U		N		R		E		O	
R	H	A	P	S	O	D	Y		D	O	R	M
	E					U					M	
I	R	A	N		Y	O	U	N	G	E	S	T
	A		U		E		N		E			
P	L	U	R	A	L		S	T	R	I	P	E
	D		S		I		E		M		E	
I	R	R	E	C	O	V	E	R	A	B	L	E
	Y		S		W		N		N		T	

92

E	M	E	R	G	E		P	E	E	L	E	D
L		F		O		C		T		A		E
I	N	F	E	R	N	O		E		V		M
J		L		S		N	A	R	R	A	T	E
A	C	U	T	E		F		N				A
H		E				I		A	R	G	O	N
		N		M	O	D	E	L		U		
S	E	T	T	O		E				E		S
T				R		N		B	U	R	S	T
Y	E	A	R	D	O	T		A		N		A
L		E		A		L	I	N	D	S	A	Y
E		O		N		Y		A		E		E
D	E	N	O	T	E		P	L	A	Y	E	D

93

S	A	M	E		S	E	T	B	A	C	K	S
N		O		P		R		R		H		O
O	U	T	D	O	O	R		E	D	I	F	Y
W		T		S		A		A		G		A
B	R	E	A	T	H	T	A	K	I	N	G	
A				G		A		T		O		S
L	O	U	V	R	E		C	H	A	N	G	E
L		R		A		A		R				A
	M	A	I	D	O	F	H	O	N	O	U	R
M		N		U		L		U		L		C
E	L	I	Z	A		A	N	G	U	I	S	H
S		U		T		M		H		V		E
H	A	M	M	E	R	E	D		F	E	N	D

94

N	A	N	C	Y		M	I	S	T	A	K	E
O		O		E		O			O		I	
M		I		L		L		S	M	I	L	E
I	N	S	U	L	A	T	E		T		N	
N		I		O		E		B	O	A	S	T
A	L	L	O	W	I	N	G		M			E
T		Y		S				D		I		R
E			I		D	E	S	I	G	N	E	R
S	P	A	D	E		X		S		T		I
	L		I		O	P	P	O	N	E	N	T
K	A	Z	O	O		O		W		N		O
	N		C			S		N		D		R
R	E	C	Y	C	L	E		S	A	S	S	Y

95

M	A	R	E		C	A	P	I	T	A	L	S
E		A		A		L		R		Q		E
T	A	N	K	F	U	L		R	O	U	G	E
A		G		T				E		A		S
P	R	E	R	E	Q	U	I	S	I	T	E	
H				R		N		I		I		I
O	R	C		T	A	I	L	S		C	O	N
R		U		H		T		T				T
	D	I	S	O	B	E	D	I	E	N	C	E
A		S		U				B		E		R
S	T	I	N	G		E	N	L	I	V	E	N
K		N		H		R		E		E		E
S	H	E	L	T	E	R	S		A	R	I	D

96

C	L	A	W		E	M	B	A	T	T	L	E
O		N		A		U		C		H		X
N	O	N	P	L	U	S		C	H	I	M	P
S		E		P		I		I		E		A
C	O	X		H		N		D	I	V	A	N
I				A	R	G	U	E		E		S
O		M		N				N		S		I
U		A		U	N	F	I	T				V
S	T	R	U	M		R		A		R	O	E
N		S		E		E		L		U		N
E	S	H	E	R		E	C	L	I	P	S	E
S		A		I		Z		Y		E		S
S	E	L	E	C	T	E	D		B	E	D	S

97

S	I	L	K		S	U	P	P	O	S	E	D
T		I		D		S		E		E		I
R	U	B	B	I	S	H		R	A	T	E	S
A		Y		S		E		A		T		C
T	R	A	M	P		R	A	M	B	L	E	R
E				L		S		B		E		E
G	L	O	B	A	L		P	U	N	D	I	T
I		V		C		S		L				I
C	L	E	M	E	N	T		A	U	D	I	O
A		R		M		U		T		R		N
L	E	A	S	E		P	R	O	R	A	T	A
L		L		N		I		R		K		R
Y	U	L	E	T	I	D	E		D	E	W	Y

98

M	I	S	S	O	U	R	I		H	E	R	B
O		P		V		E				D		E
O	Z	O	N	E		A	E	R	O	B	I	C
R		N		R		C				E		A
		G		N		T	E	N	D	R	I	L
C	R	E	D	I	T	S		U		G		M
A				G				I				E
P		T		H		D	I	S	U	S	E	D
T	R	U	S	T	E	E		A		U		
I		M				M		N		B		N
V	I	B	R	A	T	O		C	O	U	P	E
E		L				T		E		R		V
S	P	E	D		S	E	N	S	I	B	L	E

99

	B	U	T	T	E	R	F	L	I	E	S	
M		N		O		E		E		M		S
I		A		P	I	V	O	T		I	L	K
R	A	I	D	S		I		U		T		Y
R		D		P		V		P	O	S	E	S
O	N	E	L	I	N	E	R					C
R		D		N				Z		G		R
I					O	K	L	A	H	O	M	A
M	O	D	E	M		L		M		N		P
A		I		O		A		B	A	D	G	E
G	E	E		P	I	X	I	E		O		R
E		G		E		O		Z		L		S
	N	O	N	S	E	N	S	I	C	A	L	

100

	K		J		S		K		C		E	
I	N	C	O	N	C	E	I	V	A	B	L	Y
	E		V		A		N		V		E	
T	E	D	I	U	M		G	R	O	O	V	Y
			A		P		L		R		A	
I	D	E	N	T	I	T	Y		T	U	T	U
	R				A						E	
K	I	N	D		O	P	T	I	M	I	S	T
	Z		O		R		R		A			
A	Z	A	L	E	A		A	C	T	I	V	E
	L		L		T		M		R		O	
M	E	T	A	M	O	R	P	H	O	S	I	S
	D		R		R		S		N		D	

101

C	U	B	E		A	D	D	I	T	I	V	E
A		R		S		E		N		N		Y
P	R	O	M	P	T	S		C	A	C	H	E
S		A		I		I		O		I		S
I	N	D	O	C	T	R	I	N	A	T	E	
C				K		E		S		E		N
U	N	S	E	A	T		P	O	O	D	L	E
M		T		N		T		L				O
	K	I	N	D	E	R	G	A	R	T	E	N
I		R		S		I		B		U		A
S	Y	R	U	P		P	O	L	E	C	A	T
L		U		A		L		E		K		E
E	X	P	A	N	D	E	D		A	S	P	S

102

H	A	R	D		D	A	F	F	O	D	I	L
A		I		C		M		I		E		A
C	I	V	I	L	L	Y		S	I	N	G	S
I		E		E				H		I		S
E	X	T	R	A	V	A	G	A	N	Z	A	
N				R		D		N		E		G
D	A	B		S	I	D	E	D		N	O	R
A		U		I		L		C				E
	T	R	I	G	G	E	R	H	A	P	P	Y
O		R		H				I		A		N
W	A	I	S	T		C	A	P	T	U	R	E
E		T		E		O		S		S		S
S	N	O	W	D	R	O	P		S	E	T	S

103

U	R	S	A		A	M	I	C	A	B	L	E
N		T		H		A		I		U		X
P	L	A	T	E	N	S		V	O	L	G	A
A		M		A		T		I		L		G
S	I	P		D		E		L	Y	I	N	G
T				M	A	R	I	S		S		E
E		S		I				E		H		R
U		U		S	A	V	E	R				A
R	E	B	U	T		I		V		V	A	T
I		U		R		R		A		I		E
S	U	R	G	E		I	G	N	I	T	E	D
E		B		S		L		T		A		L
D	I	S	A	S	T	E	R		A	L	L	Y

104

A	S	P	E	C	T	S		Z		M	U	G
	T			H		H	E	I	D	I		U
B	U	F	F	A	L	O		N		L		N
	N			R		U		C	L	I	M	B
A	N	N	U	A	L	L	Y			T		O
	E			D		D		R		I		A
A	D	D	L	E	S		T	E	N	A	N	T
S		I		S		H		V			O	
E		S			D	E	T	E	C	T	O	R
P	A	P	A	L		N		R			D	
T		O		U		R	I	S	I	B	L	E
I		S	P	L	A	Y		E			E	
C	U	E		L		V	I	S	C	O	S	E

105

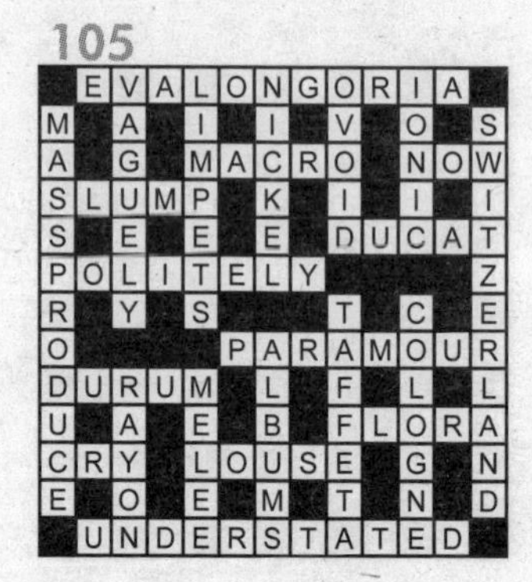

106

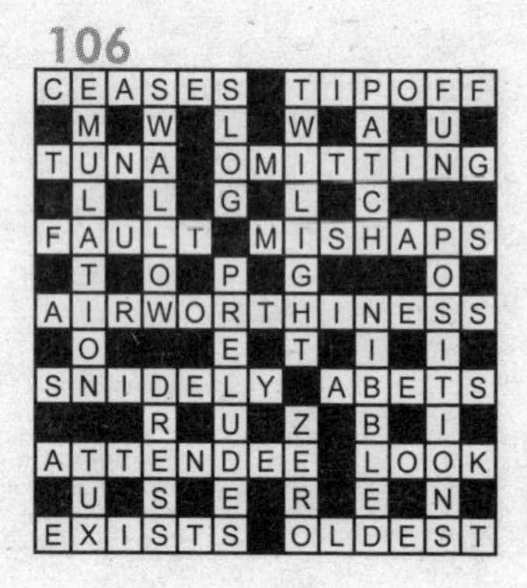

107

S	T	A	D	I	A		I		P		R	
U		U			P	A	N	T	R	I	E	S
P	E	R			I		A		I		M	
P		O	R	D	A	I	N		S	L	O	T
L		R			N		E		O		T	
Y	E	A	S	T		S	L	A	N	D	E	R
			W		B		Y		E			
A	N	G	E	L	U	S		C	R	A	N	E
	E		E		Z		M			B		X
R	U	S	T		Z	E	U	G	M	A		O
	T		E		I		S			C	U	D
H	E	L	S	I	N	K	I			U		U
	R		T		G		C	R	U	S	T	S

108

R	I	F	E		S	C	O	O	T	E	R	S
E		L		M		L		V		X		A
F	R	I	G	A	T	E		E	N	T	E	R
R		C		N		A		R		I		A
I	N	K		U		V		W	I	N	C	H
G				F	R	E	S	H		C		F
E		S		A				E		T		E
R		L		C	I	V	I	L				R
A	L	E	R	T		A		M		W	I	G
T		N		U		C		I		H		U
O	R	D	E	R		A	N	N	U	A	L	S
R		E		E		T		G		L		O
S	H	R	E	D	D	E	D		F	E	R	N

109

D	E	C	O	R	A	T	E	■	G	O	N	G
E	■	O	■	E	■	U	■	H	■	R	■	I
A	N	O	T	H	E	R	■	O	G	D	E	N
R	■	S	■	A	■	B	■	P	■	N	■	G
■	■	■	O	B	L	I	T	E	R	A	T	E
C	■	L	■	I	■	D	■	L	■	N	■	R
A	F	I	E	L	D	■	P	E	N	C	I	L
N	■	T	■	I	■	A	■	S	■	E	■	Y
B	R	E	A	T	H	L	E	S	S	■	■	■
E	■	R	■	A	■	L	■	N	■	J	■	B
R	O	A	S	T	■	U	N	E	Q	U	A	L
R	■	T	■	E	■	D	■	S	■	D	■	U
A	R	I	A	■	S	E	A	S	H	O	R	E

110

I	O	T	A	■	Y	O	U	T	H	F	U	L
N	■	W	■	I	■	L	■	R	■	A	■	E
S	W	A	R	M	E	D	■	I	S	L	E	T
E	■	I	■	P	■	■	■	G	■	L	■	S
C	O	N	V	E	N	T	I	O	N	A	L	■
U	■	■	■	R	■	H	■	N	■	C	■	S
R	U	E	■	T	O	R	S	O	■	Y	E	T
E	■	N	■	I	■	O	■	M	■	■	■	U
■	A	C	K	N	O	W	L	E	D	G	E	D
P	■	H	■	E	■	■	■	T	■	R	■	I
A	G	A	I	N	■	V	E	R	T	I	G	O
U	■	N	■	C	■	A	■	Y	■	P	■	U
L	A	T	T	E	R	L	Y	■	G	E	M	S

111

P	E	A	C	H	■	V	I	E	W	E	R	S
A	■	R	■	I	■	I	■	X	■	G	■	M
I	N	M	A	T	E	S	■	E	V	O	K	E
N	■	I	■	S	■	I	■	G	■	■	■	L
F	U	S	E	■	C	O	V	E	R	A	L	L
U	■	T	■	A	■	N	■	T	■	G	■	■
L	A	I	R	D	S	■	M	I	L	I	E	U
■	■	C	■	J	■	P	■	C	■	T	■	T
W	O	E	F	U	L	L	Y	■	R	A	K	E
O	■	■	■	T	■	A	■	S	■	T	■	N
M	A	L	T	A	■	I	V	O	R	I	E	S
E	■	O	■	N	■	N	■	A	■	O	■	I
N	E	G	A	T	E	S	■	P	A	N	E	L

112

C	A	L	L	■	A	C	O	U	S	T	I	C
O	■	I	■	M	■	E	■	N	■	R	■	H
N	U	C	L	E	A	R	■	D	R	A	M	A
T	■	I	■	L	■	I	■	E	■	V	■	R
O	U	T	D	O	■	S	Y	R	I	A	N	A
R	■	■	■	D	■	E	■	A	■	I	■	C
T	U	N	D	R	A	■	S	C	U	L	P	T
I	■	A	■	A	■	A	■	H	■	■	■	E
O	P	T	I	M	A	L	■	I	D	L	E	R
N	■	A	■	A	■	S	■	E	■	Y	■	L
I	N	S	E	T	■	A	D	V	E	R	S	E
S	■	H	■	I	■	C	■	E	■	I	■	S
T	H	A	T	C	H	E	R	■	A	C	E	S

113

D	E	R	M	I	S	■	S	■	F	■	E	■
I	■	A	■	■	E	X	P	I	R	I	N	G
A	I	D	■	■	D	■	I	■	E	■	G	■
D	■	I	M	P	A	I	R	■	S	H	I	P
E	■	U	■	■	N	■	I	■	H	■	N	■
M	I	M	I	C	■	S	T	A	M	P	E	D
■	■	■	D	■	T	■	S	■	A	■	■	■
C	A	S	I	N	O	S	■	K	N	E	L	L
■	M	■	O	■	N	■	M	■	■	S	■	A
F	A	I	L	■	S	L	A	P	U	P	■	R
■	Z	■	E	■	U	■	N	■	■	R	A	Y
C	O	N	C	E	R	T	I	■	■	I	■	N
■	N	■	T	■	E	■	C	O	R	T	E	X

114

■	S	U	B	O	R	D	I	N	A	T	E	■
U	■	N	■	U	■	E	■	E	■	E	■	S
N	■	L	■	S	T	R	E	W	■	A	C	T
C	O	U	R	T	■	A	■	T	■	S	■	A
E	■	C	■	I	■	I	■	S	H	E	E	T
R	E	K	I	N	D	L	E	■	■	■	■	E
T	■	Y	■	G	■	■	■	P	■	B	■	L
A	■	■	■	■	A	U	D	A	C	I	T	Y
I	T	C	H	Y	■	P	■	D	■	T	■	H
N	■	O	■	E	■	L	■	D	I	T	T	O
T	A	B	■	A	M	I	N	O	■	E	■	M
Y	■	R	■	R	■	F	■	C	■	R	■	E
■	P	A	I	N	S	T	A	K	I	N	G	■

115

E	L	M	S		F	A	B	U	L	I	S	T
S		O		A		B		N		R		E
C	H	O	W	D	E	R		D	U	K	E	S
A		S		M		A		E		S		S
P	R	E	C	O	N	D	I	T	I	O	N	
A				N		E		E		M		F
D	E	C	E	I	T		S	C	H	E	M	A
E		O		S		I		T				R
	E	N	T	H	U	S	I	A	S	T	I	C
J		C		M		O		B		R		I
A	D	E	L	E		M	O	L	L	U	S	C
W		A		N		E		E		C		A
S	A	L	U	T	A	R	Y		H	E	A	L

116

B	A	S	S		C	H	I	C	K	P	E	A
E		P		E		A		O		E		G
A	R	O	U	S	A	L		I	N	T	E	R
T		O		T		V		N		I		E
I	N	F	E	R		E	N	C	L	O	S	E
F				A		S		I		L		A
I	M	M	U	N	E		A	D	V	E	R	B
C		U		G		S		E				L
A	U	S	T	E	R	E		N	O	V	A	E
T		T		M		A		T		O		N
I	R	A	T	E		M	E	A	S	U	R	E
O		N		N		A		L		C		S
N	E	G	A	T	I	N	G		W	H	Y	S

117

C	O	C	K	L	E		R		A		A	
A		H			S	E	A	T	B	E	L	T
S	P	A			S		G		U		I	
H		R	E	S	E	N	T		T	U	B	E
E		G			X		I		M		I	
W	E	E	P	Y		I	M	M	E	R	S	E
			R		B		E		N			
F	O	R	E	R	U	N		S	T	U	N	G
	N		C		R		B			R		R
H	E	R	E		G	R	A	T	E	S		E
	W		P		L		S			I	R	E
P	A	S	T	R	A	M	I			N		D
	Y		S		R		C	R	E	E	P	Y

118

F	O	P	S		M	A	N	D	A	T	E	S
O		O		D		N		I		I		A
R	I	P	P	I	N	G		C	A	M	P	S
W		U		S		L		T		P		H
A	L	P	H	A	B	E	T	I	C	A	L	
R				G		S		O		N		S
D	E	B	A	R	K		E	N	R	I	C	H
S		I		E		A		A				R
	I	N	T	E	R	F	E	R	E	N	C	E
O		O		M		R		I		O		W
B	O	C	C	E		I	C	E	C	O	L	D
O		H		N		C		S		S		L
E	V	E	N	T	U	A	L		L	E	V	Y

119

V	I	C	A	R		M	A	J	E	S	T	Y
A		A		O		Y		A		E		E
R	U	M	O	U	R	S		M	E	A	N	T
N		C		T		T		B				I
I	R	O	N		T	I	M	O	R	O	U	S
S		R		R		C		R		B		
H	E	D	G	E	S		P	E	N	N	E	D
		E		P		M		E		O		E
A	G	R	A	R	I	A	N		E	X	I	T
I				O		R		R		I		R
D	A	C	H	A		G	R	A	N	O	L	A
E		O		C		I		S		U		C
D	O	L	P	H	I	N		P	O	S	I	T

120

T	R	O	U	B	L	E	S		C	A	T	S
U		U		I		X		A		N		U
B	U	R	N	O	U	T		L	O	T	U	S
A		S		C		E		L		I		P
			C	H	A	N	G	E	A	B	L	E
A		T		E		T		M		O		N
C	R	E	A	M	Y		A	B	O	D	E	S
R		A		I		G		R		Y		E
O	C	C	A	S	I	O	N	A	L			
S		H		T		A		C		L		B
T	H	E	I	R		T	R	I	V	I	A	L
I		R		Y		E		N		A		E
C	U	S	P		H	E	D	G	E	R	O	W

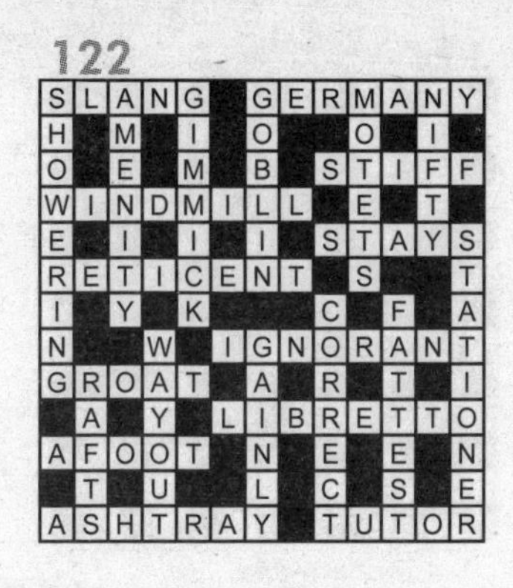

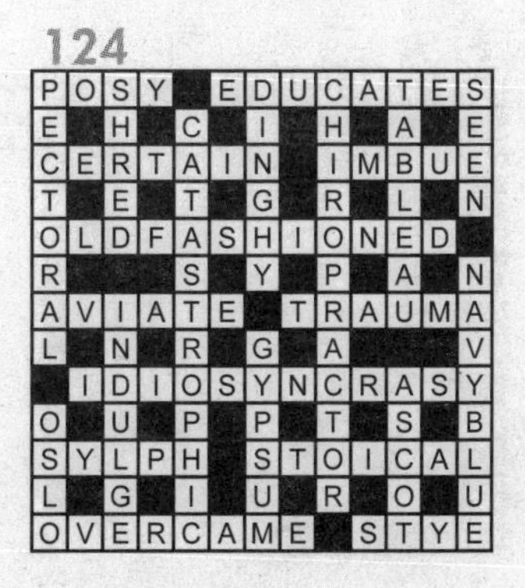

125

C	A	S	I	N	O		B		S		S	
O		L			F	L	A	T	M	A	T	E
G	N	U			F		N		A		R	
N		S	P	R	A	N	G		S	N	A	P
A		H			L		E		H		P	
C	R	Y	P	T		T	R	A	I	P	S	E
			R		W		S		N			
S	O	L	O	M	O	N		E	G	Y	P	T
	R		M		B		D			O		R
W	I	S	P		B	E	A	T	E	N		O
	G		T		L		R			D	E	W
S	I	L	L	I	E	S	T			E		E
	N		Y		D		S	P	I	R	A	L

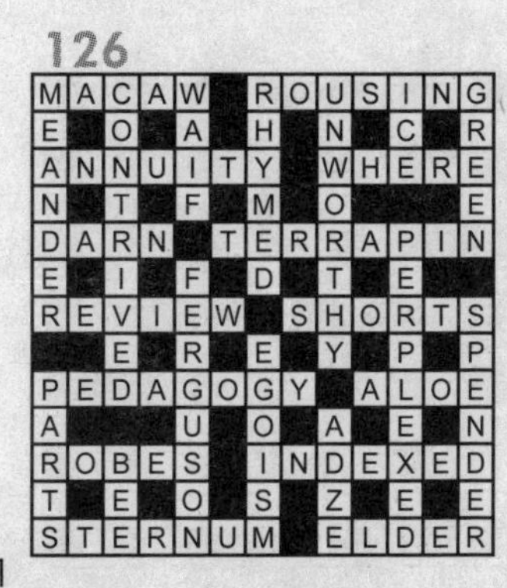

127

	D		S		S		C		B		P	
M	A	G	I	S	T	E	R	I	A	L	L	Y
	S		L		R		A		N		A	
T	H	I	E	V	E		F	I	N	I	S	H
			N		E		T		E		T	
C	A	N	T	A	T	A	S		R	E	E	F
	N					G					R	
A	T	O	M		D	A	T	A	B	A	S	E
	E		I		E		R		A			
G	L	A	Z	E	D		I	N	F	A	N	T
	O		Z		U		L		F		U	
A	P	P	L	I	C	A	B	I	L	I	T	Y
	E		E		T		Y		E		S	

128

T	R	A	S	H	Y		A	C	E	T	I	C
O		I		O		O		H		O		L
F	O	R	E	M	A	N		E		T		O
F		S		E		C	H	E	E	S	E	S
E	A	T	E	R		L		T				E
E		R				O		A	M	B	E	R
		I		R	O	U	G	H		L		
M	A	P	L	E		D				A		S
A				T		N		W	A	N	D	A
S	A	M	U	R	A	I		R		K		W
S		A		A		N	A	I	V	E	L	Y
I		R		C		E		T		T		E
F	A	T	T	E	N		L	E	S	S	E	R

129

D	E	E	P	S	E	A		W		I	L	L
	C			H		B	L	O	W	N		O
C	H	I	S	E	L	S		L		K		U
	E			E		E		F	E	W	E	R
E	L	E	C	T	R	I	C			E		D
	O			I		L		D		L		E
U	N	K	I	N	D		W	I	E	L	D	S
N		I		G		E		S			E	
E		P			I	N	S	C	R	I	B	E
A	G	L	O	W		A		O			R	
R		I		A		C	A	U	S	T	I	C
T		N	I	G	H	T		N			E	
H	U	G		E		S	A	T	I	S	F	Y

130

131

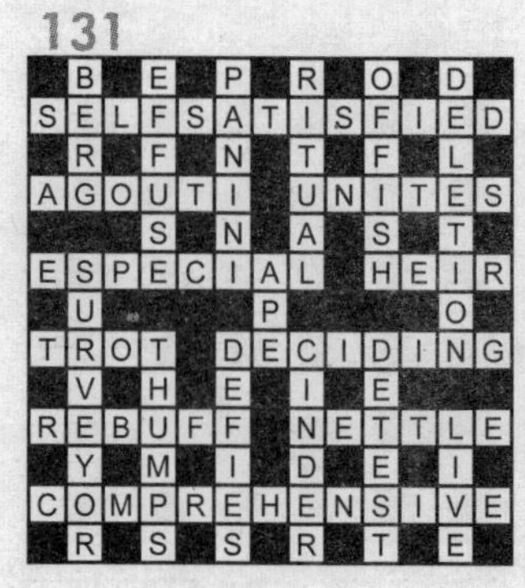

132

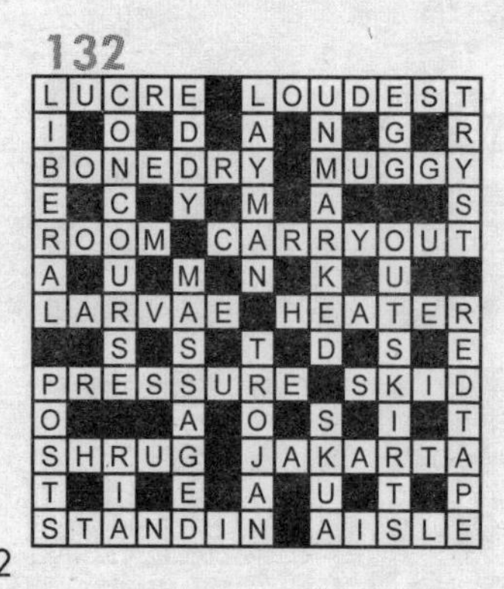

133

L	O	N	G	H	A	U	L		F	R	O	G
I		A		A		N				A		E
L	U	M	E	N		C	A	S	H	I	E	R
Y		E		D		U				S		A
		L		S		R	U	C	T	I	O	N
C	R	Y	S	T	A	L		A		N		I
O				A				V				U
N		R		N		A	M	A	L	G	A	M
F	R	E	E	D	O	M		L		A		
U		T				O		C		U		V
S	T	I	C	K	E	R		A	C	C	R	A
E		R				A		D		H		R
S	U	E	S		A	L	L	E	G	O	R	Y

134

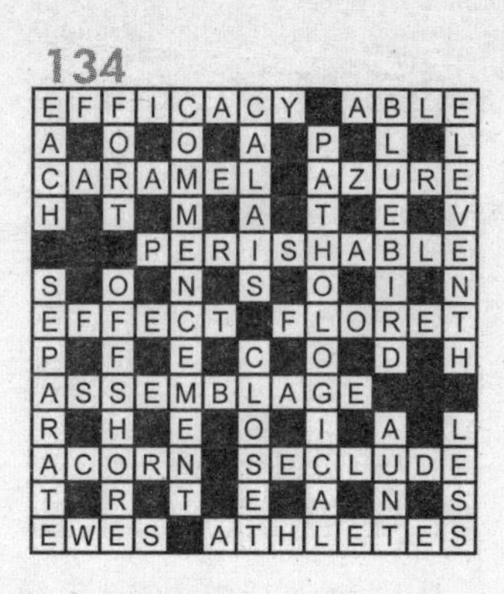

E	F	F	I	C	A	C	Y		A	B	L	E
A		O		O		A		P		L		L
C	A	R	A	M	E	L		A	Z	U	R	E
H		T		M		A		T		E		V
			P	E	R	I	S	H	A	B	L	E
S		O		N		S		O		I		N
E	F	F	E	C	T		F	L	O	R	E	T
P		F		E		C		O		D		H
A	S	S	E	M	B	L	A	G	E			
R		H		E		O		I		A		L
A	C	O	R	N		S	E	C	L	U	D	E
T		R		T		E		A		N		S
E	W	E	S		A	T	H	L	E	T	E	S

135

T	R	E	E		S	N	A	P	S	H	O	T
R		X		R		A		R		A		O
E	X	T	R	A	C	T		O	X	B	O	W
M		R		B		U		P		I		N
B	L	A	B	B	E	R	M	O	U	T	H	
L				L		E		R		A		P
E	N	T	R	E	E		S	T	A	T	O	R
D		E		R		G		I				E
	L	A	B	O	R	A	T	O	R	I	E	S
T		R		U		T		N		S		E
R	O	O	K	S		H	O	A	R	S	E	N
O		O		E		E		L		U		T
D	E	M	E	R	A	R	A		W	E	D	S

136

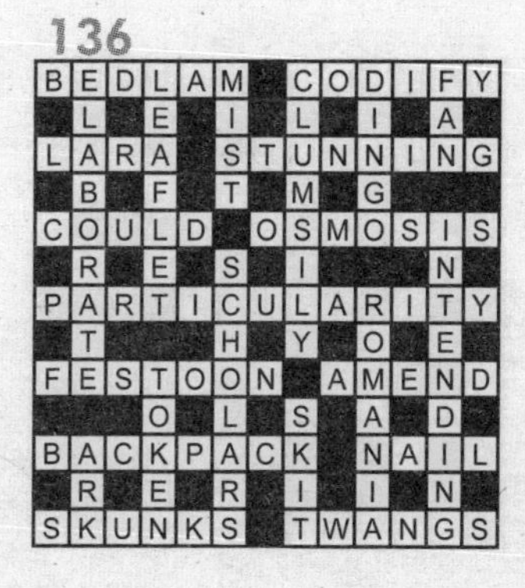

B	E	D	L	A	M		C	O	D	I	F	Y
	L		E		I		L		I		A	
L	A	R	A		S	T	U	N	N	I	N	G
	B		F		T		M		G			
C	O	U	L	D		O	S	M	O	S	I	S
	R		E		S		I				N	
P	A	R	T	I	C	U	L	A	R	I	T	Y
	T				H		Y		O		E	
F	E	S	T	O	O	N		A	M	E	N	D
			O		L		S		A		D	
B	A	C	K	P	A	C	K		N	A	I	L
	R		E		R		I		I		N	
S	K	U	N	K	S		T	W	A	N	G	S

137

P	O	L	A	N	D		S		S		S	
A		A			R	O	T	A	T	I	O	N
Y	E	W			O		O		A		U	
O		F	A	V	O	U	R		N	O	R	M
F		U			P		I		D		E	
F	I	L	M	S		S	E	C	O	N	D	S
			O		C		S		F			
P	A	U	N	C	H	Y		A	F	I	R	E
	M		I		E		A		N			X
B	A	I	T		D	U	L	C	E	T		I
	Z		I		D		O			O	P	T
C	E	N	O	T	A	P	H			N		E
	D		N		R		A	P	P	E	N	D

138

	M	O	U	N	T	A	I	N	E	E	R	
U		P		E		L		E		A		H
N		T		A	L	L	O	W		R	Y	E
D	R	I	E	R		E		E		E		A
E		C		E		Y		R	I	D	E	R
R	E	A	S	S	E	S	S					T
S		L		T				D		O		B
T					I	M	P	R	O	P	E	R
A	U	G	E	R		O		A		P		O
N		E		O		H		C	R	O	A	K
D	U	N		A	B	A	S	H		S		E
S		I		C		I		M		E		N
	N	E	T	H	E	R	L	A	N	D	S	

139

P	U	M	P		O	B	S	C	U	R	E	D
A		O		U		U		A		E		U
L	E	G	E	N	D	S		R	E	L	I	C
I		U		S				T		I		T
S	E	L	F	E	M	P	L	O	Y	E	D	
A				A		L		G		V		P
D	E	C		S	H	E	A	R		E	L	L
E		L		O		A		A				A
	C	O	R	N	I	S	H	P	A	S	T	Y
E		S		A				H		A		R
B	L	U	R	B		M	A	E	S	T	R	O
B		R		L		O		R		Y		O
S	K	E	L	E	T	O	N		C	R	A	M

140

S	I	F	T	S		T	U	S	S	L	E	S
H		O		W		A		C		I		O
A	I	R	M	A	I	L		R	E	P	E	L
K		G		M		E		I				I
I	B	E	X		U	N	A	B	A	T	E	D
N		T		M		T		B		O		
G	A	F	F	E	S		S	L	O	U	C	H
		U		T		B		E		C		U
K	A	L	A	H	A	R	I		C	H	U	M
N				O		A		K		D		E
E	A	S	E	D		C	A	N	D	O	U	R
A		A		I		E		O		W		U
D	E	D	U	C	E	D		W	I	N	K	S

141

I	N	D	I	C	T		N	A	T	T	E	R
N		E		I		H		N		A		A
J	U	M	A	N	J	I		G		X		S
U		A		C		G	A	R	N	I	S	H
R	A	N	C	H		H		I				E
E		D				P		L	A	Y	E	R
		E		A	R	R	A	Y		E		
A	D	D	E	D		O				A		B
R				J		F		V	E	R	V	E
M	A	R	C	O	N	I		O		B		I
O		O		U		L	O	W	D	O	W	N
U		L		R		E		E		O		G
R	E	L	E	N	T		F	L	A	K	E	S

142

	E		G		A		G		B		G	
I	N	C	R	E	D	U	L	O	U	S	L	Y
	D		O		S		O		R		O	
P	S	E	U	D	O		S	C	R	A	W	L
			S		R		S		O		W	
A	S	S	E	M	B	L	Y		W	O	O	F
	E					U					R	
B	R	I	G		A	G	R	O	N	O	M	Y
	E		E		D		I		O			
A	N	D	R	E	A		G	R	U	M	P	Y
	A		B		G		H		G		R	
A	D	M	I	N	I	S	T	R	A	T	O	R
	E		L		O		S		T		M	

143

	D	I	S	T	A	S	T	E	F	U	L	
P		L		A		C		T		R		A
A		L		L	O	A	C	H		G	O	D
S	U	E	D	E		L		E		E		I
S		G		N		A		R	I	S	E	N
T	R	A	I	T	O	R	S					F
H		L		S				L		M		I
E					C	O	M	E	D	O	W	N
B	U	M	P	Y		Y		V		R		I
U		A		U		S		E	L	E	C	T
C	O	Y		M	E	T	E	R		L		U
K		B		M		E		E		L		M
	D	E	H	Y	D	R	A	T	I	O	N	

144

S	H	A	M	P	O	O		E		T	O	W
	E			E		D	E	N	S	E		I
O	R	D	E	R	E	D		I		R		N
	O			S		E		D	O	M	E	D
V	I	R	T	U	O	S	I			I		I
	N			A		T		A		N		N
R	E	C	E	D	E		I	D	L	I	N	G
E		O		E		U		O			I	
P		N			S	N	I	P	P	E	T	S
L	O	V	E	D		I		T			R	
I		O		O		S	T	I	G	M	A	S
C		K	E	N	D	O		O			T	
A	G	E		E		N	A	N	N	I	E	S

145

S		M		P		N		T		B		S
T	H	I	G	H	B	O	N	E		A	S	K
O		G		A		O		N		N		A
V	E	R	G	E		D	R	O	U	G	H	T
E		A		T		L		N				I
	D	I	S	O	B	E	Y		S	P	A	N
B		N		N				I		I		G
A	W	E	D		C	A	P	S	I	Z	E	
S				F		U		O		Z		A
S	E	R	V	I	N	G		B	R	E	A	M
I		I		S		I		A		R		A
S	I	C		H	I	T	O	R	M	I	S	S
T		E		Y		E		S		A		S

146

D	U	K	E		E	G	G	S	H	E	L	L
I		O		S		R		H		S		A
S	P	A	T	U	L	A		O	P	T	I	C
T		L		B		H		R		O		K
I	N	A	P	T		A	N	T	E	N	N	A
N				E		M		C		I		D
C	O	N	T	R	A		C	I	C	A	D	A
T		I		R		S		R				I
I	N	G	R	A	T	E		C	A	S	E	S
V		E		N		A		U		A		I
E	E	R	I	E		S	E	I	S	M	I	C
L		I		A		O		T		B		A
Y	E	A	R	N	I	N	G		M	A	L	L

147

P	A	S	S		N	E	W	C	O	M	E	R
R		C		R		F		O		O		H
E	A	R	N	E	S	T		V	E	N	U	E
S		U		C				E		A		A
T	A	B	L	E	M	A	N	N	E	R	S	
I				P		L		T		C		A
G	O	O		T	Y	I	N	G		H	E	R
E		V		I		A		A				P
	D	E	M	O	N	S	T	R	A	B	L	E
S		R		N				D		R		G
K	H	A	K	I		F	E	E	D	I	N	G
I		C		S		L		N		B		I
N	A	T	A	T	I	O	N		H	E	R	O

148

A	C	A	C	I	A		J		S		B	
M		L			B	R	O	T	H	E	R	S
P	H	I			A		U		R		O	
E		C	A	E	S	A	R		E	L	K	S
R		I			E		N		D		E	
E	V	A	D	E		L	A	R	D	E	R	S
			E		B		L		E			
E	J	E	C	T	O	R		A	R	M	E	D
	A		I		R		B			A		A
C	R	O	P		E	Q	U	I	T	Y		L
	R		H		D		S			H	A	T
B	E	H	E	M	O	T	H			E		O
	D		R		M		Y	E	O	M	A	N

149

	M		U		B		U		S		C	
R	E	I	N	C	A	R	N	A	T	I	O	N
	A		B		R		A		I		M	
E	N	D	E	A	R		B	E	C	A	M	E
			N		E		L		K		A	
C	O	N	D	E	N	S	E		S	A	N	E
	U					K					D	
U	T	A	H		S	I	D	E	S	H	O	W
	S		E		T		E		M			
W	I	E	L	D	Y		B	R	O	O	C	H
	D		M		M		A		O		O	
D	E	T	E	R	I	O	R	A	T	I	O	N
	R		T		E		S		H		P	

150

R	A	D	I	U	S		B		S		S	
E		E			Q	U	A	N	T	I	T	Y
T	O	P			U		G		A		E	
I		A	I	M	I	N	G		L	I	E	D
N		R			D		A		L		R	
A	C	T	O	R		U	G	L	I	E	S	T
			I		W		E		O			
H	I	L	L	T	O	P		A	N	N	U	L
	G		I		R		S			E		Y
F	L	A	N		K	O	W	T	O	W		N
	O		E		M		E			T	A	X
M	O	U	S	S	A	K	A			O		E
	S		S		N		T	A	I	N	T	S

151

A	R	A	B	L	E		A	C	I	D	I	C
L		I		A		S		Y		E		U
P	A	R	S	N	I	P		P		M		D
I		C		C		E	A	R	R	I	N	G
N	U	R	S	E		C		E				E
E		A				T		S	T	O	O	L
		F		S	O	A	K	S		U		
P	E	T	A	L		C				T		T
U				A		U		W	E	L	S	H
R	A	D	I	C	A	L		A		I		Y
E		R		K		A	N	T	O	N	Y	M
S		O		E		R		E		E		U
T	Y	P	I	N	G		E	R	A	S	E	S

152

B	I	C	U	S	P	I	D		C	H	A	D
A		R		U		N		T		U		I
B	E	A	N	B	A	G		R	A	M	P	S
Y		G		S		E		A		P		P
			R	E	A	S	O	N	A	B	L	E
F		I		Q		T		S		A		R
L	I	N	E	U	P		S	M	O	C	K	S
A		T		E		T		I		K		E
G	R	E	E	N	H	O	U	S	E			
S		R		T		B		S		W		R
H	O	V	E	L		A	N	I	M	A	T	E
I		A		Y		G		O		I		L
P	A	L	L		D	O	W	N	P	L	A	Y

153

U	L	N	A		A	R	K	A	N	S	A	S
P		Y		M		A		D		U		I
H	A	L	C	Y	O	N		D	E	B	I	T
E		O		T				I		S		S
A	N	N	I	H	I	L	A	T	I	O	N	
V				O		U		I		I		E
A	M	P		L	I	N	G	O		L	I	V
L		R		O		G		N				A
	C	O	N	G	R	E	G	A	T	I	O	N
C		B		I				L		N		E
L	I	L	A	C		U	N	L	O	C	K	S
E		E		A		S		Y		U		C
F	A	M	I	L	I	A	R		B	R	I	E

154

H	O	N	E	S	T	L	Y		L	E	E	K
U		O		C		O				F		E
R	A	T	I	O		G	I	R	A	F	F	E
L		I		U		J				O		N
		O		N		A	L	S	O	R	A	N
K	I	N	G	D	O	M		P		T		E
I				R				A				S
L		H		E		S	I	G	N	A	L	S
O	V	E	R	L	A	P		H		L		
W		A				R		E		U		L
A	D	V	A	N	C	E		T	E	M	P	O
T		E				A		T		N		N
T	A	N	S		A	D	M	I	R	I	N	G

155

C	U	B	A		T	W	O	F	A	C	E	D
O		U		S		R		R		L		A
M	A	N	A	C	L	E		I	S	A	A	C
E		K		R		N		E		S		E
D	I	S	T	I	N	C	T	N	E	S	S	
I				P		H		D		E		L
A	D	O	P	T	S		E	L	I	S	H	A
N		V		W		G		I				R
	H	E	A	R	T	R	E	N	D	I	N	G
C		R		I		O		E		G		E
H	I	R	S	T		C	A	S	T	L	E	S
I		U		E		E		S		O		S
C	O	N	T	R	A	R	Y		M	O	T	E

156

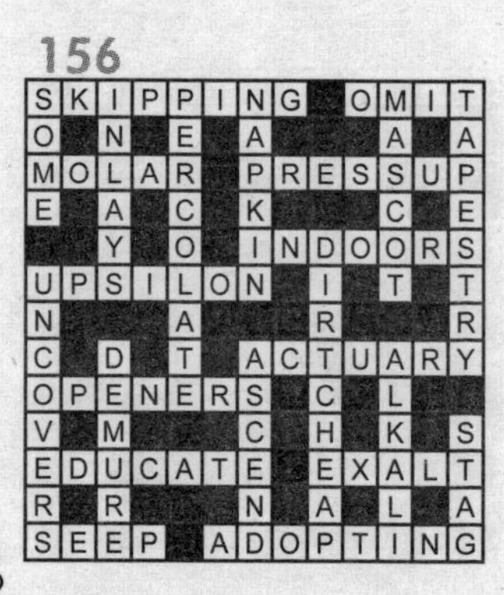

S	K	I	P	P	I	N	G		O	M	I	T
O		N		E		A				A		A
M	O	L	A	R		P	R	E	S	S	U	P
E		A		C		K				C		E
		Y		O		I	N	D	O	O	R	S
U	P	S	I	L	O	N		I		T		T
N				A				R				R
C		D		T		A	C	T	U	A	R	Y
O	P	E	N	E	R	S		C		L		
V		M				C		H		K		S
E	D	U	C	A	T	E		E	X	A	L	T
R		R				N		A		L		A
S	E	E	P		A	D	O	P	T	I	N	G

157

M	O	N	U	M	E	N	T		N	I	N	A
I		U		I		O		C		R		C
M	I	N	D	S	E	T		H	A	R	S	H
E		S		R		A		A		I		I
			C	E	N	T	I	M	E	T	R	E
S		T		P		E		P		A		V
O	D	O	U	R	S		V	I	R	T	U	E
U		M		E		G		O		E		R
T	R	A	N	S	P	L	A	N	T			
H		H		E		A		S		E		E
P	L	A	I	N		S	C	H	E	M	E	D
A		W		T		S		I		I		G
W	A	K	E		S	Y	M	P	A	T	H	Y

158

	G		I		D		M		J		S	
A	L	U	M	N	A		E	V	I	C	T	S
	U		P		I		N		G		U	
T	E	A	R		S	L	U	G	G	A	R	D
			A		I		S		E		G	
S	P	E	C	I	E	S		C	R	I	E	R
	L		T		S		F		Y		O	
N	O	W	I	N		C	O	U	P	O	N	S
	D		C		M		O		O			
I	D	E	A	L	I	S	T		K	I	L	N
	I		B		D		M		E		U	
K	N	O	L	L	S		E	R	R	O	R	S
	G		E		T		N		Y		K	

159

P	A	C	E		O	U	T	C	L	A	S	S
R		R		D		S		R		R		E
E	P	I	T	O	M	E		O	P	I	N	E
P		M		M				S		Z		D
A	P	P	R	E	H	E	N	S	I	O	N	
R				S		M		C		N		E
E	O	N		T	A	B	O	O		A	W	L
S		I		I		E		U				E
	O	B	S	C	U	R	A	N	T	I	S	M
C		B		A				T		N		E
A	L	L	O	T		M	A	R	I	L	Y	N
L		E		E		O		Y		A		T
M	A	R	K	D	O	W	N		B	Y	E	S

160

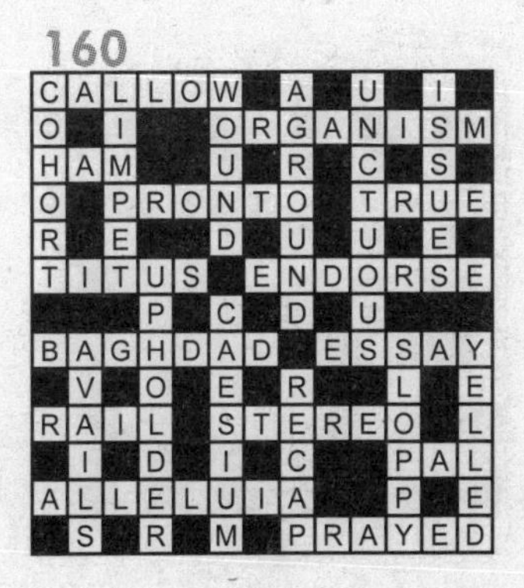

C	A	L	L	O	W		A		U		I	
O		I			O	R	G	A	N	I	S	M
H	A	M			U		R		C		S	
O		P	R	O	N	T	O		T	R	U	E
R		E			D		U		U		E	
T	I	T	U	S		E	N	D	O	R	S	E
			P		C		D		U			
B	A	G	H	D	A	D		E	S	S	A	Y
	V		O		E		R			L		E
R	A	I	L		S	T	E	R	E	O		L
	I		D		I		C			P	A	L
A	L	L	E	L	U	I	A			P		E
	S		R		M		P	R	A	Y	E	D

161

G	A	L	I	L	E	O		Y		M	A	D
	S			E		S	C	U	B	A		A
T	S	U	N	A	M	I		L		R		Y
	A			P		E		E	D	I	C	T
V	I	N	E	Y	A	R	D			M		I
	L			E		S		F		B		M
I	S	O	B	A	R		P	A	L	A	C	E
N		S		R		T		I			Y	
E		T			P	R	O	T	E	I	N	S
R	E	R	U	N		A		H			I	
T		I		I		D	E	F	U	N	C	T
I		C	Y	C	L	E		U			A	
A	S	H		K		S	O	L	I	D	L	Y

162

S	T	A	D	I	U	M	S		C	O	M	E
A		W		N		A		R		P		V
F	L	A	T	T	E	N		E	L	I	D	E
E		Y		E		T		P		N		R
			I	N	F	I	D	E	L	I	T	Y
W		S		S		S		T		O		D
R	E	T	A	I	L		S	I	E	N	N	A
I		R		F		C		T		S		Y
G	R	A	V	Y	T	R	A	I	N			
G		P		I		E		V		T		F
L	U	P	I	N		C	H	E	E	R	I	O
E		E		G		H		L		A		L
D	A	D	O		D	E	W	Y	E	Y	E	D

163

E	D	D	I	E		P	O	P	C	O	R	N
A		E		X		U		R		W		O
R	E	N	T	A	L	S		O	V	E	N	S
S		I		M		H		C				E
H	U	G	E		R	E	F	L	E	C	T	S
O		R		R		D		A		R		
T	H	A	M	E	S		V	I	Z	I	E	R
		T		S		A		M		S		E
C	R	E	E	P	I	N	G		S	T	E	M
A				O		C		G		I		O
B	A	S	I	N		H	O	L	L	A	N	D
I		E		S		O		A		N		E
N	E	W	Y	E	A	R		D	R	O	L	L

164

M	I	F	F		E	C	L	I	P	S	E	S
U		L		F		A		M		H		I
S	C	O	U	R	E	R		P	R	A	W	N
I		U		A				R		L		K
C	U	R	M	U	D	G	E	O	N	L	Y	
I				D		R		V		O		A
A	S	P		U	S	A	G	E		W	A	S
N		A		L		S		M				S
	I	N	T	E	R	P	R	E	T	I	V	E
S		A		N				N		N		S
U	N	C	U	T		O	C	T	O	P	U	S
C		E		L		R		S		U		O
H	E	A	V	Y	S	E	T		S	T	A	R

165

L	A	C	E	S		P	U	D	D	L	E	S
O		O		O		A			U		V	
U		R		M		R		A	B	B	E	Y
S	E	N	T	E	N	C	E		L		R	
I		E		D		E		V	I	N	Y	L
N	O	R	M	A	L	L	Y		N			E
E		S		Y				R		V		M
S			U		J	A	L	A	P	E	N	O
S	H	O	P	S		N		V		S		N
	O		K		A	T	L	A	N	T	I	S
S	T	E	E	R		H		G		I		O
	E		E			E		E		G		L
C	L	I	P	P	E	R		S	C	E	N	E

166

E	L	E	G	Y		H	U	D	D	L	E	D
X		X		A		O		O		E		R
C	R	E	W	M	A	N		G	R	E	B	E
I		C		S		I		M				A
T	H	U	D		E	N	L	A	R	G	E	D
E		T		S		G		T		R		
D	R	I	V	E	N		G	I	V	E	U	P
		V		A		F		C		N		R
F	R	E	E	W	I	L	L		T	A	T	E
A				A		O		A		D		S
G	H	O	S	T		R	E	C	O	I	L	S
I		H		E		A		H		E		E
N	U	M	E	R	A	L		E	R	R	E	D

167

V	A	N	I	L	L	A		A		K	E	N
	L			E		D	U	B	A	I		E
F	L	Y	O	V	E	R		E		N		W
	T			E		I		T	I	E	I	N
S	I	M	P	L	I	F	Y			T		E
	M			L		T		A		I		S
L	E	N	S	E	S		E	R	E	C	T	S
A		A		D		R		R			R	
C		T			G	O	V	E	R	N	E	D
O	D	I	U	M		B		S			S	
N		O		O		U	N	T	R	U	T	H
I		N	O	D	E	S		E			L	
C	O	S		E		T	I	D	D	L	E	R

168

M	O	A	T	S		J	U	N	G	L	E	S
I		L		E		O		A		A		W
L	O	O	S	E	L	Y		U	M	B	R	A
K		N		K		F		T				B
S	I	G	N		M	U	T	I	N	O	U	S
O		S		R		L		C		C		
P	R	I	Z	E	D		L	A	P	T	O	P
		D		S		H		L		O		O
S	P	E	C	I	F	I	C		S	P	A	T
T				S		D		O		U		T
E	V	E	R	T		D	E	M	E	S	N	E
P		L		O		E		E		E		R
S	A	F	F	R	O	N		N	A	S	T	Y

169

C	A	S	T		D	A	R	I	N	G	L	Y
R		I		C		N		N		R		A
I	G	N	E	O	U	S		C	H	I	C	K
B		E		L		W		O		N		S
B	E	W	I	L	D	E	R	M	E	N	T	
A				A		R		P		E		G
G	A	Z	E	B	O		P	A	N	D	E	R
E		O		O		R		R				A
	C	O	O	R	D	I	N	A	T	I	O	N
S		M		A		B		B		R		D
E	V	I	C	T		B	E	L	L	O	W	S
R		N		O		O		Y		N		O
F	I	G	U	R	I	N	E		R	Y	A	N

170

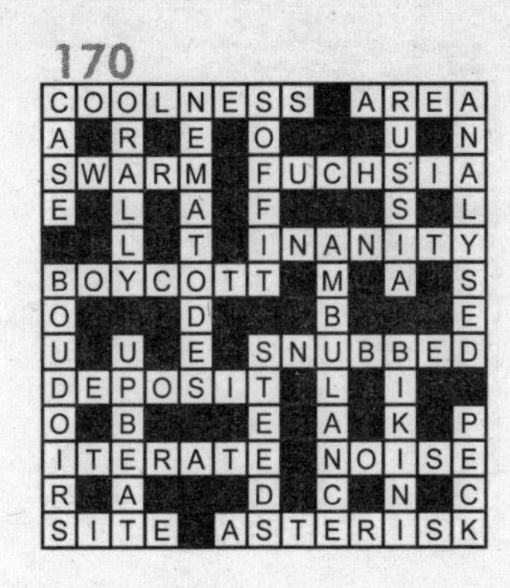

C	O	O	L	N	E	S	S		A	R	E	A
A		R		E		O				U		N
S	W	A	R	M		F	U	C	H	S	I	A
E		L		A		F				S		L
		L		T		I	N	A	N	I	T	Y
B	O	Y	C	O	T	T		M		A		S
O				D				B				E
U		U		E		S	N	U	B	B	E	D
D	E	P	O	S	I	T		L		I		
O		B				E		A		K		P
I	T	E	R	A	T	E		N	O	I	S	E
R		A				D		C		N		C
S	I	T	E		A	S	T	E	R	I	S	K

171

F	I	A	S	C	O		S		A		L	
A		P			M	A	C	A	Q	U	E	S
B	O	O			E		H		U		A	
L		G	A	G	G	L	E		E	N	V	Y
E		E			A		M		D		E	
S	W	E	E	T		R	E	Q	U	I	R	E
			V		K		R		C			
B	A	N	E	F	U	L		S	T	O	R	K
	L		N		M		M			O		E
C	L	O	T		Q	U	A	R	T	Z		E
	U		F		U		D			I	M	P
B	R	O	U	H	A	H	A			N		E
	E		L		T		M	A	N	G	E	R

172

D	I	S	M	O	U	N	T		I	T	C	H
U		O		R		U				U		A
S	I	R	E	N		A	I	L	E	R	O	N
K		R		A		N				T		D
		E		M		C	O	B	B	L	E	S
M	Y	L	E	E	N	E		U		E		O
I				N				T				M
L		O		T		A	R	T	I	S	T	E
D	E	B	A	S	E	D		E		A		
N		T				O		R		L		S
E	N	A	M	O	U	R		C	L	A	I	M
S		I				E		U		M		O
S	A	N	D		A	D	A	P	T	I	N	G

173

C	A	M	E		S	P	A	C	I	O	U	S
O		A		A		A		O		V		O
L	O	G	I	C	A	L		N	E	E	D	S
L		M		H		L		Q		R		O
A	V	A	R	I	C	I	O	U	S	L	Y	
P				E		D		I		I		O
S	T	A	R	V	E		A	S	L	E	E	P
E		P		E		E		T				E
	C	O	M	M	E	N	D	A	T	I	O	N
B		S		E		J		D		R		I
E	A	T	E	N		O	X	O	N	I	A	N
E		L		T		I		R		S		G
P	H	E	A	S	A	N	T		O	H	M	S

174

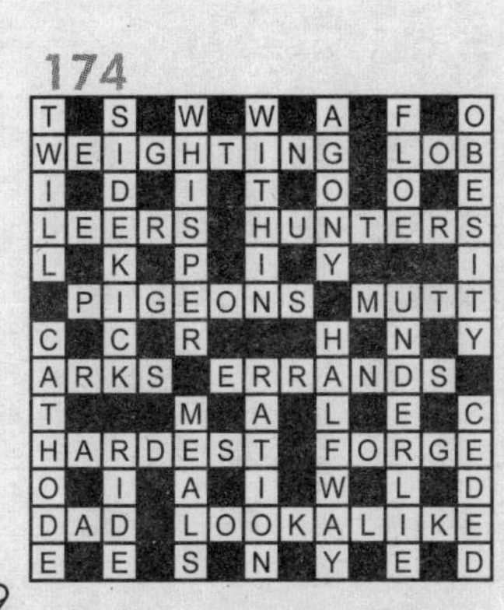

T		S		W		W		A		F		O
W	E	I	G	H	T	I	N	G		L	O	B
I		D		I		T		O		O		E
L	E	E	R	S		H	U	N	T	E	R	S
L		K		P		I		Y				I
	P	I	G	E	O	N	S		M	U	T	T
C		C		R				H		N		Y
A	R	K	S		E	R	R	A	N	D	S	
T				M		A		L		E		C
H	A	R	D	E	S	T		F	O	R	G	E
O		I		A		I		W		L		D
D	A	D		L	O	O	K	A	L	I	K	E
E		E		S		N		Y		E		D

175

L	I	F	E		A	C	A	D	E	M	I	C
I		E		C		A		E		O		R
G	A	L	L	I	U	M		M	O	T	T	O
H		O		R		E		O		I		S
T	O	N		R		R		N	E	V	I	S
F				O	V	A	L	S		E		C
I		A		S				T		S		U
N		W		T	O	W	E	R				L
G	R	E	E	R		E		A		S	A	T
E		S		A		A		T		I		U
R	O	O	S	T		P	L	O	D	D	E	R
E		M		U		O		R		L		A
D	R	E	S	S	I	N	G		Z	E	A	L

176

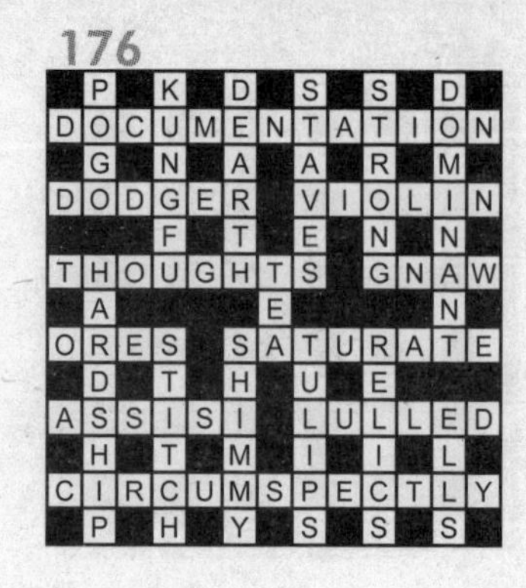

	P		K		D		S		S		D	
D	O	C	U	M	E	N	T	A	T	I	O	N
	G		N		A		A		R		M	
D	O	D	G	E	R		V	I	O	L	I	N
			F		T		E		N		N	
T	H	O	U	G	H	T	S		G	N	A	W
	A					E					N	
O	R	E	S		S	A	T	U	R	A	T	E
	D		T		H		U		E			
A	S	S	I	S	I		L	U	L	L	E	D
	H		T		M		I		I		L	
C	I	R	C	U	M	S	P	E	C	T	L	Y
	P		H		Y		S		S		S	

177

A	G	E	I	S	M		S	T	A	F	F	S
	U		M		A		T		M		A	
C	A	M	P		Z	E	A	L	O	T	R	Y
	C		E		E		R		U			
L	A	P	A	Z		U	S	U	R	P	E	D
	M		C		E		H				X	
S	O	P	H	I	S	T	I	C	A	T	E	D
	L				C		P		T		R	
B	E	E	S	W	A	X		S	T	A	T	E
			I		P		B		E		I	
A	N	G	E	L	I	C	A		S	O	O	N
	A		V		S		L		T		N	
I	N	F	E	S	T		M	I	S	U	S	E

178

G	A	S	T	R	I	C		R		N	A	P
	P			E		H	A	I	K	U		E
O	R	I	F	I	C	E		L		R		A
	I			N		R		L	U	T	E	S
N	O	W	A	D	A	Y	S			U		A
	R			E		L		T		R		N
S	I	G	H	E	D		B	E	R	E	F	T
U		A		R		V		T			A	
C		L			H	I	T	H	E	R	T	O
C	O	A	C	H		V		E			I	
E		H		I		A	R	R	A	I	G	N
E		A	S	P	I	C		E			U	
D	U	D		S		E	N	D	U	R	E	S

179

D	E	B	T		A	D	H	E	R	E	N	T
I		L		E		Y		M		P		R
S	H	U	F	F	L	E		B	U	S	T	A
P		N		F		I		A		I		N
A	R	T		E		N		R	U	L	E	S
S				R	O	G	E	R		O		P
S		P		V				A		N		A
I		R		E	A	V	E	S				R
O	B	O	E	S		E		S		L	Y	E
N		S		C		S		I		L		N
A	M	A	Z	E		P	E	N	D	A	N	T
T		I		N		E		G		M		L
E	T	C	E	T	E	R	A		C	A	V	Y

180

	F	R	E	N	C	H	F	R	I	E	S	
W		E		U		A		O		D		C
O		U		N	E	W	L	Y		G	E	L
R	U	N	I	N		K		A		A		O
D		I		E		E		L	U	R	E	S
P	R	O	T	R	U	D	E					E
E		N		Y				A		L		F
R					B	R	O	C	C	O	L	I
F	A	T	E	D		O		R		N		S
E		A		I		S		E	I	G	H	T
C	U	B		V	A	C	U	A		E		E
T		L		O		O		G		S		D
	S	E	T	T	L	E	M	E	N	T	S	

181

S	C	H	E	R	Z	O		U		H	O	W
	H			U		C	O	R	G	I		R
B	A	B	Y	S	I	T		N		L		I
	P			H		A		S	P	L	A	T
C	L	A	S	H	I	N	G			O		T
	I			O		T		B		C		E
U	N	T	R	U	E		K	R	A	K	E	N
P		W		R		R		I			X	
H		I			D	E	V	E	L	O	P	S
O	W	N	E	R		W		F			A	
L		K		A		A	S	I	N	I	N	E
D		L	U	N	A	R		N			D	
S	E	E		G		D	O	G	F	I	S	H

182

A	N	T	E	R	O	O	M			I	B	I	S

A	N	T	E	R	O	O	M		I	B	I	S
N		R		E		N				A		H
T	H	E	F	T		R	A	T	T	L	E	R
S		B		A		U				T		U
		L		L		S	A	P	L	I	N	G
F	L	E	M	I	S	H		O		C		G
L				A				T				E
A		N		T		C	L	E	A	R	E	D
S	Q	U	E	E	Z	E		N		E		
H		N				L		T		F		C
I	N	C	L	I	N	E		I	V	O	R	Y
N		I				R		A		R		A
G	L	O	W		C	Y	C	L	A	M	E	N

183

C	O	N	V	E	R	G	E		C	L	U	B
U		E		A		U		U		A		A
B	E	R	M	U	D	A		N	A	M	E	D
S		O		D		R		D		P		G
			M	E	D	D	L	E	S	O	M	E
C		S		C		S		R		O		R
R	A	P	T	O	R		T	W	I	N	G	E
U		I		L		A		R		S		D
C	E	N	S	O	R	S	H	I	P			
I		S		G		S		T		Z		H
B	A	T	O	N		E	V	I	L	E	Y	E
L		E		E		R		N		T		A
E	A	R	L		S	T	A	G	N	A	N	T

184

	T	R	E	A	C	H	E	R	O	U	S	
T		E		F		E		A		N		A
C		L		F	R	A	U	D		P	A	D
H	Y	E	N	A		D		A		I		O
A		A		B		O		R	E	N	A	L
I	N	S	O	L	E	N	T					E
K		E		Y				V		S		S
O					M	A	J	E	S	T	I	C
V	A	L	E	T		B		R		A		E
S		A		U		O		B	A	R	O	N
K	I	D		B	R	A	V	O		L		C
Y		E		E		R		S		E		E
	I	N	G	R	E	D	I	E	N	T	S	

185

T	R	A	V	E	S	T	Y		S	H	O	O
A		C		X		H		Q		O		U
C	H	I	P	P	E	R		U	P	S	E	T
T		D		E		O		E		T		B
			A	R	T	N	O	U	V	E	A	U
E		O		I		E		E		L		R
M	I	N	I	M	A		F	J	O	R	D	S
I		E		E		A		U		Y		T
G	O	O	D	N	E	S	S	M	E			
R		N		T		P		P		L		B
A	R	O	M	A		I	M	I	T	A	T	E
N		N		L		R		N		I		D
T	H	E	N		K	E	D	G	E	R	E	E

186

A	R	C	S		T	A	M	P	E	R	E	D
P		U		C		V		R		E		E
P	U	R	P	O	S	E		A	Z	T	E	C
R		V		U		R		I		R		O
O	C	E	A	N		S	U	S	T	A	I	N
P				T		E		E		I		T
R	I	G	G	E	R		R	W	A	N	D	A
I		R		R		S		O				M
A	N	A	R	C	H	Y		R	I	C	C	I
T		N		L		N		T		O		N
I	N	D	I	A		O	P	H	E	L	I	A
O		M		I		D		Y		O		T
N	E	A	R	M	I	S	S		O	N	C	E

187

	U		O		C		U		P		B	
A	P	P	R	E	H	E	N	S	I	B	L	E
	O		I		A		R		F		A	
U	N	C	O	I	L		O	F	F	I	C	E
			L		E		L		L		K	
P	E	D	E	S	T	A	L		E	R	O	S
	M					C					U	
S	P	U	D		V	E	N	E	R	A	T	E
	E		E		I		I		A			
P	R	I	C	E	S		P	E	D	A	N	T
	O		A		A		P		I		O	
T	R	A	N	S	G	R	E	S	S	I	O	N
	S		T		E		R		H		N	

188

I	M	P	A	C	T		W		A		A	
R		A			S	W	E	E	P	E	R	S
O	A	R			A		T		O		R	
N		T	H	E	R	O	N		S	K	I	P
E		L			S		E		T		V	
D	O	Y	E	N		E	S	C	A	P	E	E
			N		H		S		T			
E	D	I	T	I	O	N		L	E	O	N	A
	A		I		M		A			R		B
E	W	E	R		I	O	D	I	N	E		I
	D		E		N		A			G	A	D
C	L	O	T	H	I	N	G			O		E
	E		Y		D		E	A	R	N	E	D

189

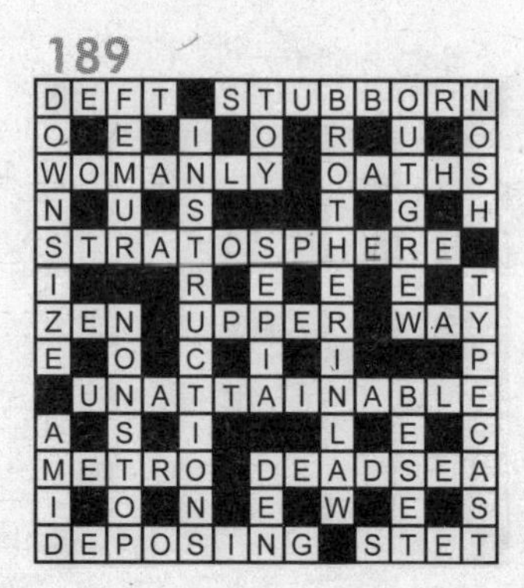

D	E	F	T		S	T	U	B	B	O	R	N
O		E		I		O		R		U		O
W	O	M	A	N	L	Y		O	A	T	H	S
N		U		S				T		G		H
S	T	R	A	T	O	S	P	H	E	R	E	
I				R		E		E		E		T
Z	E	N		U	P	P	E	R		W	A	Y
E		O		C		I		I				P
	U	N	A	T	T	A	I	N	A	B	L	E
A		S		I				L		E		C
M	E	T	R	O		D	E	A	D	S	E	A
I		O		N		E		W		E		S
D	E	P	O	S	I	N	G		S	T	E	T

190

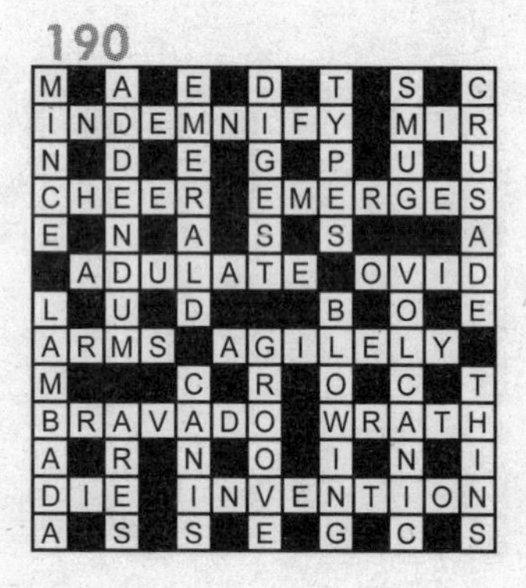

M		A		E		D		T		S		C
I	N	D	E	M	N	I	F	Y		M	I	R
N		D		E		G		P		U		U
C	H	E	E	R		E	M	E	R	G	E	S
E		N		A		S		S				A
	A	D	U	L	A	T	E		O	V	I	D
L		U		D				B		O		E
A	R	M	S		A	G	I	L	E	L	Y	
M				C		R		O		C		T
B	R	A	V	A	D	O		W	R	A	T	H
A		R		N		O		I		N		I
D	I	E		I	N	V	E	N	T	I	O	N
A		S		S		E		G		C		S

191

C	A	B	S		P	E	R	I	O	D	I	C
A		O		O		U		M		I		O
T	U	B	U	L	A	R		M	E	L	O	N
E		B		D		O		E		A		G
B	O	Y		T		P		A	F	T	E	R
L				E	V	A	N	S		E		E
A		E		S				U		D		S
N		S		T	U	N	E	R				S
C	O	P	R	A		U		A		L	O	W
H		O		M		M		B		E		O
E	T	U	D	E		B	E	L	G	I	U	M
T		S		N		E		E		G		A
T	W	E	E	T	E	R	S		S	H	U	N

192

C	R	A	Y	O	N		A	D	A	G	E	S
Y		R		W		C		R		A		E
M	E	M	E	N	T	O		I		U		N
B		C		E		N	O	Z	Z	L	E	S
A	P	H	I	D		C		Z				E
L		A				L		L	I	M	B	S
		I		C	A	U	S	E		O		
P	E	R	C	H		S				N		U
I				I		I		B	E	G	A	N
C	A	L	Y	P	S	O		O		O		U
K		U		P		N	O	X	I	O	U	S
U		N		E		S		E		S		E
P	A	G	O	D	A		F	R	I	E	N	D

193

V	I	B	R	A	T	E	S		P	L	O	P
E		A		N		M				I		A
T	R	I	T	E		P	A	R	T	N	E	R
O		L		C		L				T		A
		E		D		O	S	T	L	E	R	S
A	N	Y	B	O	D	Y		R		L		O
G				T				I				L
E		A		A		G	R	A	S	S	E	S
N	E	B	U	L	A	E		T		Y		
C		L				N		H		L		P
I	M	A	G	I	N	E		L	E	V	E	R
E		Z				R		O		I		O
S	L	E	W		M	A	I	N	L	A	N	D

194

C	H	O	K	E	R		E	N	M	I	T	Y
	E		I		U		N		A		U	
S	P	U	N		T	U	T	O	R	I	N	G
	T		S		S		I		G			
P	A	T	H	S		A	T	T	E	M	P	T
	G		I		K		L				R	
C	O	M	P	R	E	H	E	N	S	I	O	N
	N				Y		D		H		S	
A	S	C	R	I	B	E		L	I	M	P	S
			U		O		M		E		E	
G	R	A	D	U	A	T	E		L	U	R	E
	I		D		R		N		D		E	
O	B	E	Y	E	D		U	P	S	I	D	E

195

	J		I		C		S		U		D	
B	U	R	N	E	R		W	I	N	N	E	R
	N		D		A		E		J		F	
M	E	R	E		C	H	E	R	U	B	I	C
			T		K		P		S		A	
Q	U	I	E	T	L	Y		S	T	I	N	T
	N		R		E		T		I		C	
B	A	L	M	Y		S	W	I	F	T	E	R
	W		I		S		O		I			
M	A	G	N	A	T	E	S		A	R	M	Y
	R		A		U		O		B		O	
B	E	A	C	O	N		M	E	L	L	O	W
	S		Y		S		E		E		N	

196

	D	I	S	C	O	U	R	A	G	E	D	
P		N		O		R		L		N		A
E		C		M	A	C	H	O		J	A	G
C	H	I	R	P		H		O		O		O
U		S		L		I		F	O	Y	E	R
L	O	O	S	E	E	N	D					A
I		R		X				S		V		P
A					W	H	I	P	L	A	S	H
R	A	L	L	Y		U		E		C		O
I		A		U		B		C	R	U	M	B
T	U	B		C	A	R	A	T		O		I
Y		E		C		I		R		L		A
	C	L	E	A	N	S	H	A	V	E	N	

197

S	O	D	A	S		S	U	S	P	E	N	D
P		E		A		M		T		V		I
E	N	L	A	R	G	E		R	E	E	S	E
N		I		I		L		A				T
C	A	V	E		E	L	L	I	P	S	I	S
E		E		A		S		G		T		
R	A	R	I	N	G		C	H	E	R	U	B
		E		E		S		T		E		R
A	B	D	I	C	A	T	E		M	A	L	I
C				D		O		E		M		D
T	A	N	G	O		N	A	G	G	I	N	G
E		E		T		E		G		N		E
D	I	T	H	E	R	S		S	A	G	A	S

198

P	E	R	M	E	A	T	E		G	I	L	L
E		E		M		A				C		I
A	N	G	L	E		U	P	F	R	O	N	T
R		I		R		G				N		I
		M		G		H	I	T	T	I	N	G
P	R	E	F	E	C	T		A		C		A
E				N				X				N
A		C		C		B	R	I	S	K	E	T
C	H	I	M	E	R	A		D		I		
E		R				T		E		M		N
F	U	R	T	I	V	E		R	I	O	J	A
U		U				A		M		N		V
L	U	S	T		B	U	S	Y	B	O	D	Y

199

	U		N		W		A		I		O	
O	R	N	I	T	H	O	L	O	G	I	S	T
	D		C		O		C		N		B	
C	U	C	K	O	O		O	R	I	S	O	N
			E		P		V		T		U	
W	I	N	D	P	I	P	E		E	A	R	S
	M					O					N	
S	P	I	T		A	T	T	A	C	K	E	R
	U		R		U		R		R			
E	D	G	I	N	G		O	C	E	A	N	S
	E		P		U		U		D		U	
I	N	C	O	R	R	U	P	T	I	B	L	E
	T		D		Y		E		T		L	

200

Q	U	A	Y		P	E	N	U	M	B	R	A
U		X		A		N		N		R		S
A	M	I	A	B	L	E		E	D	I	T	S
D		O		S		R		M		S		E
R	A	M		O		G		P	O	K	E	R
I				L	O	Y	A	L		L		T
L		T		U				O		Y		I
A		H		T	A	T	T	Y				V
T	R	O	P	E		R		M		H	O	E
E		U		Z		I		E		O		N
R	O	G	U	E		V	E	N	T	U	R	E
A		H		R		I		T		S		S
L	I	T	T	O	R	A	L		B	E	E	S

201

M	I	T	E		F	R	U	I	T	F	U	L
I		I		S		H		N		L		A
N	A	T	T	I	L	Y		A	B	Y	S	S
I		L		N		T		D		L		T
S	L	E	D	G	E	H	A	M	M	E	R	
T				L		M		I		A		A
R	A	P	I	E	R		U	S	E	F	U	L
Y		L		M		B		S				L
	C	A	P	I	T	A	L	I	S	T	I	C
L		C		N		R		B		R		L
A	W	A	R	D		M	I	L	E	A	G	E
N		T		E		A		E		Y		A
K	N	E	A	D	I	N	G		T	S	A	R

202

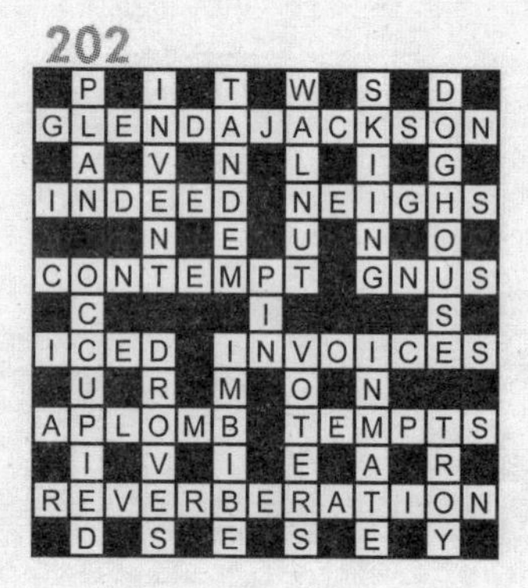

203

M	O	D	E	L	S		F		L		L	
U		I			C	R	I	T	I	C	A	L
G	A	S			A		N		B		T	
G		U	N	C	L	O	G		E	V	E	N
E		S			P		E		R		S	
D	O	E	R	S		B	R	E	A	D	T	H
			E		S		S		T			
S	M	A	S	H	E	S		B	E	S	O	M
	Y		E		M		D			E		E
G	R	A	M		I	C	E	B	O	X		T
	I		B		N		S			T	O	E
C	A	L	L	B	A	C	K			O		O
	D		E		R		S	I	N	N	E	R

204

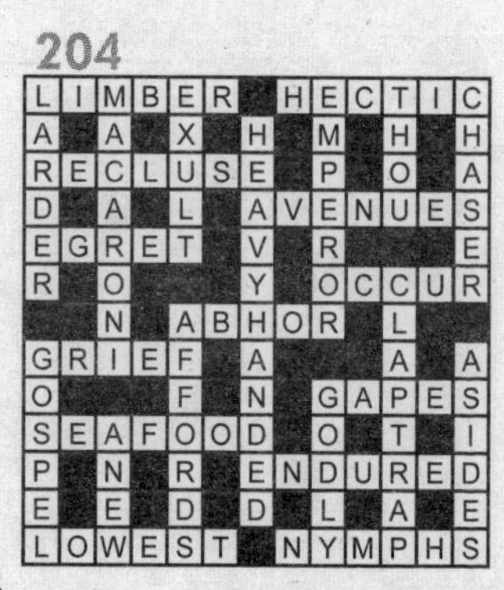

205

S	C	I	E	N	C	E	S		P	A	P	A
O		N		E		N				M		U
R	E	F	E	R		L	E	N	I	E	N	T
T		O		V		I				L		O
		R		O		S	O	P	H	I	S	M
C	O	M	B	U	S	T		E		E		A
R				S				P				T
E		U		L		E	M	P	O	R	I	A
A	N	N	O	Y	E	D		E		E		
M		C				I		R		M		E
T	A	L	L	E	S	T		O	D	O	U	R
E		E				E		N		V		A
A	L	S	O		A	D	M	I	R	E	R	S

206

	W		A		I		E		C		B	
C	A	R	B	O	N	I	F	E	R	O	U	S
	N		S		T		F		A		C	
S	E	C	U	R	E		I	N	V	O	K	E
			R		R		G		E		A	
S	U	D	D	E	N	L	Y		N	I	R	O
	N					A					O	
F	L	I	P		A	D	D	I	T	I	O	N
	I		O		B		E		O			
S	K	E	W	E	R		V	A	N	D	A	L
	E		E		O		O		G		I	
F	L	I	R	T	A	T	I	O	U	S	L	Y
	Y		S		D		D		E		S	

207

S	O	L	I	C	I	T		W		B	I	D
	B			R		R	A	R	E	R		O
I	S	O	N	O	M	Y		I		A		S
	C			S		I		T	A	K	E	S
G	U	E	S	S	I	N	G			I		I
	R			B		G		D		N		E
N	E	C	T	A	R		S	I	N	G	E	R
A		A		R		R		L			R	
P		P			H	E	R	E	U	P	O	N
K	E	T	C	H		V		M			D	
I		A		A		A	M	M	O	N	I	A
N		I	D	I	O	M		A			N	
S	O	N		R		P	A	S	S	A	G	E

208

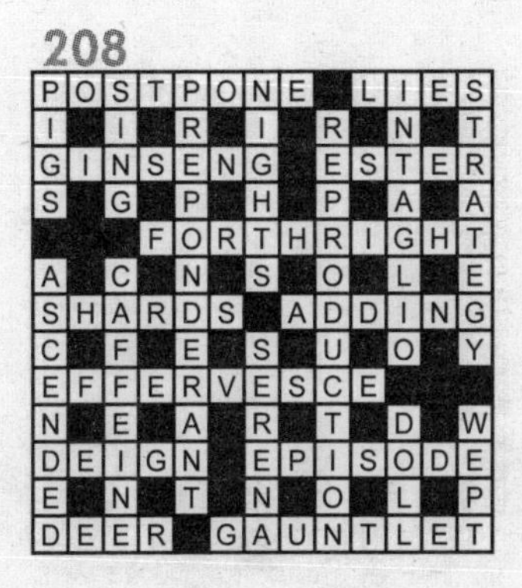

P	O	S	T	P	O	N	E		L	I	E	S
I		I		R		I		R		N		T
G	I	N	S	E	N	G		E	S	T	E	R
S		G		P		H		P		A		A
			F	O	R	T	H	R	I	G	H	T
A		C		N		S		O		L		E
S	H	A	R	D	S		A	D	D	I	N	G
C		F		E		S		U		O		Y
E	F	F	E	R	V	E	S	C	E			
N		E		A		R		T		D		W
D	E	I	G	N		E	P	I	S	O	D	E
E		N		T		N		O		L		P
D	E	E	R		G	A	U	N	T	L	E	T

209

A	C	C	E	D	E		A	F	R	A	I	D
R		A		E		D		L		N		O
D	I	V	U	L	G	E		A		N		O
O		A		F		F	I	R	E	A	R	M
U	N	L	I	T		E		E				E
R		I				R		U	N	D	I	D
		E		S	T	E	E	P		I		
B	U	R	N	T		N				C		S
U				O		T		E	R	A	S	E
R	A	V	I	O	L	I		T		P		P
E		I		P		A	T	H	I	R	S	T
A		S		E		L		O		I		E
U	G	A	N	D	A		E	S	C	O	R	T

210

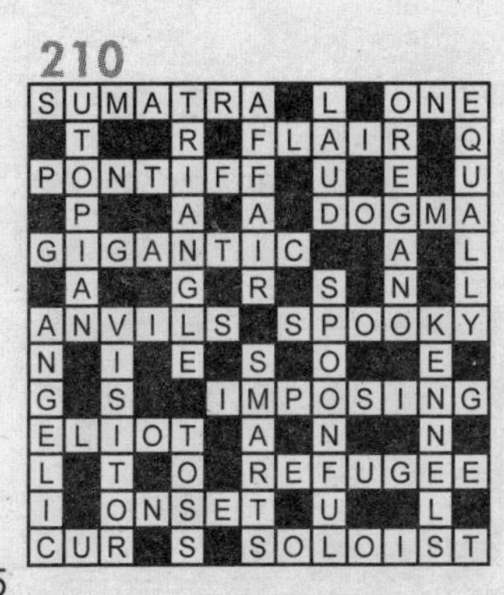

S	U	M	A	T	R	A		L		O	N	E
	T			R		F	L	A	I	R		Q
P	O	N	T	I	F	F		U		E		U
	P			A		A		D	O	G	M	A
G	I	G	A	N	T	I	C			A		L
	A			G		R		S		N		L
A	N	V	I	L	S		S	P	O	O	K	Y
N	I			E		S		O		E		
G	S				I	M	P	O	S	I	N	G
E	L	I	O	T		A		N		N		
L	T		O			R	E	F	U	G	E	E
I		O	N	S	E	T		U		L		
C	U	R		S		S	O	L	O	I	S	T

211

A	C	M	E		P	R	O	P	O	S	E	D
S		A		C		U		L		Q		A
T	U	R	N	O	U	T		A	D	U	L	T
O		I		N				I		A		A
U	N	A	S	S	U	M	I	N	G	L	Y	
N				E		O		C		L		O
D	A	M		Q	U	I	L	L		Y	E	N
S		U		U		S		O				E
	A	D	V	E	N	T	I	T	I	O	U	S
S		D		N				H		L		I
T	A	I	N	T		W	I	E	L	D	E	D
A		E		L		A		S		E		E
B	A	R	N	Y	A	R	D		G	R	I	D

212

C	O	W	S		E	M	P	O	R	I	U	M
O		O		W		U		S		M		I
M	A	R	S	H	E	S		T	A	M	E	S
P		S		O		C		E		E		C
A	P	T		L		L		N	I	N	T	H
S				E	V	E	N	T		S		I
S		S		H				A		E		E
I		H		E	R	E	C	T				V
O	B	A	M	A		R		I		W	H	O
N		K		R		R		O		I		U
A	D	E	P	T		A	L	U	M	N	U	S
T		U		E		N		S		C		L
E	X	P	E	D	I	T	E		V	E	R	Y

213

D	U	F	F		S	H	A	M	P	O	O	S
I		U		D		Y		O		U		T
S	I	N	N	E	R	S		U	N	T	I	E
H		G		L		S		N		L		R
O	R	I	B	I		O	U	T	D	O	N	E
N				Q		P		A		O		O
O	P	A	Q	U	E		T	I	C	K	E	T
U		R		E		A		N				Y
R	E	S	I	S	T	S		S	T	R	I	P
A		E		C		T		I		O		I
B	I	N	G	E		E	N	D	E	M	I	C
L		I		N		R		E		E		A
Y	A	C	H	T	I	N	G		H	O	W	L

214

T	H	A	N	K	Y	O	U		K	I	E	V
O		C		O		B				B		I
F	A	U	N	A		T	R	A	D	E	I	N
U		M		L		U				R		E
		E		A		S	T	A	G	I	N	G
I	G	N	O	B	L	E		P		A		A
N				E				O				R
N		A		A		R	E	C	E	N	C	Y
O	B	V	E	R	S	E		R		A		
C		A				D		Y		S		F
E	N	T	H	U	S	E		P	O	S	S	E
N		A				E		H		A		T
T	O	R	Y		I	M	M	A	T	U	R	E

215

L	O	C	A	L	E		S		P		E	
E		O			D	E	C	I	S	I	V	E
T	I	P			G		A		A		E	
T		P	O	S	E	U	R		L	E	N	S
E		E			S		P		M		E	
R	U	R	A	L		B	E	L	I	N	D	A
			N		L		R		S			
W	A	R	T	H	O	G		S	T	O	M	A
	L		I		O		V			P		P
T	I	E	D		F	O	I	B	L	E		A
	G		O		A		S			N	O	T
W	H	I	T	E	H	O	T			E		H
	T		E		S		A	F	F	R	A	Y

216

H	I	G	H	B	R	O	W		T	R	I	O
U		R		U		W		D		E		B
S	M	I	T	T	E	N		E	Q	U	A	L
H		N		T		E		C		N		I
			D	E	B	R	I	E	F	I	N	G
C		M		R		S		L		O		I
O	B	O	I	S	T		V	E	R	N	O	N
M		O		C		V		R		S		G
P	E	R	I	O	D	I	C	A	L			
U		I		T		R		T		G		R
T	U	N	I	C		A	G	I	T	A	T	E
E		G		H		G		O		F		D
R	I	S	K		T	O	A	N	D	F	R	O

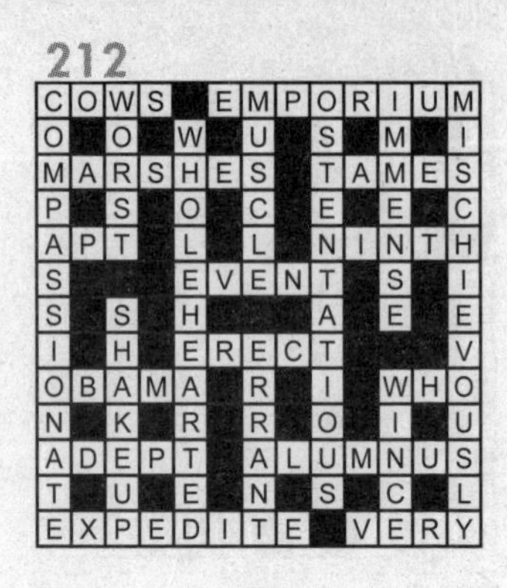

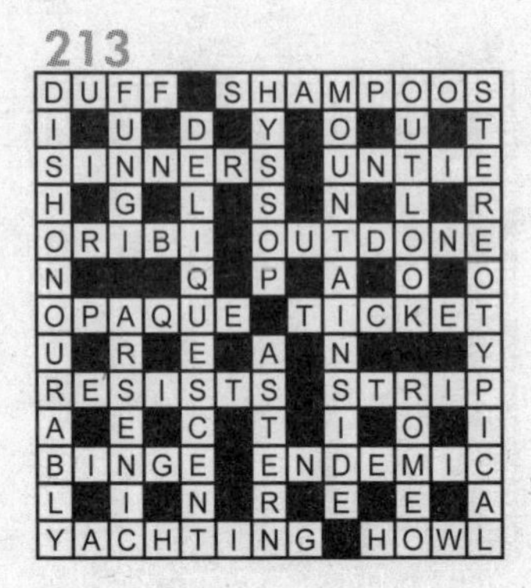

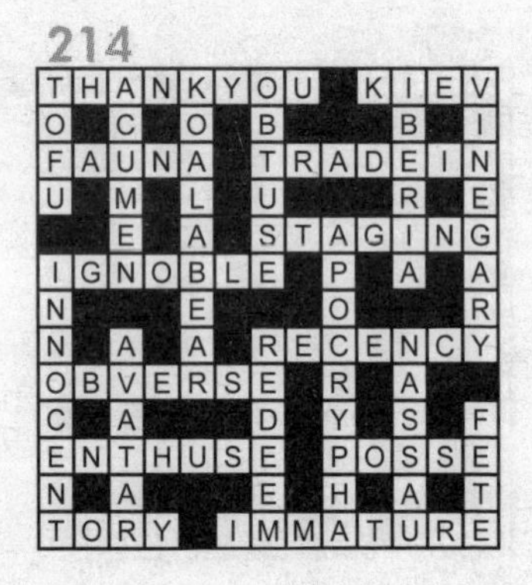

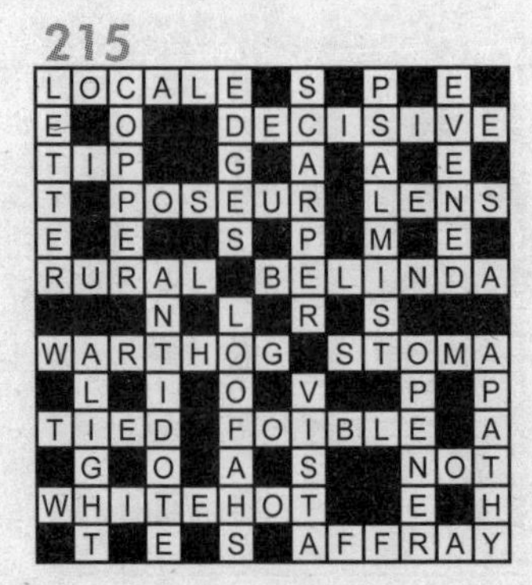

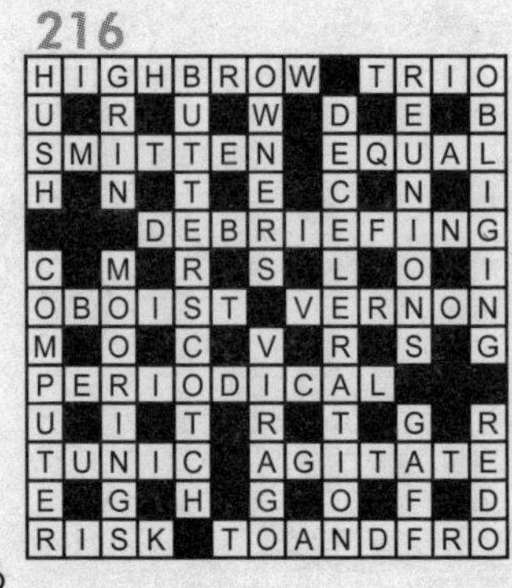

217

I	M	B	U	E	D		A		A		R	
N		E			R	E	G	A	R	D	E	D
P	O	D			A		E		A		N	
U		B	O	X	F	U	L		C	H	E	W
T		U			T		E		H		G	
S	I	G	H	S		A	S	U	N	D	E	R
			E		B		S		I			
E	R	R	A	T	U	M		A	D	D	O	N
	U		D		L		S			A		E
L	E	I	A		L	A	W	S	O	N		W
	F		C		D		A			D	U	E
M	U	S	H	R	O	O	M			E		S
	L		E		G		P	A	R	R	O	T

218

I	V	O	R		I	R	R	I	T	A	N	T
N		U		P		E		L		E		R
F	I	G	U	R	E	S		L	A	R	G	E
I		H		E		I		U		O		A
N	O	T	E	D		N	E	M	E	S	I	S
I				E		S		I		O		U
T	R	U	S	T	Y		A	N	T	L	E	R
E		P		E		L		A				E
S	P	L	U	R	G	E		T	A	R	O	T
I		I		M		S		I		E		R
M	U	F	T	I		S	C	O	R	P	I	O
A		T		N		E		N		A		V
L	I	S	T	E	N	E	R		B	Y	T	E

219

D	O	W	N	C	A	S	T		V	O	L	T
O		E		O		I		C		U		H
C	I	N	E	M	A	S		U	T	T	E	R
K		T		M		K		M		M		E
			M	E	T	I	C	U	L	O	U	S
R		D		N		N		L		D		H
O	T	I	O	S	E		C	O	H	E	R	E
O		A		U		A		N		D		D
F	U	T	U	R	I	S	T	I	C			
L		R		A		T		M		L		A
E	X	I	S	T		R	U	B	B	I	N	G
S		B		E		A		U		M		E
S	H	E	D		B	L	O	S	S	O	M	S

220

O	C	C	U	L	T		S	H	A	R	K	S
T		H		I		C		U		E		H
T	O	R	O	N	T	O		N		S		O
A		O		E		N	E	G	A	T	E	D
W	O	M	A	N		D		A				D
A		I				I		R	O	O	M	Y
		U		N	U	T	T	Y		B		
C	A	M	E	O		I				S		I
A				D		O		S	I	T	A	R
S	O	J	O	U	R	N		A		A		I
K		U		L		A	F	F	E	C	T	S
E		D		E		L		E		L		E
T	H	E	I	S	M		G	R	E	E	N	S

221

S	T	U	B	B	E	D		W		H	A	Y
	H			O		R	A	I	N	Y		E
R	O	Y	A	L	T	Y		L		G		A
	R			D		I		T	R	I	E	R
F	E	M	I	N	I	N	E			E		N
	A			E		G		E		N		E
C	U	B	I	S	T		E	X	T	E	N	D
A		E		S		E		E			A	
T		L			I	S	O	M	E	T	R	Y
E	P	O	C	H		C		P			W	
R		V		A		A	T	T	A	C	H	E
E		E	Q	U	I	P		E			A	
R	E	D		L		E	L	D	E	R	L	Y

222

L	O	F	T	Y		S	C	A	T	T	E	R
A		O		A		I		U		I		E
N	E	U	T	R	O	N		T	O	N	E	S
C		N		D		F		O				E
E	A	T	S		J	U	M	B	O	J	E	T
T		A		M		L		A		E		
S	W	I	V	E	L		S	H	U	T	U	P
		N		C		R		N		T		R
M	I	S	C	H	I	E	F		H	I	F	I
O				A		B		E		S		C
U	R	B	A	N		U	N	B	L	O	C	K
S		A		I		K		O		N		L
E	A	R	A	C	H	E		R	U	S	T	Y

223

E	X	C	U	S	E		A	P	P	L	E	S
S		O		P		L		A		E		L
C	O	C	H	L	E	A		T		E		E
R		K		I		U	T	T	E	R	E	D
O	C	T	E	T		G		E				G
W		A				H		R	O	U	S	E
		I		U	N	I	O	N		N		
H	A	L	T	S		N				K		E
E				H		G		N	I	N	O	N
I	C	E	B	E	R	G		A		O		Z
G		P		R		A	R	C	H	W	A	Y
H		E		E		S		H		N		M
T	R	E	A	D	S		M	O	U	S	S	E

224

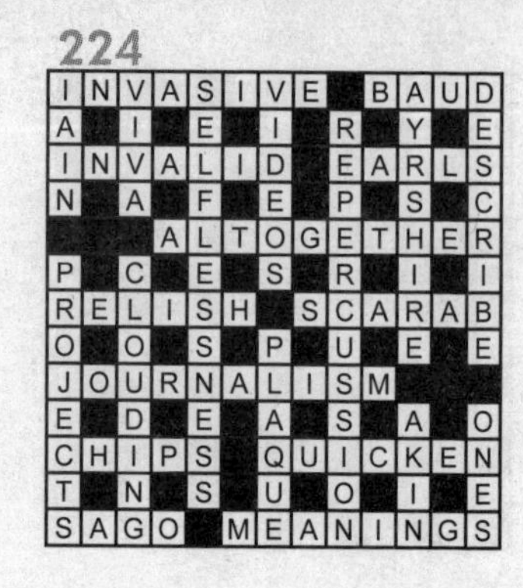

225

C	L	A	V	I	C	L	E		L	A	M	P
H		L		N		A				L		U
A	B	B	O	T		N	O	S	E	B	A	G
T		E		E		D				I		I
		D		R		E	T	H	A	N	O	L
E	V	O	L	V	E	D		A		O		I
G				A				P				S
Y		A		L		A	S	P	H	A	L	T
P	E	R	U	S	A	L		E		V		
T		D				P		N		I		A
I	K	E	B	A	N	A		I	N	D	E	X
A		N				C		N		L		L
N	E	T	S		G	A	R	G	O	Y	L	E

226

227

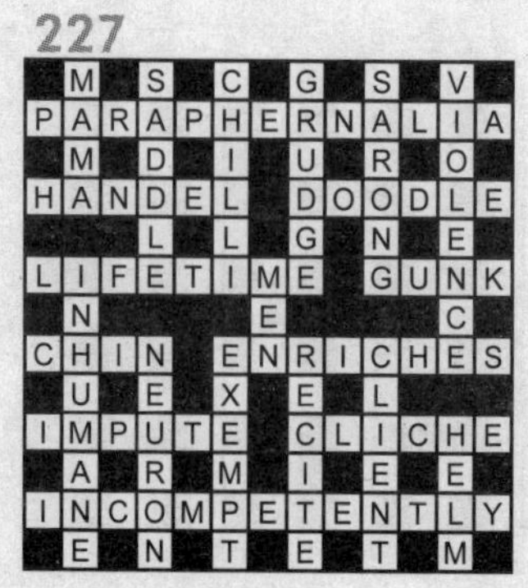

228

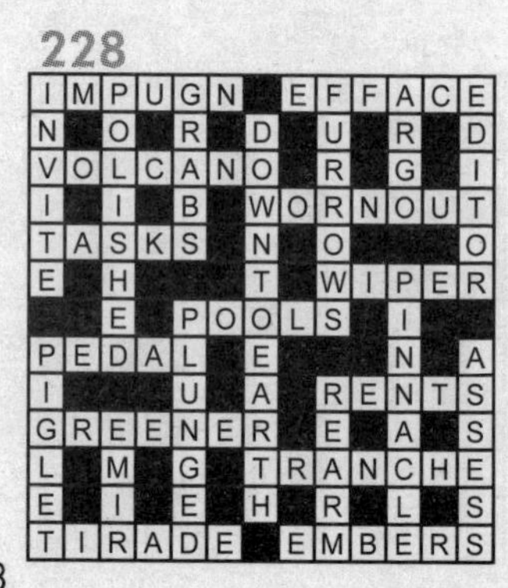

229

P	A	R	A	S	I	T	E		J	E	E	P
U		E		O		O		U		S		A
S	T	E	A	M	E	R		N	I	P	P	Y
H		K		N		R		F		O		M
			C	A	R	I	C	A	T	U	R	E
E		B		M		D		V		S		N
P	H	O	E	B	E		M	O	Z	A	R	T
I		O		U		O		U		L		S
D	I	S	C	L	O	S	U	R	E			
E		T		I		T		A		B		L
M	A	I	D	S		L	I	B	E	R	I	A
I		N		M		E		L		A		D
C	O	G	S		A	R	D	E	N	T	L	Y

230

E	S	C	A	P	E	S		O		T	H	Y
	C			L		I	M	P	L	Y		O
S	A	R	C	A	S	M		A		P		U
	N			Y		P		L	O	H	A	N
U	N	S	E	T	T	L	E			O		G
	E			I		Y		D		O		E
D	R	E	A	M	S		S	I	G	N	E	R
E		M		E		C		S			N	
E		B			E	A	S	T	W	A	R	D
P	A	L	E	R		T		A			A	
F		E		A		N	E	S	T	E	G	G
R		M	E	N	S	A		T			E	
Y	E	S		K		P	R	E	C	E	D	E

231

M	E	R	I	N	G	U	E		P	E	E	R
O		A		A		N		C		N		O
W	A	T	E	R	E	D		O	D	D	L	Y
S		S		R		U		N		U		A
			C	O	L	L	A	T	E	R	A	L
A		A		W		Y		R		I		I
R	E	S	U	M	E		H	A	U	N	T	S
T		S		I		A		D		G		T
F	R	I	E	N	D	S	H	I	P			
U		S		D		S		C		X		O
L	A	T	T	E		U	N	T	A	M	E	D
L		E		D		R		E		E		E
Y	O	D	A		W	E	D	D	I	N	G	S

232

	M	I	S	C	H	I	E	V	O	U	S	
P		N		A		T		E		N		I
L		G		B	I	S	O	N		I	O	N
A	O	R	T	A		E		O		T		C
Y		A		R		L		M	A	Y	O	R
W	R	I	T	E	O	F	F					E
R		N		T				S		E		M
I					C	A	N	T	I	C	L	E
G	L	E	A	N		C		U		H		N
H		X		A		Q		T	W	I	S	T
T	H	E		V	A	U	L	T		D		A
S		R		E		I		E		N		L
	U	T	I	L	I	T	A	R	I	A	N	

233

R	A	P	T		E	S	C	A	P	E	E	S
O		A		F		H		P		X		U
U	P	R	A	I	S	E		P	E	A	L	S
N		T		E		K		R		C		A
D	A	Y		L		E		O	U	T	E	N
T				D	E	L	T	A		E		S
H		S		G				C		D		A
E		U		L	A	R	C	H				R
C	O	N	G	A		E		A		V	I	A
L		R		S		W		B		E		N
O	M	I	T	S		O	B	L	I	G	E	D
C		S		E		R		E		A		O
K	E	E	P	S	A	K	E		A	N	O	N

234

F	A	L	L		S	K	I	M	M	I	N	G
A		I		E		E		A		N		A
R	E	M	O	V	A	L		G	A	S	E	S
R		I		O		V		N		U		H
I	N	T	E	L	L	I	G	I	B	L	Y	
E				U		N		F		A		H
R	E	F	U	T	E		P	I	E	R	C	E
S		L		I		S		C				L
	R	U	N	O	F	T	H	E	M	I	L	L
S		V		N		U		N		M		B
C	H	I	N	A		D	E	C	L	A	R	E
A		A		R		I		E		G		N
B	A	L	L	Y	H	O	O		N	E	A	T

235

M	O	B	S		H	I	N	D	M	O	S	T
A		E		U		N		I		T		H
L	E	A	R	N	E	D		C	A	T	E	R
A		S		C		I		T		O		E
D	U	T	C	H		A	N	A	E	M	I	A
M				A		N		T		A		T
I	N	F	I	R	M		L	O	U	N	G	E
N		E		I		A		R				N
I	N	V	I	T	E	D		S	A	U	D	I
S		E		A		J		H		S		N
T	H	R	O	B		U	N	I	T	I	N	G
E		E		L		R		P		N		L
R	E	D	D	E	N	E	D		U	G	L	Y

236

E	D	U	C	E		C	U	S	T	O	M	S
Y		N		X		I			H		U	
E		M		C		N		G	R	A	D	E
O	D	O	M	E	T	E	R		O		D	
P		V		R		M		S	W	A	Y	S
E	X	E	M	P	L	A	R		N			W
N		D		T				D		M		E
E			O		D	O	V	E	C	O	T	E
R	E	I	N	S		V		M		R		T
	X		I		M	O	N	O	T	O	N	E
L	U	T	O	N		I		N		C		N
	D		N			D		I		C		E
V	E	S	S	E	L	S		C	H	O	I	R

237

F	L	O	O	D	I	N	G		L	I	M	P
I		A		E		E		I		N		R
V	E	R	A	N	D	A		N	A	C	R	E
E		S		U		T		E		U		C
			I	N	F	L	E	X	I	B	L	E
D		E		C		Y		P		A		D
R	U	S	T	I	C		F	E	T	T	L	E
E		O		A		R		R		E		S
A	N	T	I	T	H	E	S	I	S			
D		E		I		S		E		P		L
F	O	R	G	O		C	O	N	S	O	L	E
U		I		N		U		C		O		A
L	A	C	Y		D	E	T	E	R	R	E	D

238

L	O	W	S		O	V	E	R	A	L	L	S
I		O		C		O		E		A		H
T	E	R	N	A	R	Y		P	A	N	T	O
T		L		R		A		R		T		R
L	I	D		E		G		E	J	E	C	T
E				L	E	E	K	S		R		T
M		G		E				E		N		E
E		R		S	U	D	A	N				M
R	I	O	T	S		U		T		C	E	P
M		W		N		F		I		H		E
A	L	I	V	E		F	U	N	N	I	E	R
I		N		S		L		G		L		E
D	I	G	E	S	T	E	D		B	E	N	D

239

S	O	C	I	A	L		A	D	V	I	C	E
A		I		N		O		O		N		D
V	E	R	N	I	E	R		O		F		I
A		C		O		C	U	R	I	O	U	S
G	L	U	O	N		H		W				O
E		L				E		A	S	H	E	N
		A		A	S	S	A	Y		E		
S	H	R	U	B		T				A		C
A				A		R		L	A	V	E	R
P	E	T	U	N	I	A		E		I		I
P		E		D		T	E	M	P	E	R	S
E		A		O		E		O		S		P
R	A	K	I	N	G		K	N	O	T	T	Y

240

L	A	N	D	F	I	L	L		E	V	E	S
A		A		L		I		D		E		E
Z	E	P	H	Y	R	S		I	B	S	E	N
Y		S		I		T		S		U		T
			U	N	D	E	R	C	O	V	E	R
M		O		G		N		O		I		I
I	N	F	U	S	E		I	N	D	U	C	E
S		F		A		C		N		S		S
S	T	I	P	U	L	A	T	E	D			
P		C		C		N		C		M		C
E	L	I	T	E		A	N	T	H	I	L	L
N		A		R		D		E		E		A
D	U	L	Y		H	A	R	D	E	N	E	D

241

	C	A	L	L	O	U	S	N	E	S	S	
C		B		Y		N		E		T		S
A		R		C	I	V	I	C		A	R	E
L	O	A	T	H		E		K		V		L
C		D		E		I		S	H	E	A	F
U	N	E	V	E	N	L	Y					C
L		S		S				D		O		E
A					A	M	E	R	I	C	A	N
T	A	R	T	S		A		E		T		T
I		O		E		K		S	T	A	I	R
N	E	W		V	E	E	R	S		G		E
G		E		E		U		E		O		D
	T	R	A	N	S	P	A	R	E	N	T	

242

P	O	M	P		V	A	G	A	B	O	N	D
E		O		F		S		L		R		A
N	A	T	U	R	E	S		L	O	L	L	Y
D		E		O		I		I		A		S
A	S	T	O	N	I	S	H	M	E	N	T	
N				T		T		P		D		C
T	H	E	S	I	S		R	O	C	O	C	O
S		L		S		S		R				N
	H	I	P	P	O	P	O	T	A	M	U	S
E		S		I		R		A		I		I
P	O	I	S	E		A	W	N	I	N	G	S
I		O		C		Y		T		I		T
C	A	N	O	E	I	S	T		I	M	P	S

243

	R	O	C	K	A	N	D	R	O	L	L	
I		R		I		A		I		O		B
N		A		T	A	M	E	D		T	A	R
S	O	N	I	C		I		E		T		O
T		G		H		N		S	C	O	R	N
I	C	E	B	E	R	G	S					Z
N		S		N				F		T		E
C					J	E	R	O	B	O	A	M
T	A	L	O	N		L		X		R		E
I		A		O		I		T	A	P	E	D
V	O	W		R	E	C	U	R		E		A
E		N		S		I		O		D		L
	O	S	T	E	N	T	A	T	I	O	N	

244

H	I	V	E		G	U	N	M	E	T	A	L
O		I		A		R		O		E		I
L	E	G	I	B	L	E		T	I	M	I	D
O		G		S				H		P		O
G	O	O	D	T	E	M	P	E	R	E	D	
R				E		O		R		R		D
A	N	A		M	E	R	I	T		A	W	E
M		B		I		P		O				T
	H	Y	P	O	C	H	O	N	D	R	I	A
C		S		U				G		U		I
O	A	S	E	S		T	H	U	R	M	A	N
M		A		L		E		E		B		E
A	L	L	A	Y	I	N	G		P	A	T	E

245

G	R	A	F	T		W	E	A	K	E	S	T
L		V		E		A			R		W	
U		E		S		L		M	O	S	E	S
T	H	R	O	T	T	L	E		N		A	
I		A		A		O		H	E	A	R	S
N	I	G	H	T	O	W	L		R			E
O		E		E				E		P		C
U			P		S	C	E	N	A	R	I	O
S	M	E	A	R		A		G		E		N
	A		L		S	P	A	R	K	L	E	D
K	N	E	L	T		T		A		A		A
	I		O			O		V		T		R
F	A	R	R	I	E	R		E	M	E	R	Y

246

A	L	T	O		C	O	S	M	E	T	I	C
S		E		A		P		E		E		H
T	E	N	A	B	L	E		A	D	D	E	R
O		O		S		N		L		I		O
N	E	R	V	E		L	A	Y	D	O	W	N
I				N		Y		M		U		O
S	A	F	E	T	Y		F	O	S	S	I	L
H		E		M		L		U				O
I	N	S	P	I	R	E		T	W	A	N	G
N		T		N		S		H		L		I
G	R	I	N	D		S	C	E	P	T	I	C
L		V		E		E		D		E		A
Y	I	E	L	D	I	N	G		O	R	A	L

247

S	P	E	A	R	S		E	G	R	E	S	S
P		N		O		S		R		L		I
L	I	G	H	T	U	P		A		A		E
I		R		O		R	E	M	I	N	D	S
C	H	A	I	R		I		M				T
E		V				N		A	L	P	H	A
		E		W	A	G	E	R		H		
F	U	D	G	E		F				A		C
E				L		I		P	A	S	T	E
R	E	V	O	L	V	E		I		E		N
R		E		O		L	I	Q	U	O	R	S
E		E		F		D		U		U		O
T	H	R	I	F	T		B	E	T	T	E	R

248

I	N	T	O		I	D	L	E	N	E	S	S
N		E		C		E		L		C		E
D	A	M	S	O	N	S		E	A	S	E	L
E		P		M		P		C		T		F
S	I	T		M		O		T	H	A	N	E
C				O	U	T	E	R		S		V
R		V		N				O		Y		I
I		I		W	H	O	O	P				D
B	A	T	H	E		P		L		F	E	E
A		I		A		P		A		R		N
B	R	A	W	L		U	N	T	W	I	S	T
L		T		T		G		E		A		L
E	L	E	P	H	A	N	T		X	R	A	Y

249

D	E	C	E	M	B	E	R		D	I	S	C
A		O		O		N				N		O
L	A	T	I	N		S	H	E	A	R	E	R
E		T		O		I				O		R
		O		L		G	R	E	N	A	D	E
P	O	N	T	O	O	N		N		D		C
R				G				A				T
E		S		U		B	E	C	O	M	E	S
S	U	P	R	E	M	O		T		A		
S		I				N		M		N		S
M	E	L	L	O	W	S		E	X	T	O	L
E		L				A		N		R		A
N	O	S	E		D	I	S	T	R	A	C	T

250

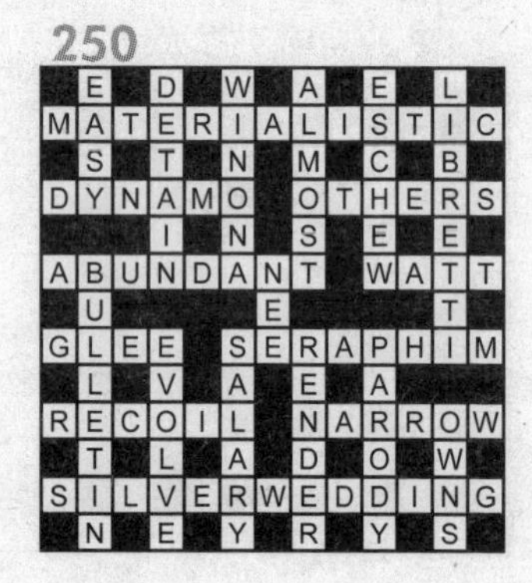

	E		D		W		A		E		L	
M	A	T	E	R	I	A	L	I	S	T	I	C
	S		T		N		M		C		B	
D	Y	N	A	M	O		O	T	H	E	R	S
			I		N		S		E		E	
A	B	U	N	D	A	N	T		W	A	T	T
	U					E					T	
G	L	E	E		S	E	R	A	P	H	I	M
	L		V		A		E		A			
R	E	C	O	I	L		N	A	R	R	O	W
	T		L		A		D		O		W	
S	I	L	V	E	R	W	E	D	D	I	N	G
	N		E		Y		R		Y		S	

251

U	N	I	F	Y		R	E	C	T	I	F	Y
N		M		E		E			O		E	
D		P		L		S		L	U	C	I	D
E	N	R	O	L	L	E	D		C		G	
C		E		I		L		G	A	U	N	T
I	N	S	A	N	E	L	Y		N			I
D		S		G				T		A		M
E			A		S	T	R	A	D	D	L	E
D	R	I	V	E		R		X		M		T
	U		O		B	A	S	I	L	I	C	A
A	L	B	U	S		N		I		R		B
	E		C			C		N		E		L
A	R	C	H	I	V	E		G	O	R	G	E

252

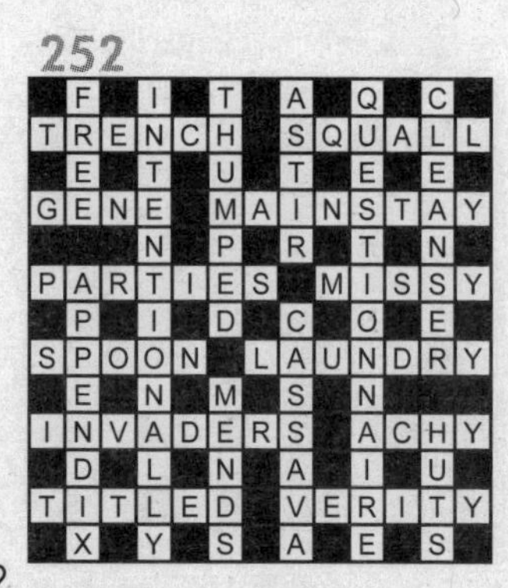

	F		I		T		A		Q		C	
T	R	E	N	C	H		S	Q	U	A	L	L
	E		T		U		T		E		E	
G	E	N	E		M	A	I	N	S	T	A	Y
			N		P		R		T		N	
P	A	R	T	I	E	S		M	I	S	S	Y
	P		I		D		C		O		E	
S	P	O	O	N		L	A	U	N	D	R	Y
	E		N		M		S		N			
I	N	V	A	D	E	R	S		A	C	H	Y
	D		L		N		A		I		U	
T	I	T	L	E	D		V	E	R	I	T	Y
	X		Y		S		A		E		S	

253

F	I	G	S		S	U	S	P	E	C	T	S
O		A		C		P		R		A		O
R	A	T	I	O	N	S		O	I	L	E	D
E		E		M		H		T		D		A
M	A	S	S	P	R	O	D	U	C	E	D	
O				L		T		B		R		C
S	E	E	M	E	D		N	E	V	A	D	A
T		X		T		A		R				N
	S	P	R	E	A	D	E	A	G	L	E	D
A		I		N		R		N		E		I
L	E	A	V	E		O	R	C	H	A	R	D
E		T		S		I		E		S		L
C	R	E	O	S	O	T	E		W	H	E	Y

254

	G		T		G		T		U		S	
M	O	T	H	E	R	C	O	U	N	T	R	Y
	B		I		E		P		R		I	
S	I	E	R	R	A		I	D	E	A	L	S
			S		S		C		A		A	
S	C	A	T	T	E	R	S		L	O	N	E
	O					E					K	
U	N	I	T		O	V	E	R	D	R	A	W
	T		R		R		U		O			
V	A	L	U	E	D		R	E	B	E	L	S
	I		M		E		O		B		U	
I	N	A	P	P	R	O	P	R	I	A	T	E
	S		S		S		E		N		E	

255

R	O	U	T	E	S		T		V		A	
E		N			T	E	R	R	I	B	L	E
S	U	M			R		A		E		I	
O		A	T	T	A	I	N		W	R	E	N
R		S			Y		S		I		N	
T	A	K	E	N		C	O	Y	N	E	S	S
			M		E		M		G			
M	E	M	B	E	R	S		A	S	I	D	E
	L		E		O		S			N		L
F	I	Z	Z		S	U	P	E	R	B		A
	X		Z		I		A			O	A	T
K	I	L	L	J	O	Y	S			R		E
	R		E		N		M	A	N	N	E	D

256

E	T	C	H		F	I	L	I	G	R	E	E
Y		O		M		N		N		I		R
E	M	P	R	E	S	S		C	O	V	E	N
P		E		T		I		O		I		E
I	N	D	I	A	N	S	U	M	M	E	R	
E				P		T		P		R		B
C	A	T	C	H	Y		H	A	W	A	I	I
E		H		Y		P		R				C
	P	E	R	S	P	I	C	A	C	I	T	Y
S		R		I		S		B		N		C
C	O	M	I	C		C	O	L	O	N	E	L
A		O		A		E		E		E		E
R	E	S	T	L	E	S	S		P	R	O	S

257

G	R	A	N	D	P	A		A		A	U	K
	A			I		S	U	P	E	R		R
A	P	P	E	A	L	S		E		M		Y
	P			L		A		S	T	R	O	P
M	O	N	G	O	L	I	A			E		T
	R			G		L		P		S		O
A	T	R	I	U	M		P	R	O	T	O	N
Z		E		E		P		E			S	
I		C			W	O	R	S	H	I	P	S
M	E	E	T	S		T		U			R	
U		D		C		A	D	M	I	R	E	D
T		E	N	A	C	T		E			Y	
H	A	S		N		O	D	D	N	E	S	S

258

E	M	B	L	E	M		E	V	A	D	E	D
S		A		T		G		I		A		E
C	A	T	C	H	E	R		N		U		A
U		H		I		A	C	E	R	B	I	C
D	O	R	I	C		S		G				O
O		O				S		A	L	I	E	N
		O		U	S	H	E	R		M		
D	E	M	O	N		O				P		R
E				D		P		T	H	E	R	E
C	O	V	E	R	U	P		R		R		A
A		O		E		E	V	O	K	I	N	G
M		T		S		R		U		A		A
P	L	E	A	S	E		S	T	O	L	E	N

259

A	S	C	E	T	I	C		T		P	A	R
	C			E		A	R	O	S	E		A
C	H	E	V	R	O	N		E		R		I
	E			M		O		S	A	T	E	D
P	R	O	V	I	D	E	D			U		E
	Z			N		S		B		R		R
D	I	S	M	A	L		G	L	O	B	E	S
R		C		L		N		I			M	
O		R			C	I	N	N	A	M	O	N
P	L	A	Y	S		M		D			T	
O		P		A		B	R	I	T	A	I	N
F		P	I	L	A	U		N			O	
F	L	Y		E		S	E	G	M	E	N	T

260

S	O	B	S		C	O	N	F	L	I	C	T
T		I		E		T		O		T		E
A	D	J	U	N	C	T		R	E	A	L	M
C		O		C		E		M		L		P
Y	O	U	T	H		R	E	A	L	I	S	E
F				A		S		L		C		R
E	B	B	I	N	G		O	D	E	S	S	A
R		E		T		I		E				M
G	O	S	L	I	N	G		H	I	N	G	E
U		T		N		N		Y		I		N
S	P	R	I	G		O	D	D	M	E	N	T
O		E		L		R		E		C		A
N	E	W	L	Y	W	E	D		T	E	A	L

261

D	U	S	T	S		C	H	A	N	G	E	D
E		T		E		O			O		N	
M		R		V		P		S	T	E	E	L
E	X	E	G	E	S	I	S		A		M	
A		A		N		E		D	R	A	Y	S
N	E	M	A	T	O	D	E		Y			E
I		S		H				P		S		N
N			A		T	R	O	U	S	E	R	S
G	R	O	W	N		E		B		V		A
	A		H		E	A	R	L	I	E	S	T
A	N	V	I	L		L		I		R		I
	K		L			M		S		A		O
A	S	C	E	N	T	S		H	E	L	E	N

262

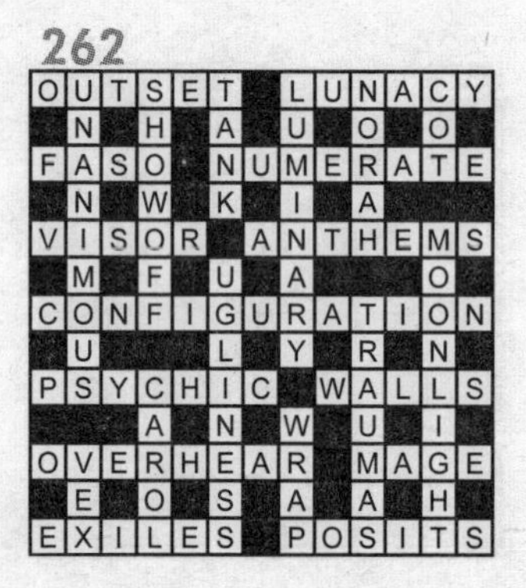

O	U	T	S	E	T		L	U	N	A	C	Y
	N		H		A		U		O		O	
F	A	S	O		N	U	M	E	R	A	T	E
	N		W		K		I		A			
V	I	S	O	R		A	N	T	H	E	M	S
	M		F		U		A				O	
C	O	N	F	I	G	U	R	A	T	I	O	N
	U				L		Y		R		N	
P	S	Y	C	H	I	C		W	A	L	L	S
			A		N		W		U		I	
O	V	E	R	H	E	A	R		M	A	G	E
	E		O		S		A		A		H	
E	X	I	L	E	S		P	O	S	I	T	S

263

C	A	D	E	N	Z	A		T		C	H	I
	S			E		G	U	A	V	A		N
S	T	O	R	A	G	E		L		R		V
	O			T		O		C	A	I	R	O
J	U	V	E	N	I	L	E			B		I
	N			E		D		R		O		C
A	D	J	U	S	T		B	E	M	U	S	E
T		O		S		U		H			C	
H		U			O	R	I	E	N	T	A	L
E	A	R	L	Y		B		A			N	
I		N		O		A	L	R	E	A	D	Y
S		E	L	L	E	N		S			A	
M	A	Y		K		E	Y	E	B	A	L	L

264

R	O	B	S		A	R	R	I	V	A	L	S
E		Y		L		A		N		L		P
C	A	L	L	I	N	G		C	E	L	L	O
E		A		C		I		O		E		R
P	A	W		K		N		R	I	G	H	T
T				E	A	G	E	R		R		S
I		B		T				I		O		M
V		R		Y	O	U	N	G				A
E	P	I	C	S		N		I		P	A	N
N		O		P		S		B		E		S
E	X	C	E	L		U	N	L	E	A	S	H
S		H		I		R		E		R		I
S	W	E	E	T	P	E	A		F	L	O	P

265

T	U	C	K		S	T	R	E	A	M	E	R
O		R		R		O		X		E		E
A	M	U	L	E	T	S		P	S	A	L	M
D		E		S		S		E		N		O
I	N	L	E	T		E	A	R	L	I	E	R
N				A		D		I		N		S
T	O	R	Q	U	E		B	E	A	G	L	E
H		E		R		G		N				L
E	P	I	T	A	X	Y		T	R	I	P	E
H		G		T		R		I		D		S
O	U	N	C	E		A	Z	A	L	E	A	S
L		E		U		T		L		A		L
E	N	D	O	R	S	E	S		C	L	O	Y

266

A	L	L	I	A	N	C	E		H	A	L	F
I		A		F		O				N		R
D	I	G	I	T		A	B	A	L	O	N	E
E		G		E		T				R		N
		E		R		E	N	S	N	A	R	E
W	I	D	E	N	E	D		T		K		T
A				O				E				I
Y		C		O		P	L	A	S	T	I	C
F	L	A	U	N	T	Y		D		R		
A		M				T		F		I		F
R	E	B	I	R	T	H		A	W	F	U	L
E		E				O		S		L		E
R	A	R	E		A	N	A	T	H	E	M	A

267

D	I	V	E	R		A	P	R	I	C	O	T
O		U		E		V			N		O	
D		L		C		E		B	L	A	Z	E
E	G	G	P	L	A	N	T		A		E	
C		A		I		U		S	N	I	D	E
A	T	T	E	N	D	E	D		D			M
G		E		E				P		T		P
O			U		C	H	A	R	C	O	A	L
N	Y	M	P	H		Y		E		R		O
	O		H		H	E	A	V	E	N	L	Y
F	L	U	I	D		N		I		A		I
	K		L			A		E		D		N
U	S	E	L	E	S	S		W	R	O	N	G

268

C	E	D	I	L	L	A		G		E	N	D
	G			I		S	C	R	U	M		E
N	O	S	E	G	A	Y		I		B		F
	T			N		L		P	I	A	N	O
V	I	T	R	E	O	U	S			R		R
	S			O		M		B		G		M
S	T	E	P	U	P		G	R	O	O	M	S
C		P		S		R		A			A	
A		I			M	E	A	N	D	E	R	S
P	U	T	O	N		G		D			T	
U		A		O		G	R	I	F	F	I	N
L		P	A	S	T	A		S			N	
A	A	H		Y		E	X	H	I	B	I	T

269

A	L	L	E	G	E		J	A	C	K	A	L
B		I		L		M		I		I		A
J	A	M	A	I	C	A		R		W		R
E		E		D		L	O	P	P	I	N	G
C	U	R	I	E		E		O				E
T		I				D		R	A	Z	O	R
		C		F	A	I	N	T		I		
J	O	K	E	R		C				M		O
E				I		T		C	U	B	E	S
J	A	C	U	Z	Z	I		U		A		P
U		A		Z		O	C	T	O	B	E	R
N		V		L		N		U		W		E
E	R	A	S	E	D		S	P	E	E	D	Y

270

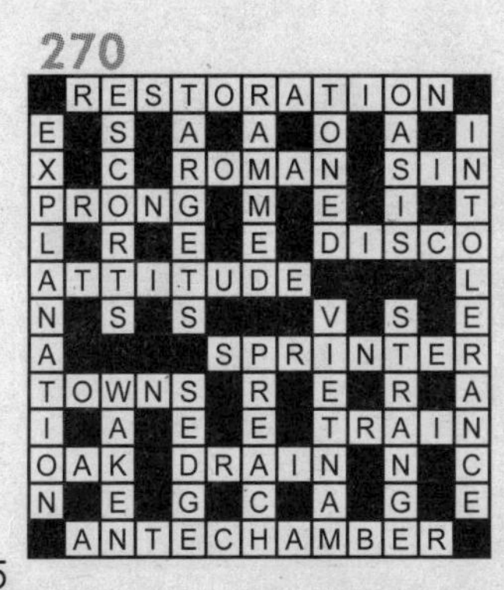

	R	E	S	T	O	R	A	T	I	O	N	
E		S		A		A		O		A		I
X		C		R	O	M	A	N		S	I	N
P	R	O	N	G		M		E		I		T
L		R		E		E		D	I	S	C	O
A	T	T	I	T	U	D	E					L
N		S		S				V		S		E
A					S	P	R	I	N	T	E	R
T	O	W	N	S		R		E		R		A
I		A		E		E		T	R	A	I	N
O	A	K		D	R	A	I	N		N		C
N		E		G		C		A		G		E
	A	N	T	E	C	H	A	M	B	E	R	

271

A	R	C	H		E	P	I	P	H	A	N	Y
R		H		M		S		L		B		A
T	H	E	R	A	P	Y		A	S	S	A	M
I		W		L		C		Y		O		S
F	L	Y	O	N	T	H	E	W	A	L	L	
I				O		E		I		V		L
C	I	T	R	U	S		A	T	H	E	N	A
E		H		R		W		H				D
	D	E	L	I	G	H	T	F	U	L	L	Y
Y		O		S		I		I		E		B
E	A	R	T	H		F	E	R	R	A	R	I
T		E		E		F		E		D		R
I	M	M	O	D	E	S	T		U	S	E	D

272

273

D	O	W	N	Y		G	R	A	V	I	T	Y
E		R		A		R			A		I	
T		I		W		E		S	C	A	L	D
E	N	G	I	N	E	E	R		A		L	
C		G		I		C		A	N	G	S	T
T	A	L	E	N	T	E	D		T			H
I		E		G				M		R		R
O			E		O	B	L	I	G	A	T	E
N	O	I	S	Y		R		N		D		A
	A		T		P	O	P	U	L	I	S	T
S	K	U	A	S		L		T		A		E
	U		T			L		E		T		N
A	M	N	E	S	T	Y		S	E	E	M	S

274

275

L	O	B	S		E	D	U	C	A	T	E	D
I		O		D		O		A		E		O
F	E	N	C	I	N	G		R	O	A	R	S
E		G		S				B		S		E
B	O	O	G	I	E	W	O	O	G	I	E	
O				N		H		H		N		O
A	N	Y		G	R	A	V	Y		G	O	B
T		A		E		R		D				S
	T	R	A	N	S	F	E	R	A	B	L	E
A		D		U				A		L		S
G	U	A	N	O		G	U	T	T	E	R	S
U		G		U		I		E		A		E
E	V	E	N	S	O	N	G		S	T	U	D

276

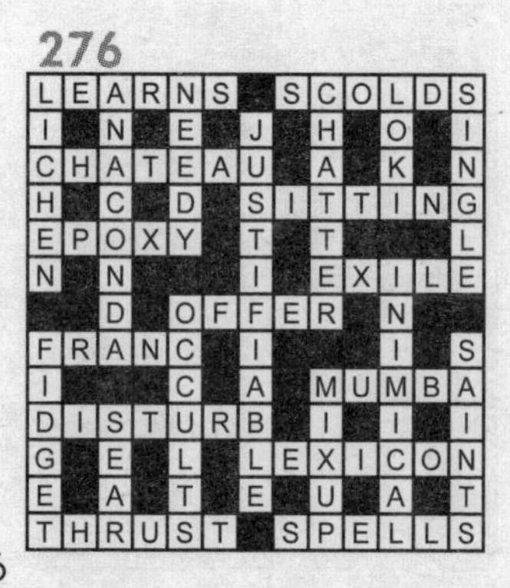

277

I	N	C	U	R	S		D		T		V	
R		U			K	E	R	C	H	I	E	F
O	D	D			I		E		A		I	
N		D	I	P	P	E	D		I	L	L	S
I		L			S		G		L		E	
C	R	E	P	T		D	E	M	A	N	D	S
			R		N		R		N			
S	P	E	E	D	U	P		A	D	A	P	T
	L		C		M		D			V		I
M	A	I	L		B	R	O	N	C	O		M
	N		U		E		O			W	O	E
W	A	N	D	E	R	E	R			A		R
	R		E		S		S	T	Y	L	U	S

278

M	O	P	S		I	S	O	L	A	T	E	S
I		E		D		T		E		R		T
S	E	C	R	E	T	E		G	R	A	T	E
C		A		L		A		I		C		A
E	N	N	U	I		M	A	T	C	H	E	D
L				C		Y		I		E		F
L	I	N	E	A	R		I	M	P	A	L	A
A		E		T		M		A				S
N	O	U	V	E	A	U		T	W	E	E	T
E		T		S		E		E		R		N
O	G	R	E	S		S	I	L	E	N	C	E
U		A		E		L		Y		I		S
S	P	L	E	N	D	I	D		H	E	N	S

279

S	H	A	B	B	Y		I	M	P	O	R	T
T		N		L		C		A		I		R
O	R	I	N	O	C	O		G		N		E
D		M		A		M	A	N	I	K	I	N
G	I	A	N	T		M		U				D
Y		T				I		M	I	S	T	Y
		E		C	O	N	E	S		T		
B	A	S	I	L		G				A		L
I				A		L		C	U	R	I	A
S	A	S	H	I	M	I		E		F		W
H		E		M		N	U	L	L	I	F	Y
O		E		E		G		L		S		E
P	O	M	A	D	E		E	S	T	H	E	R

280

F	U	N	K		D	E	E	R	S	K	I	N
R		E		E		Y		E		N		O
A	B	S	E	N	C	E		S	T	E	R	N
G		T		T				U		E		E
R	E	S	E	R	V	E	P	R	I	C	E	
A				E		R		R		A		N
N	O	D		P	R	O	V	E		P	E	A
T		R		R		D		C				M
	L	I	F	E	S	E	N	T	E	N	C	E
A		B		N				I		A		D
C	A	B	L	E		W	H	O	E	V	E	R
N		L		U		O		N		A		O
E	Y	E	B	R	O	W	S		S	L	A	P

281

C	L	A	N		R	E	V	A	M	P	E	D
O		D		M		A		R		R		I
L	O	I	T	E	R	S		C	R	O	S	S
L		E		Z		T		H		V		R
A	B	U	Z	Z		E	D	I	F	I	C	E
B				O		R		T		S		S
O	P	P	O	S	E		R	E	C	O	U	P
R		E		O		A		C				E
A	P	R	O	P	O	S		T	O	P	I	C
T		S		R		T		U		L		T
I	B	I	Z	A		H	E	R	S	E	L	F
O		S		N		M		E		A		U
N	O	T	I	O	N	A	L		I	D	O	L

282

B		D		T		S		C		H		A
R	A	I	N	W	A	T	E	R		O	W	N
I		S		I		R		A		A		O
M	Y	T	H	S		I	G	N	O	R	E	D
S		A		T		K		K				Y
	I	N	D	E	X	E	S		T	H	I	N
F		C		R				P		I		E
A	L	E	S		R	I	C	H	E	S	T	
N				F		M		R		T		S
C	L	E	A	R	U	P		A	L	O	N	E
I		G		O		E		S		R		R
F	O	G		W	O	N	D	E	R	I	N	G
Y		Y		N		D		S		C		E

283

	P	E	R	S	O	N	I	F	I	E	S	
I		N		M		E		A		N		I
N		G		A	S	T	E	R		D	I	N
T	A	R	N	S		T		M		O		A
E		O		H		E		S	E	W	E	D
M	I	S	D	E	E	D	S					V
P		S		D				V		S		E
E					D	E	C	A	N	T	E	R
R	A	K	E	S		L		N		R		T
A		E		E		D		E	L	U	D	E
T	E	E		G	L	E	N	S		D		N
E		L		U		S		S		E		T
	E	S	S	E	N	T	I	A	L	L	Y	

284

H	O	B	N	O	B		A		G		B	
A		L			I	N	C	U	R	R	E	D
P	S	I			N		R		A		N	
P		G	U	N	G	H	O		F	O	I	L
E		H			O		B		F		G	
N	A	T	T	Y		R	A	D	I	A	N	S
			A		P		T		T			
A	B	Y	S	M	A	L		B	I	R	C	H
	R		T		P		D			H		I
H	I	D	E		R	A	R	I	T	Y		A
	G		F		I		A			M	A	T
S	H	R	U	N	K	E	N			E		U
	T		L		A		K	A	N	S	A	S

285

P	L	A	N	K	T	O	N		S	P	U	R
A		B		I		S				U		H
R	E	S	I	N		I	M	P	I	N	G	E
K		O		S		R				I		O
		R		W		I	N	F	U	S	E	S
R	I	B	B	O	N	S		O		H		T
E				M				R				A
D		S		A		B	I	G	G	E	S	T
F	L	A	N	N	E	L		A		T		
A		U				E		T		H		E
C	A	N	T	A	T	A		H	E	I	S	T
E		A				C		E		C		N
D	E	S	K		C	H	A	R	I	S	M	A

286

P	O	K	Y		A	L	F	R	E	S	C	O
E		E		C		E		E		P		V
R	A	M	B	L	E	S		A	B	O	V	E
I		P		A		S		S		N		R
O	U	T		I		O		S	A	G	E	S
D				R	I	N	S	E		E		T
I		S		V				S		S		A
C		H		O	G	L	E	S				T
T	R	U	L	Y		E		M		D	Y	E
A		T		A		N		E		R		M
B	R	O	W	N		T	O	N	N	A	G	E
L		F		C		I		T		W		N
E	N	F	E	E	B	L	E		K	N	O	T

287

A	L	G	A		S	C	I	S	S	I	O	N
S		O		A		O		T		M		O
C	H	U	F	F	E	D		R	I	P	E	N
E		G		F		D		A		O		A
R	E	E	V	E		L	A	W	S	U	I	T
T				C		E		B		N		T
A	D	A	P	T	S		M	E	D	D	L	E
I		I		I		S		R				N
N	O	R	F	O	L	K		R	A	G	E	D
A		D		N		I		I		L		A
B	U	R	M	A		L	E	E	R	Y	A	N
L		O		T		L		S		P		C
E	S	P	R	E	S	S	O		S	H	O	E

288

N	I	G	H		N	I	T	R	O	G	E	N
O		A		U		C		E		R		E
N	O	M	I	N	E	E		P	R	O	W	L
A		U		D		A		O		U		S
P	A	T		E		G		S	I	S	Q	O
P				R	E	E	K	S		E		N
E		O		G				E		S		M
A		S		A	N	D	E	S				A
R	I	S	E	R		O		S		V	A	N
A		I		M		M		I		I		D
N	I	C	H	E		I	S	O	T	O	P	E
C		L		N		N		N		L		L
E	J	E	C	T	I	O	N		S	A	G	A

289

U	R	G	E		C	O	N	F	I	N	E	D
N		I		C		B		R		U		I
C	E	L	L	A	R	S		E	X	A	M	S
O		D		L		E		U		N		T
N	A	S	A	L		S	I	D	E	C	A	R
D				I		S		I		E		E
I	N	D	I	G	O		M	A	S	S	E	S
T		E		R		D		N				S
I	N	S	T	A	T	E		S	U	S	H	I
O		K		P		A		L		H		N
N	O	T	C	H		D	R	I	V	I	N	G
A		O		E		E		P		N		L
L	E	P	O	R	I	N	E		B	E	V	Y

290

	B		C		C		S		Z		A	
V	I	G	O	U	R		C	L	E	F	T	S
	L		M		I		O		R		T	
A	L	U	M		C	H	O	C	O	L	A	T
			U		K		T		T		I	
P	L	A	N	T	E	D		M	O	U	N	D
	E		I		T		T		L		E	
S	A	U	C	E		T	H	R	E	A	D	S
	F		A		P		E		R			
F	L	O	T	I	L	L	A		A	U	R	A
	E		I		I		T		N		I	
S	T	R	O	B	E		R	E	C	K	O	N
	S		N		S		E		E		T	

291

R	I	C	H	L	Y		S	T	R	E	A	M
E		A		I		T		O		A		E
D	E	L	I	V	E	R		O		R		D
U		A		E		A	T	L	A	N	T	A
C	O	M	E	S		N		B				L
E		A				S		O	P	A	L	S
		R		A	F	F	I	X		G		
A	L	I	G	N		I				N		O
B				Y		G		B	L	O	W	S
J	U	J	I	T	S	U		E		S		C
U		U		I		R	E	G	A	T	T	A
R		T		M		E		I		I		R
E	Y	E	L	E	T		K	N	O	C	K	S

292

	I	N	S	E	N	S	I	T	I	V	E	
I		U		A		T		E		I		M
L		D		S	E	E	D	S		R	E	A
L	I	G	H	T		L		T		U		G
U		I		E		L		S	U	S	A	N
S	O	N	I	N	L	A	W					I
I		G		D				S		L		F
O					D	A	I	Q	U	I	R	I
N	O	B	L	E		R		U		M		C
I		U		B		C		A	P	P	L	E
S	L	Y		B	E	T	E	L		O		N
T		E		E		I		L		P		T
	P	R	E	D	E	C	E	S	S	O	R	

293

S	I	F	T		C	U	L	P	A	B	L	E
O		I		S		R		E		A		L
M	E	N	T	I	O	N		N	E	P	A	L
B		A		T				N		T		E
R	E	L	A	T	I	O	N	S	H	I	P	
E				I		L		Y		S		G
R	O	B		N	A	D	A	L		M	A	R
O		R		G		E		V				E
	C	O	N	D	E	N	S	A	T	I	O	N
A		U		U				N		N		A
M	A	G	I	C		O	M	I	T	T	E	D
M		H		K		W		A		R		E
O	B	T	U	S	E	L	Y		J	O	B	S

294

P	I	N	I	O	N		A	B	A	T	E	D
O		I		S		F		R		O		E
T	O	B	A	C	C	O		E		R		P
A		B		A		R	A	W	H	I	D	E
S	O	L	A	R		G		E				N
H		I				E		R	I	L	E	D
		N		D	O	T	T	Y		U		
S	U	G	A	R		M				N		E
I				I		E		D	U	C	K	S
S	T	I	F	F	E	N		R		H		S
T		O		T		O	C	A	R	I	N	A
E		N		E		T		W		N		Y
R	E	S	I	D	E		A	L	I	G	N	S

295

D	I	S	P	A	T	C	H		S	T	O	W
U		L		B		L		V		A		E
S	T	U	M	B	L	E		I	D	L	E	S
T		R		R		R		C		L		T
			R	E	S	I	S	T	A	N	C	E
V		C		V		C		O		E		R
I	T	A	L	I	C		P	R	I	S	O	N
N		R		A		C		I		S		S
C	H	A	T	T	E	R	B	O	X			
I		P		I		I		U		H		R
B	R	A	W	N		M	E	S	S	A	G	E
L		C		G		E		L		L		E
E	K	E	S		B	A	B	Y	H	O	O	D

296

297

	I		B		G		B		G		C	
I	N	D	E	F	A	T	I	G	A	B	L	E
	C		D		T		L		U		I	
W	H	E	E	Z	E		L	U	C	E	N	T
			C		A		E		H		C	
B	A	N	K	R	U	P	T		E	C	H	O
	V						I				E	
H	O	O	P		W	E	S	T	W	A	R	D
	I		O		E		H		I			
A	D	H	E	R	E		R	I	D	D	L	E
	I		T		V		O		E		O	
I	N	D	I	V	I	D	U	A	L	I	T	Y
	G		C		L		D		Y		S	

298

299

	C	O	N	S	O	L	I	D	A	T	E	
A		P		C		E		I		I		A
N		E		R	E	A	C	T		G	A	P
T	E	N	S	E		S		C		E		P
I		A		E		E		H	I	R	E	R
C	H	I	L	D	I	S	H					O
Y		R		S				M		I		P
C					S	P	L	A	T	T	E	R
L	O	B	E	S		A		C		A		I
O		E		O		T		B	A	L	S	A
N	I	B		N	A	I	V	E		I		T
E		O		A		N		T		A		E
	A	P	P	R	O	A	C	H	I	N	G	

300

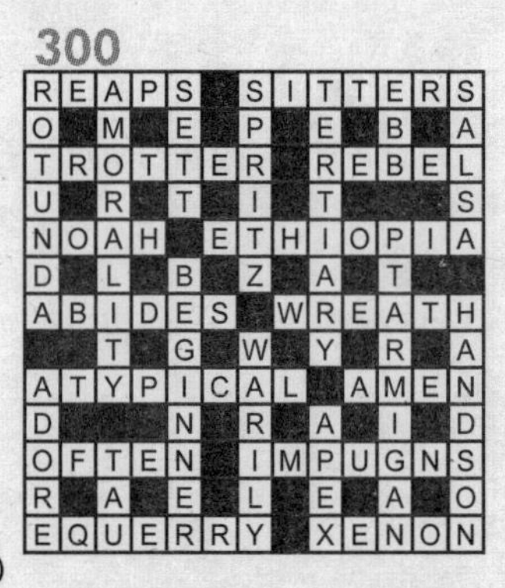

NOTES

NOTES